COINS OF THE WORLD

Twentieth Century Issues

1901—1950

Containing a complete list of all the coins issued by the countries of the whole world, their colonies or dependencies, with illustrations of most of the types and the average valuation among collectors and dealers.

FOURTH EDITION

EDITED BY
WAYTE RAYMOND

PUBLISHED BY
WAYTE RAYMOND, INCORPORATED
NEW YORK

GENERAL INFORMATION

DATES

Illustrations have been given for nearly every type of coin listed in this catalogue and the first and last date of issue given. A range of dates 1903-16 does not necessarily mean that all dates in that period are known, but that the first and last dates have been seen.

NUMERALS

The chart of numerals formerly reproduced in the front of the book will now be found with the Index and List of Denominations.

VALUES

The values given have been arrived at by a careful study of the current coin market and with the cooperation of coin collectors and dealers throughout the world. In each instance they are for the commonest date and mint mark of each type. As the condition of a coin is important to collectors it is assumed that recent dates are in mint condition and coins of the earlier part of the century at least very fine. Worn or mutilated coins are of no value to collectors.

DEFINITIONS OF METALS USED IN COINAGE

Aluminum-Bronze—An alloy having the approximate composition of 90-93% copper, 7-10% aluminum with, perhaps, a little iron. (This is not true of bronze).

Brass—An alloy consisting essentially of copper (50-95%) and zinc (50-5%).

Bronze—An alloy of copper and tin in which the tin content is generally well below 20%. The name bronze is loosely used to cover many copper alloys (as, for example, "aluminum bronze" above).

Copper-Nickel—A generic term applying to alloys composed entirely of copper and nickel. The principal copper nickel alloys at present contain nickel in following percentages: 2.5, 5, 10, 15, 20, 25, and 30.

Copper-Silver—The alloy adopted for U.S. 5 Cent pieces in 1942 consisting of silver 35%, copper 56%, manganese 9%.

Nickel-Bronze—A bronze alloy with a small percentage of nickel.

ABBREVIATIONS

Obv.—Obverse; ℞—Reverse; l.—to the left; r.—to the right;
stg.—standing; std.—seated; m.—Millimeters.

AFGHANISTAN

In Asia, bounded on the north by Turkoman S.S.R. of the USSR, on the east by British India, on the south by Baluchistan (Br. India) and on the west by Iran. The government is a constitutional monarchy.

Mints: Kabul, Herat, Kandahar.

Inscriptions in Arabic. The dates are given in the Mohammadan Era. The earliest dates are in the regular or lunar years of 354 days, but in 1920 the Amir Amanullah changed the calendar to a solar year, thereby making the old date of 1338 to be 1298, or 40 years earlier. On the expulsion of Amanullah in 1929 the dates again appear in accordance with the lunar year.

60 Paissas = 12 Shahis or 90 Puls = 1 Rupee. (Indian)
2 Qirans = 1 Rupee.
100 Puls = 1 Afghani.
20 Afghanis = 1 Amani.

An Afghani is about nine-tenths of a Rupee.

Usual type—Throne room over crossed guns, in star or plain.

Habibullah Khan—1319-1337 A.H. or 1901-1919 A.D.

GOLD

A 1 Dinar 1319, 1320 (1901,02) 50.00

SILVER

1 5 Rupees 1319, 24 (1901,06). Toughra 20.00
2 1 Rupee 1319,20 .... 1.50
3 5 Rupees 1322. Inscription rev. ... 20.00
4 1 Rupee 1322,24 .... 1.50
5 1 Rupee 1330,34 .... 1.50
6 1/8 Rupee 1331 .... .75

BRASS

7 1 Paissa 1329,32 .... .35
8 1 Paissa 1336. Reduced size ...... .35

COPPER

9 1 Paissa 1321,22 .... .25
10 1 Paissa 1333 .... .25
11 1 Paissa 1329,30 .... .25

Amanullah 1337-1347 A.H. or 1919-1929 A.D.

GOLD

13 1 Amani 1337 (old era = 1919). Throne room in star in wreath. ℞ Inscription in wreath 25.00
13a 1 Amani 1337. Type of following 25.00

12 2 Amani 1298, 1299 (new era = 1920, 21). Similar but different inscription 50.00

12a 2 Amani 1299. Throne room. ℞ Toughra in wreath 50.00
12b 1 Amani 1299. Similar 25.00
12c 1/2 Amani 1299. Similar 15.00

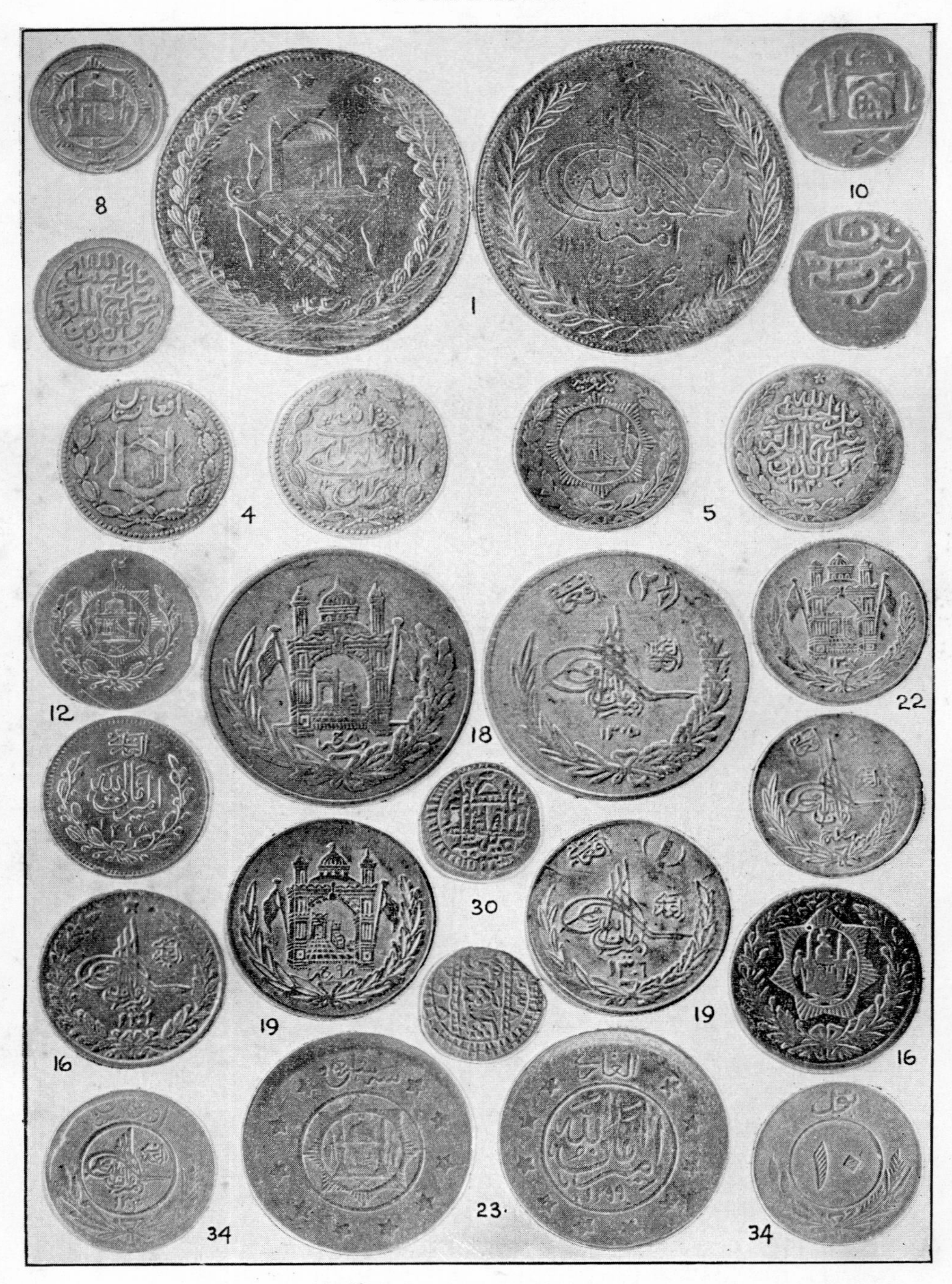

AFGHANISTAN

14	1 Amani 1304. Similar	25.00
15	½ Amani 1304. Similar	15.00

SILVER

16	1 Rupee 1301-03. Toughra in wreath. ℞ Throne room in star in wreath	1.50
17	½ Rupee 1337 (old Era). 1302-03. Similar	1.00
18	2½ Afghani 1304-6. Toughra in wreath. ℞ Throne room in wreath	15.00
19	1 Afghani 1304-06. Similar	2.00
20	½ Afghani 1304-06. Similar	1.25
21	1 Afghani 1308. Similar but date on reverse	2.00
22	½ Afghani 1308. Similar	1.25

COPPER AND BRASS

23	3 Shahi 1298-1300. 33 mm.	.75
24	1 Shahi 1337. Similar. 25 mm.	.40
25	1 Paissa 1299-1302. Similar. Brass. 20 mm.	.50
26	3 Shahi 1300-01. 33 mm.	.50
27	1 Abassi (4 shahi) 1299-1301. Yellow bronze. Thick. 25 mm.	.75
28	15 Paissas 1299.	.50
29	1 Paissa 1299. Similar. 17 mm.	.30
30	1 Shahi 1338-39 and 1298-99 (1901-21).	.40
31	1 Paissa 1298. 17 mm.	.40
32	1 Paissa 1299. 14 mm.	.40
33	25 Puls 1304. Toughra in circle in wreath. ℞ Value in circle in wreath	1.00
34	10 Puls 1304. Similar	.75
35	5 Puls 1304. Similar	.75
36	2 Puls 1304. Similar	.50
37	1 Pul 1304. Similar	.50

Rebel Bacha-i-Sakao as Habibullah Ghazi-1347 A.H. or 1929 A.D.

GOLD

38	6 Rupees 1347= 1929. Arms. ℞ Inscription	50.00

SILVER

39	1 Rupee 1347 (Lunar year). Similar to the last rupee of Habibullah 1330-34	3.50
40	1 Qiran (½ Rupee) 1347. Similar	1.50

YELLOW BRONZE

41	20 Paissas 1347. Similar to the silver	1.50

Mohammed Nadir Shah—1347-1351 A.H. or 1929-1933 A.D.

SILVER

42	1 Afghani 1348. Similar to the 1308 Afghani of Amanullah —	5.00
43	½ Afghani 1350	3.00

COPPER

44	25 Puls 1349	1.00

Mohammed Zahir Shah
A.H. 1351 = 1933 A.D.

Types of preceding reigns
Solar year dates beginning 1313=1935

SILVER

45 1 Afghani 3.50
46 ½ Afghani 2.00

VARIOUS METALS

47 25 Puls. Bronze 1313 .... 1.25

48 25 Puls. Copper-Nickel .... .75

49 10 Puls. Copper-Nickel .... .50
50 5 Puls. Bronze .... .50
51 3 Puls. Bronze .... .50
52 2 Puls. Bronze .... .35

ALGERIA

(L'Algerie)

A government-general of the French Republic in Northern Africa.

Mint: Paris

100 Centimes = 1 Franc

COPPER-NICKEL

Turin Type

1 100 Francs 1950
2 50 Francs 1949,50
3 20 Francs 1949,50

ALBANIA

(Shqiperia)

Between Yugoslavia and Greece on the Adriatic Sea in southeastern Europe. After the Italian invasion in 1939, King Zogu fled, and the crown was given to Victor Emmanuel of Italy.

Republic 1925-1928. Kingdom 1928-1939. Republic since 1946.
Mints: Rome (R), Vienna (V), London (L).
The Franka Ari or Franc gold = 5 Lek. 1 Lek = 40 Qindar.

Ahmed Zogu, Pres.—later Zog I King

GOLD

1 100 Franka Ari 1926, 27. Head of Zog *l.* ℞ Two horse chariot 100.00

a. Same with star under head.

b. Same with 2 stars under head.

The 1926 coin has a slightly different arrangement of the reverse legend.

2 20 Franka Ari 1926, 27. Head *l.* ℞ Eagle 20.00

3 10 Franka Ari 1927. Similar 12.50

4 20 Franka Ari 1926, 27. Bust of Skanderbeg *r.* ℞ Winged lion facing 25.00

SILVER

5 5 Franka Ari 1925-27. Similar head *r.* ℞ Plowing scene 15.00

a. Same with star under head 15.00

6 2 Franka Ari 1926-1928 Sower. ℞ Eagle 3.00

7 1 Franka Ari 1927, 28. Helmeted head *r.* ℞ Prow of galley 2.00

8 2 Franka Ari 1935. Head of Zog I *r.* ℞ Arms 3.00

9 1 Franka Ari 1935. Similar 1.50

NICKEL

15 1 Lek. 1926-27, 1930-31. Classical head *r.* ℞ Horseman .... .75

16 ½ Lek 1926. Double headed eagle. ℞ Hercules and lion .... .50

17 ½ Lek 1930-31. Arms. ℞ Hercules and lion .... .50

18 ¼ Lek 1926-27. Lion *l.* ℞ Oak spray and value .... .25

BRONZE

21 10 Qindar Lek 1926. Eagle head to *r.* ℞ Value between sprays .... .35

22 5 Qindar Lek 1926. Lion head *l.* ℞ Value over oak spray .... .25

23 2 Qindar Ar. 1935. Double headed eagle. ℞ Value and spray .... .25

24 1 Qindar Ar. 1935. Same .... .15

Commemorating the 25th Anniversary of Independence, Nov. 28, 1937

GOLD

Type—Head of Zog *r.* ℞ Arms, denomination and 28. XI. 1912-37.

25 100 Franka Ari 1937 .... 200.00

26 20 Franka Ari 1937 .... 35.00

SILVER

Type—Head of Zog *r.* ℞ Arms.

27 2 Franka Ari 1937 .... 5.00

28 1 Franka Ari 1937 .... 3.00

4
5
1
6
7
17
16
18
18
8
15
22
21
24
SKANDERBEGU
SHQIPNI
ALBANIA
1926
Fr. 5
ALBANIA-SHQIPNI
1927
FR.A.100
ZOG·I·MBRET·I·SHQIPTAREVET
1935
2 FRANGA AR
1 LEK
QINDAR AR

ALBANIA

Commemorating the marriage of the king (April 27, 1938) to Countess Geraldine Appony

Type—Head of Zog *r.* ℞ Draped arms, value and date.

GOLD

29 100 Franka Ari 1938 ....150.00

30 20 Franka Ari 1938 .... 35.00

Commemorating the 10th year jubilee of reign of Zog as king. I.IX. 1928-1938

Type—Head of Zog *r.* ℞ Arms.

GOLD

31 100 Franka Ari 1938 ....150.00

32 50 Franka Ari 1938 .... 90.00
33 20 Franka Ari 1938 .... 35.00

Under Italian Domination With Head of Victor Emanuel III as king and emperor

1 Lek = 1 Lira.

SILVER

34 10 Lek 1939 Head *r.* ℞ Albanian arms and fasces 6.00
35 5 Lek 1939 Head *l.* ℞ Similar...... 3.00

ACMONITAL

36 2 Lek 1939 Bust *l.* in helmet........... 1.00
37 1 Lek 1939-41 .... .75
38 0.50 Lek 1939-41 .... .50
39 0.20 Lek 1939-41 .... .35

BRONZE

40 0.10 Lek 1940-42 Bare head *l.* ℞ Branch .... .50
41 0.05 Lek 1940-42 Bare head *r.* ℞ Branch .... .50

ALBANIA

Peoples republic formed in 1946.

Type-Arms and stars. ℞ Value and date, border of stars.

42 5 Lek 1947 Zinc ....

44 1 Lek 1947 ....

43 2 Lek 1947 ....

45 ½ Lek 1947 ....

ANNAM

French Protectorate

Nguyen Dynasty.

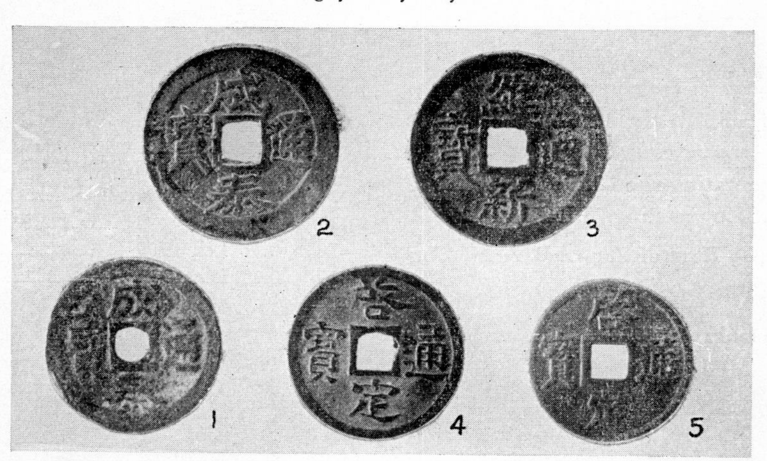

Than Thoi—1889-1914

Cast.

1 1 Sapeque. Four characters around central hole. ℞ Blank. Brass ....

2 10 Sapeque. Similar. ℞ Two characters. Copper ....

Duy Tan—1914-1916

3 10 Sapeque. Similar. ℞ Two characters. Brass ....

Khai Dinh—1916-1926

4 1 Sapeque. Similar. ℞ Blank. Copper ....

5 1 Sapeque. Same but struck. Brass ....

Bao Dai—1926

6 1 Sapeque. Similar to preceding.

ANGOLA

(Portuguese West Africa)

Situated on the African coast between the Belgian Congo and South West Africa

Mints: Birmingham (H), Lisbon

100 Centavos = 1 Escudo

5 Centavos = 1 Macuta

Republic 1910-1926

NICKEL

Type—Liberty head. ℞ Arms

1 50 Centavos 1922,23 (H) 3.00

COPPER-NICKEL

Type—Liberty head. ℞ Value

2 20 Centavos 1921-24 .... .50

3 10 Centavos 1921-24 .... .35

BRONZE

Type—Arms. ℞ Value

4 5 Centavos 1921-24 .... .35

5 2 Centavos 1921,22 .... .50

6 1 Centavo 1921,22 .... .50

New State 1926

NICKEL-BRONZE

Type—Republic head. ℞ Arms over value

7 50 Centavos 1927,28 .... 1.50

8 20 Centavos 1927,28 .... .75

9 10 Centavos 1927,28 .... .50

10 5 Centavos 1927 .... .25

Type—Arms over date. ℞ Value

11 50 Centavos 1948,49 ....

BRONZE

Type—Arms over date. ℞ Value

12 20 Centavos 1948,49 ....

13 10 Centavos 1948,49 ....

ARGENTINA

(Republica Argentina)

Occupies the greater part of southern South America.

Mint: Buenos Aires.

100 Centavos = 1 Peso.

No gold or silver coins struck in the twentieth century.

NICKEL

Type—Liberty head ℞ Value in wreath

1 50 Centavos 1941 .... 1.00

COPPER-NICKEL

Type of preceding.

2 20 Centavos 1905-42 .... .25
3 10 Centavos 1905-42 .... .15
4 5 Centavos 1903-42 .... .10

BRONZE

Type—Arms. ℞ Value.

5 2 Centavos 1939-49 .... .15
6 1 Centavo 1939-48 .... .10

BRASS

Type—Draped Liberty head. ℞ Value.

7 20 Centavos 1942-50 .... .25

8 10 Centavos 1942-50 .... .15

9 5 Centavos 1942-50 .... .10

San Martin Centennial

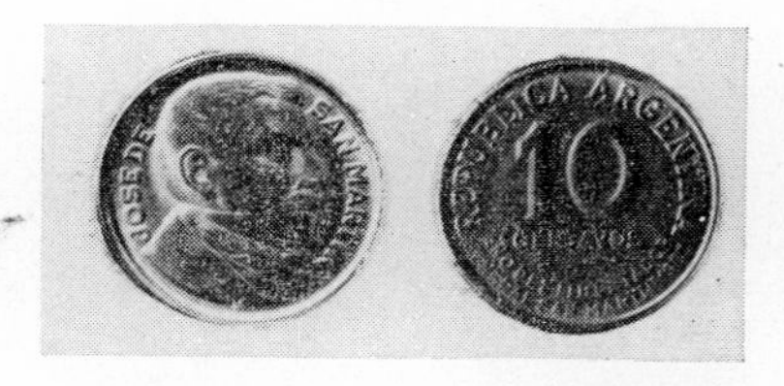

Type—Head of Gen. San Martin. ℞ Value

10 20 Centavos 1950. Nickel .... .25

11 10 Centavos 1950. Copper-Nickel .15

12 5 Centavos 1950. Copper-Nickel .10

AUSTRALIA

A continent in the Pacific Ocean with the Indian Ocean on the west and the Southern Ocean on the south. A self-governing Dominion of the British Commonwealth of Nations.

Mints: Melbourne (M), Sydney, Perth, London, Birmingham (H); Calcutta (I); San Francisco, Denver, Bombay

British Currency: 12 Pence=1 Shilling. 20 Shillings=1 Pound.

GOLD

British Sovereigns have been struck at Sydney, Perth and Melbourne nearly every year until 1931, and ½ Sovereigns at times. For details see Great Britain.

Edward VII

SILVER

Type—Head *r.* ℞ Australian arms.

1 Florin (2 shillings). 1910 .... 2.50
2 Shilling. 1910 .... 1.25
3 6 Pence. 1910 .... .75
4 3 Pence. 1910 .... .50

George V
SILVER

5 Florin. 1911-1936 .... 1.50
6 Shilling. 1911-1936 .... .75
7 6 Pence. 1911-1936 .... .50
8 3 Pence. 1911-1936 .... .35

The Sydney Mint was closed in 1926. No Mint Marks on silver coins after 1921.

COMMEMORATIVE SILVER

9 Florin. 1927. Opening of Parliament at Canberra. 2.50

10 Florin. 1935. Centenary of Victoria and Melbourne 5.00

BRONZE

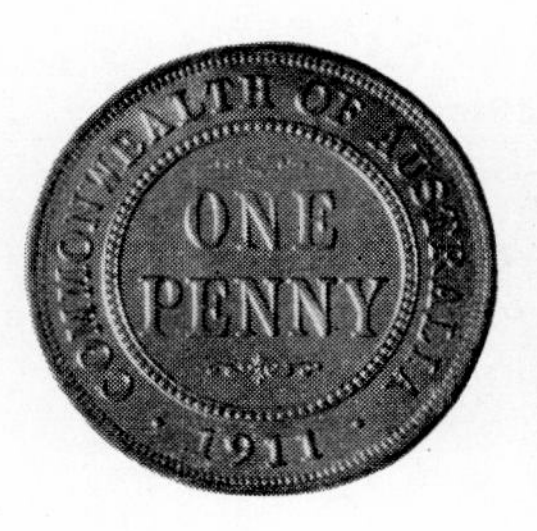

11 Penny. 1911-1936 .... .25

12 ½ Penny. 1911-1936. Similar......... .20
There are no Mint Marks on the bronze coins struck in Australia.

George VI

SILVER

All with bare head of king facing left. Reverses are described.

13 Crown 1937, 38. Large crown 3.50

14 Florin 1938-47. Arms 1.00

15 Shilling 1938-48. Ram's head .... .50
16 Sixpence 1938-48. Arms .... .25

17 Threepence 1938-48. Wheat ears... .15

During 1947 the fineness of the silver coins was reduced from .925 to .500.

BRONZE

18 Halfpenny 1938, 39. Value in circle .... .15

19 Penny 1938-48. Kangaroo .... .15
20 Halfpenny 1939-48. Kangaroo .... .10

Without title—IND. IMP.

SILVER

21 Florin 1951 ....
22 Shilling 1950 ....
23 Sixpence 1950,51 ....
24 Threepence 1949-51 ....

BRONZE

25 Penny 1949-51 ....
26 Halfpenny 1949-51 ....

AUSTRIA

As Part of the Austro-Hungarian Empire

Mint: Vienna.
100 Heller = 1 Corona

Francis Joseph—1848-1916

GOLD

1 100 Corona 1908. 60 Year Jubilee of reign. Head *r.* ℞ Reclining figure 100.00
2 100 Corona 1909-15. Similar. ℞ Arms of the Empire and double headed eagle 85.00
3 20 Corona 1901-1905, 1909. Type of 1892. Laureated head *r.* ℞ Double head eagle 12.50
4 20 Corona 1909-16. Plain head *r.* ℞ Similar to above 12.50
5 20 Corona 1908. 60 Year Jubilee. 15.00
6 10 Corona 1905-1909. Type of 1892. Laureated head *r.* ℞ Arms on eagle 7.50
7 10 Corona 1908. Jubilee type.... 10.00
8 10 Corona 1909-12. Plain head *r.* as on the 20 kr. 7.50

SILVER

9 5 Corona 1909. Plain head to *r.* ℞ Arms in circle and wreath.... 3.50
10 5 Corona 1908. 60 Year Jubilee. Plain head *r.* ℞ Running figure of Fame 4.00

11 5 Corona 1907, 09. Laureated head ℞ Same as No. 9 .... 3.50
12 2 Corona 1912-13. Plain head *r.* ℞ Arms on Eagle 1.00
13 1 Corona 1901-07. Laureated head to *r.* ℞ Crown and value in wreath .... .75
14 1 Corona 1908. Jubilee issue. Plain head r. Crown value and laurel spray 1.00
15 1 Corona 1912-16. Plain head *r.* ℞ As on 1901 issue .... .50

NICKEL

16 20 Heller 1907-09, 1911, 1914. Type of 1893 issue, Eagle .... .25
17 10 Heller 1907-11. Similar .... .20
18 10 Heller 1915-16. *Obv.* Same. ℞ Value in wreath .... .20

BRONZE

19 2 Heller 1901-15. Type of 1893 issue. Arms. ℞ 2 and spray in cartouche .... .15
20 1 Heller 1901-03. 1909-1916. Similar to the 2 Heller. .... .10

Pieces dated 1916 have two different shields, one with the arms of the Empire, the other with the arms of Austria.

Karl—1916-18

IRON

21 20 Heller 1916-18. Arms of Austria. ℞ Value in wreath .... .25
22 2 Heller 1916-18. Similar .... .25

Trade Coins

GOLD

23 4 Ducats 1901-15. Bust to *r.* ℞ Arms 35.00
24 1 Ducat 1901-15. Similar 10.00

These coins are broad and thin and sold largely to gypsies.

SILVER

25 Maria Theresa Thaler 1780. Bust *r.* ℞ Arms 1.50

These coins bearing the date 1780 are still being struck and have been used extensively in Ethiopia and Arabia. Recent issues have been made at London, Brussels, Bombay and Vienna.

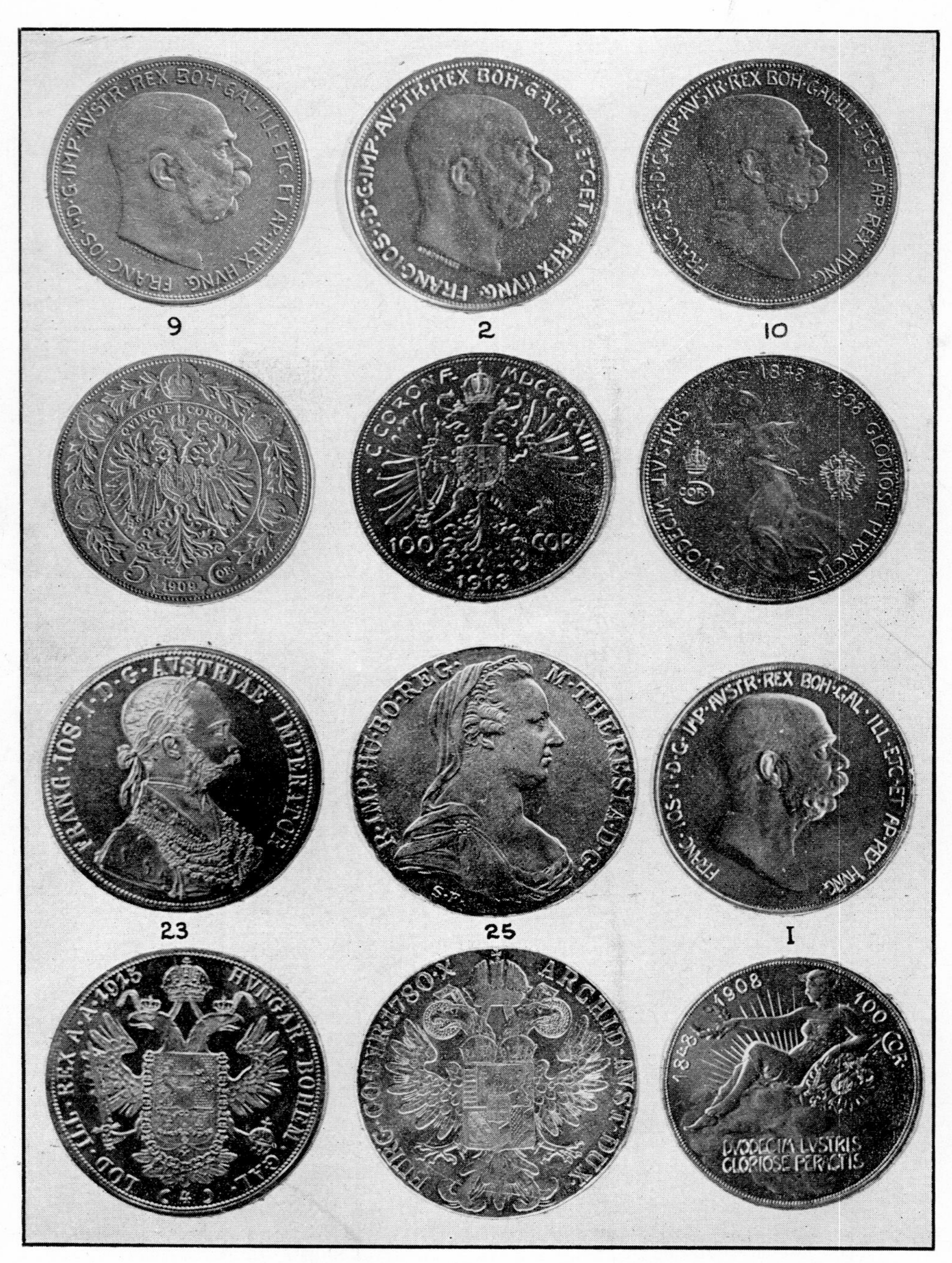

AUSTRIAN EMPIRE

AUSTRIA

Republik Osterreich

In Central Europe. A Republic until 1939 when absorbed by the German Reich and known as "Ostmark." Republic restored in 1945.

Mint: Vienna.
100 Heller = 1 Krone.
10,000 Kronen = 1 Schilling.
100 Groschen = 1 Schilling.

Iron 20 Heller and 2 Heller pieces were struck during the first two years of the Republic but as they were of the same design and bore the date 1918, they are consequently not distinguished from those of the monarchy.

GOLD

1 100 Kronen 1923-24. Arms on single head eagle. ℞ Value in wreath 150.00

2 20 Kronen 1923-24. Similar 35.00

3 100 Schillings 1926-31, 1933-34. Arms on single headed eagle. ℞ Value and sprays........ 50.00

4 25 Schillings 1926-31, 1933-34. Similar 15.00

5 100 Schillings 1935-38. Double head eagle. ℞ Madonna of Maria Zell. 1935 very rare 75.00

6 25 Schillings 1935-37. Same as the 100 Schillings. ℞ St. Leopold 25.00

TRADE COINS

4 and 1 Ducat pieces have been coined every year but they all bear the date 1915 and are from the same dies as were used during the Empire.

Law of Dec. 21, 1923

18 1 Schilling. Silver 1924. Parliament. ℞ Shield and value .... .50

26 1000 Kronen. Copper Nickel 1924. Tirolese woman's head. ℞ Value .... .25

36 200 Kronen. Bronze 1923, 24, Teutonic cross. ℞ Value .... .20

38 100 Kronen. Bronze 1923, 24, Head of eagle. ℞ Value .... .15

Reform of Dec. 20, 1924

SILVER

19 1 Schilling 1925, 26, 1932. Similar to No. 18 but size reduced .... .50

20 ½ Schilling (50 groschen) 1925, 26. Arms ℞ ½ in diamond .... .35

AUSTRIAN REPUBLIC

8	2 Schillings 1928. Head of Franz Schubert	1.50
9	2 Schillings 1929. Head of Dr. Theodor Billroth	1.50
10	2 Schillings 1930. Seated figure of Walther von der Vogelweide	2.50
11	2 Schillings 1931. Bust of Mozart	2.50
12	2 Schillings 1932. Bust of Haydn	2.50
13	2 Schillings 1933. Head of Dr. Seipel	2.50
14	2 Schillings 1934. Head of Dr. Dollfuss	1.50
15	2 Schillings 1935. Bust of Dr. Lueger	1.50
16	2 Schillings 1936. Head of Prince Eugene of Savoy	1.50
17	2 Schillings 1937. Karlskirche in Vienna	1.00

7 5 Schillings 1934-36. Arms. ℞ Madonna of Mariazell 2.50

COPPER NICKEL

27	10 Groschen 1925, 1928, 29. Head of Tirolese woman. ℞ Value in wreath	.25
28	5 Groschen 1931, 32, 1934, 1936. Cross. ℞ Value	.20

29 1 Schilling 1934-35. Arms. ℞ Value and ears of wheat .... .50

30	50 Groschen 1934. Arms. ℞ Value	.30
31	50 Groschen 1935, 36. Smaller eagle. ℞ Value	.30

BRONZE

37	2 Groschen 1925-30, 1934-35. Cross. ℞ Value	.20
39	1 Groschen 1925-36. Head of eagle. ℞ Value	.15

Law of July 25, 1946

40 2 Schilling 1946-48. Aluminum...

41 1 Schilling 1946-49. Aluminum...

42 50 Groschen 1946-49. Aluminum

43 20 Groschen 1950.
Aluminum bronze ....

44 10 Groschen 1947-49. Zinc ....

45 5 Groschen 1948-49. Zinc ....

46 2 Groschen 1950. Aluminum .....

47 1 Groschen 1947-49. Zinc ....

AZORES

Three groups of islands in the North Atlantic Ocean, west of Portugal. Part of the Republic of Portugal.

Mint: Lisbon.

Carlos I—1889-1908

COPPER

1 10 Reis 1901. Arms. ℞ Value in wreath .... .35

2 5 Reis 1901. Similar .... .25

BELGIUM

(Royaume de Belgique—Koniglijk Belgie)

A part of the Low Countries, bordering on the North Sea in Western Europe. A constitutional Monarchy. A Regency since 1945 with Prince Charles as regent.

Mints: Brussels, Birmingham.

100 Centimes = 1 Franc. 5 Francs = 1 Belga.

As two languages are spoken in Belgium, part of the coinage since 1886 is inscribed in French and part is inscribed in Flemish. Therefore unless definitely stated only one description will be given for a coin although there were two varieties minted.

Leopold II—1865-1909

SILVER

1 2 Francs 1904, 1909. Head *l.* ℞ Value in wreath 1.00
2 1 Franc 1904, 1909. Similar to the 2 Francs .... .60
3 50 Centimes 1901. Head *l.* ℞ Sitting lion and shield .... .35
4 50 Centimes 1907, 1909. Head *l.* ℞ Value in wreath .... .35

COPPER NICKEL

Type: Lion l. ℞ Value. Type of 1861 issue

8 10 Centimes 1901 .... .50
8a 5 Centimes 1901 .... .35

Type: Crowned L's. ℞ Value and spray

5 25 Centimes 1908, 09 .... .20
6 10 Centimes 1901-06 .... .15
7 5 Centimes 1901-07 .... .10

COPPER

9 2 Centimes 1902, 1905, 1909. Lion and shield. ℞ Crowned script *l* .... .20
10 1 Centime 1901-02, 1907. Similar .... .15

Albert I—1909-1934

GOLD

11 20 Francs 1914. Bust *l.* ℞ Shield on crowned mantle 20.00
Legend in Flemish or French.

SILVER

12 20 Francs 1933, 34. Head l. ℞ Shield 3.00

Type: Head l. Value in wreath.

13 2 Francs 1910-12 .... 1.50
14 1 Franc 1910-14, 1917, 18 .... .75

The pieces dated 1914, 1917 and 1918 were struck in Birmingham because of the German occupation of Belgium.

15 50 Centimes 1910-14 .... .35

NICKEL

16 20 Francs or 4 Belgas 1931, 32. Head l. ℞ Shield 3.50
17 10 Francs or 2 Belgas 1930, 31 (Centenary of the Kingdom). Heads of the three rulers of modern Belgium. ℞ Values 2.50
18 5 Francs or 1 Belga 1930-34. Head l. ℞ Value .... .50

Type: Allegory of Belgium wounded but victorious. ℞ Caduceus and value.

19 2 Francs 1923, 24, 1930 .... .35
20 1 Franc 1922, 23, 1928-30, 1933-35 .... .25
21 50 Centimes 1922, 23, 1927-30, 1932-34 .... .15

COPPER NICKEL

Type: Crowned A around center hole. ℞ Value.

22 25 Centimes 1910-14, 1920-23, 1926-29 .... .15
23 10 Centimes 1911, 1920-29, 1930-32 .... .10
24 5 Centimes 1910, 1913, 14, 1920-28, 1930-32 .... .10

COPPER

Type: Lion. ℞ Crowned A.

25 2 Centimes 1910-12, 1914, 1919 .10
26 1 Centime 1911, 12, 1914 .... .10

LEOPOLD II KONING DER BELGEN
2
ALBERT·ROI·DES·BELGES
16
20 FR
1931
13
1 FRANK 1904
9
2 CENT
2 FRANK 1911
EENDRACHT MAAKT MACHT
LEOPOLD I LEOPOLD II ALBERT
1830–1930
17
ROYAUME DE BELGIQUE
EXPOSITION DE BRUXELLES
50 FR
27
CENTENAIRE DES CHEMINS DE FER BELGES
1835 1935
KONINKRIJK BELGIË
1908
5
31
BELGIQUE·BELGIE
25 CENT
1916
BELGIE
19
25 CEN
ALBERT·ROI·DES·BELGES
12
20 FR
1934
GOED VOOR
2 F
1923
LEOPOLD III
29
BELGIË
5 FR
LEOPOLD III
1934
28
ROYAUME DE BELGIQUE
20 FR
KONINKRIJK BELGIË

BELGIUM

German Occupation—World War I

ZINC

30 50 Centimes 1918 Hole in cinquefoil. ℞ Arms .... .75

Type: Lion. ℞ Value.

31 25 Centimes 1915-18 .... .25
32 10 Centimes 1915-17 .... .20
33 5 Centimes 1915, 16 .... .15

Leopold III 1934-1940

SILVER

27 50 Francs 1935. Exhibition at Brussels and Centenary of the Belgian Railroads. St. Michael and the Dragon. ℞ Exposition Hall 6.00

28 20 Francs 1934, 35. Head, l. ℞ Crowned laurel, wheat and oak 2.50

34 50 Francs 1939, 40. Head, l. ℞ Shields of nine provinces 4.00

NICKEL

29 5 Francs 1936, 37. Head, l. ℞ Value .... .50

35 5 Francs. 1938, 39. Lion. ℞ Three Shields .... .50

36 1 Franc 1939, 40. Similar but different shields .... .25

COPPER NICKEL

Type: Crowned L's. ℞ Three shields

37 25 Centimes 1938, 39 .... .15
38 10 Centimes 1938, 39 .... .10
39 5 Centimes 1939, 40 .... .10

German Occupation—World War II

ZINC

40

41

45

40 5 Francs 1941-45. Head of Leopold. ℞ Value .... .25

41 1 Franc 1941-45. Lion. ℞ Crowned double L .... .15

Type: Similar to preceding Copper Nickel.

42 25 Centimes 1942-45 .... .15
43 10 Centimes 1941-45 .... .10
44 5 Centimes 1941-43 .... .10

Allied Forces

45 2 Francs. Zinc plated steel 1944. Legend. ℞ Value .... .15

Post War Coinage

SILVER

46 100 Francs 1948. Heads of the four kings, Leopold I, II, III and Albert I.
Dedicated to the Belgian dynasty

47 50 Francs 1948. Mercury head ......
48 20 Francs 1949. Mercury head ......

COPPER-NICKEL

49 5 Francs 1948. Ceres head ....

50 1 Franc 1950. Ceres head ....

BELGIAN CONGO

(Congo Belge or Belgisch Congo)

In Central Africa, having a short coastline on the South Atlantic Ocean. A Belgian Colony.
Mints: Brussels, Birmingham, Philadelphia, Pretoria
100 Centimes = 1 Congo Franc

As an independent state before 1909

Leopold II

COPPER-NICKEL

1 20 Centimes 1906, 1908. With inscription LEOP.II.R.D. BELGES SOUV.DE L'ETAT INDEP. DU CONGO. Five L's crowned. ℞ Star .... .50
2 10 Centimes 1906, 1908. Similar .40
3 5 Centimes 1906, 1908. Similar .35

As a Belgian Colony

4 20 Centimes 1909. Similar .... .75
5 10 Centimes 1909. Similar .... .50
6 5 Centimes 1909. Similar .... .35

Albert

COPPER-NICKEL

7 1 Franc 1920-1930. King's head *l.* ℞ Palm tree 1.25
8 50 Centimes 1921-29. Similar ...... .75
9 20 Centimes 1910-11. Similar to the coins of Leopold but five crowned A's .... .35
10 10 Centimes 1910-28 .... .35
11 5 Centimes 1910-28 .... .25

COPPER

12 2 Centimes 1910, 19, 20 .... .35
13 1 Centime 1910, 19, 20 .... .25

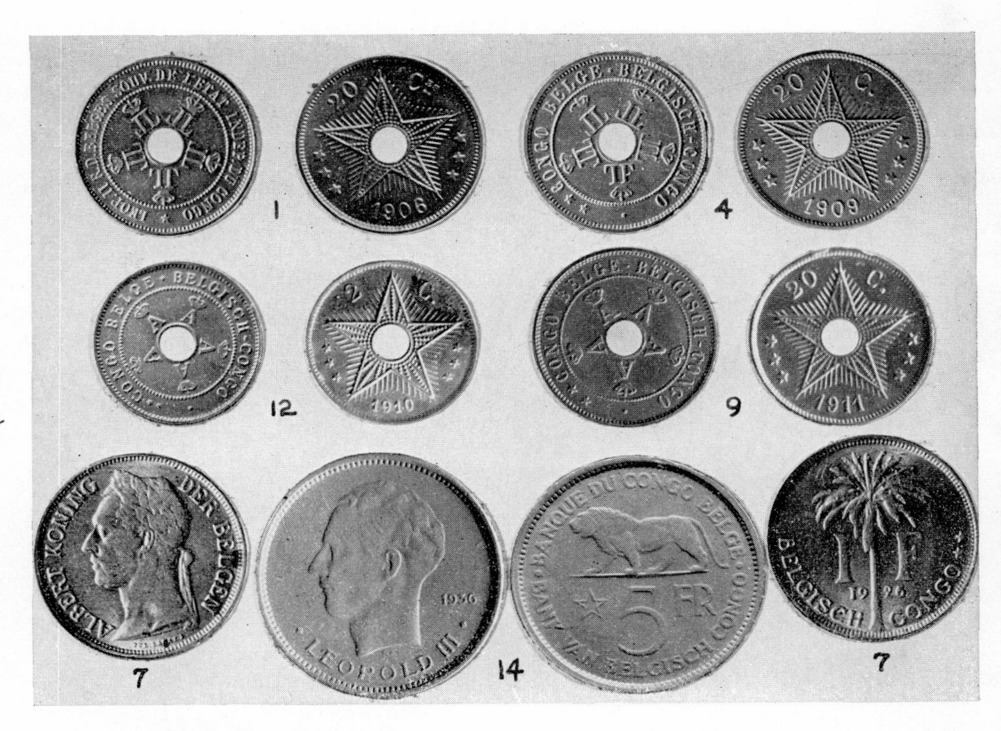

Leopold III—1934-1950
Bank of Belgian Congo

NICKEL-BRONZE

14 5 Francs 1936-38. Head of Leopold III l. ℞ Lion 1.50

SILVER

15 50 Francs 1944. Elephant. ℞ Value 3.50

BRASS

Type of silver coin.

16 5 Francs 1947 .... .75

17 2 Francs 1943. Hexagonal .... .50

18 2 Francs 1946. Round .... .35

19 1 Franc 1944-48 .... .25

BOLIVIA

(Republica Boliviana)

Occupies the central part of South America, with Peru and Chile on the west, Brazil on the north and east, Paraguay on the east, and Argentina on the south.

Mints: Potosi (monogram). Paris (A) or symbols. Birmingham (H). Vienna, Philadelphia.

100 Centavos = 1 Boliviano.

SILVER

1 50 Centavos 1901, 1904-08. Arms, stars above. ℞ Value in wreath. Potosi mint 2.00

2 50 Centavos 1909. Arms. Stars below. Birmingham mint. 2.00
3 20 Centavos 1907. Arms, stars above. Potosi mint .... .35
4 20 Centavos 1909. Arms, stars below. Birmingham Mint .... .35

BRASS

5 50 Centavos 1902. Arms, stars below 1.50
6 20 Centavos. Similar 1.00

COPPER-NICKEL

5 and 10 Centavo coins dated 1883 were re-issued at a later date after being punched with a small hole.

7 10 Centavos. 1902-19. Arms. ℞ Caduceus and value........ .15

8 5 Centavos 1902-19. Similar........ .10
9 10 Centavos 1935. Smaller .... .15
10 5 Centavos 1935. Smaller .... .10

11 50 Centavos 1937. Arms. ℞ Arm grasping torch ....
12 10 Centavos 1937. Similar .... .35

Caduceus type

13 50 Centavos 1939-41. Size 28 m...... .50
14 10 Centavos 1939-41. Size reduced to 23 m. .... .25

BRONZE

Caduceus type

15 50 Centavos 1942-49. Size 24 m.... .25

ZINC

Caduceus type size reduced.

16 20 Centavos 1942. Size 21 m........ .20
17 10 Centavos 1942. Size 17 m........ .15

BRAZIL

(Estados Unidos do Brasil)

The largest state in South America, bounded on the north by Venezuela and the Guianas, on the east by the Atlantic Ocean, on the south by Uruguay, Argentina and Paraguay, and on the west by Bolivia, Peru and Colombia.

Mints: Rio de Janeiro. Also Birmingham, Brussels, Berlin, Vienna, Hamburg.

1000 Reis = 1 Milreis.

GOLD

1 20 Milreis. 1901-22. Liberty head *l.* ℞ Southern Cross in circle of stars 100.00

2 10 Milreis. 1901-22. Liberty head in circle. ℞ Arms on star in wreath 75.00

SILVER

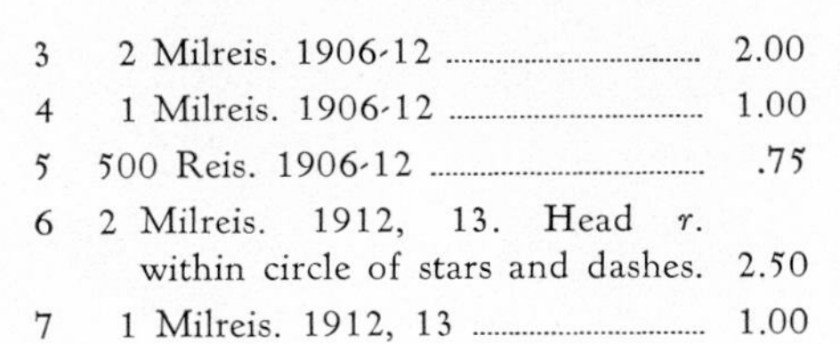

3 2 Milreis. 1906-12 .... 2.00

4 1 Milreis. 1906-12 .... 1.00

5 500 Reis. 1906-12 .... .75

6 2 Milreis. 1912, 13. Head *r.* within circle of stars and dashes. 2.50

7 1 Milreis. 1912, 13 .... 1.00

8 500 Reis. 1912 .... 1.50

9 2 Milreis. 1913. Similar but stars only in circle 2.50

10 1 Milreis. 1913 .... 1.00

11 500 Reis. 1913 .... .50

12 2 Milreis. 1922 (Centenary of Independence). Busts of Dom Pedro I and Pres. Pessoa *l.* ℞ Shields of Empire and Republic 2.00

13 2 Milreis. 1924-34. Head *r.* Outer circle of stars. ℞ Fasces and value in wreath 1.50

14 5 Milreis. 1936-38. Head of Santos Dumont *l.* ℞ Wing and value 2.50

15 2 Milreis. 1935. Head of Caxias *l.* ℞ sword and value 2.00

REPUBLICA DOS ESTADOS UNIDOS DO BRASIL
1907
3
ORDEM E PROGRESSO
2000
RÉIS
XX GRAMMAS
REPUBLICA DOS ESTADOS UNIDOS DO BRASIL
1913
6
ORDEM E PROGRESSO
2000
RÉIS
BRASIL
16
REPUBLICA DOS ESTADOS UNIDOS DO BRAZIL
1913
9
ORDEM E PROGRESSO
2000
RÉIS
BRASIL
12
1822
1822
25
REPUBLICA DOS ESTADOS UNIDOS DO
200
BRASIL
CENTENARIO
2
18
BRASIL
1000
REIS
1927
29
REPUBLICA DOS ESTADOS UNIDOS DO BRASIL
200
REIS
1931
31
50
REIS
1921
BRASIL
500
RÉIS
1928
32
20
REIS
1921
19
REPUBLICA DOS ESTADOS UNIDOS
100
BRASIL
26
26
38
20
REIS
13
REPUBLICA DOS ESTADOS UNIDOS DO BRASIL
2.000
RÉIS
1934

BRAZIL

ALUMINUM—BRONZE

16 1 Milreis. 1922 (Centenary of Independence). Busts of Dom Pedro I and Pres. Pessoa *l.* ℞ Torch, crown and liberty cap...... .50

a. Error BBASIL 1.50

17 500 Reis. 1922. Similar ...... .35

a. Error: BBASIL 7.50

18 1 Milreis. 1924-31 Kneeling figure of Plenty to *r.* ℞ Value in wreath .60

19 500 Reis. 1924-30. Similar ...... .40

20 2 Milreis. 1936-38. Caxias *r* ...... .75

20a 2 Milreis. 1938. Polygonal ...... .75

21 1 Milreis. 1935. Anchieta ...... .75

22 1 Milreis. 1936-38. Size reduced .35

23 500 Reis. 1935. Facing head of Feijo. Weight 4 gr. 2.50

23a 500 Reis. 1936-38. Weight 5 gr.... .25

COPPER-NICKEL

24 400 Reis. 1901. Liberty head 1.00

25 200 Reis. 1901. Similar 1.25

26 100 Reis. 1901. Similar 1.00

28 400 Reis. 1918-35. Head *r.* Stars .50

29 200 Reis. 1918-35. Similar...... .25

30 100 Reis. 1918-35. Similar ...... .40

31 50 Reis. 1918-31. Similar ...... .15

32 20 Reis. 1918-27. Similar ...... .10

33 400 Reis. 1936-38. Cruz ...... .35

34 300 Reis. 1936-38. Gomes ...... .60

35 200 Reis. 1936-38. Maua ...... .35

36 100 Reis. 1936-38. Tamandare ...... .35

BRONZE

37 40 Reis. 1901-12. Southern Cross .15

38 20 Reis. 1901-12. Similar...... .10

COMMEMORATIVE SERIES 1932

4th Centenary of the Colonization of Brazil

39 2 Milreis. Bust of John III ℞ Arms. Silver 2.00

40 1 Milreis. Standing figure of da Sousa. ℞ Arms. Al.Bronze 2.00

41 500 Reis. Facing bust of Ramalho. ℞ Quilted jacket. Al.Bronze 1.50

42 400 Reis. Map of South America. ℞ Cross. Nickel 1.25

43 200 Reis. Sphere. ℞ Ship. Nickel .50

44 100 Reis. Facing bust of Cazique Tiberica. ℞ Weapons. Nickel 35

New State

With bust of Pres. Getulio Vargas

COPPER-NICKEL

45 400 Reis. 1938-42 .... .20
46 300 Reis. 1938-42 .... .15
47 200 Reis. 1938-42 .... .10
48 100 Reis. 1938-42 .... .10

The coins of 1942 have a higher content of copper.

ALUMINUM BRONZE
Celebrated Men.

49 2000 Reis. 1939. Marshal Peixoto 1.00

50 1000 Reis. 1939. Tobias Barreto...... .75

51 500 Reis. 1939. Machado de Assis .50

New Monetary Standard
100 centavos=1 cruzeiro

COPPER-NICKEL

Type—Bust of Vargas *l.* ℞ Value.

52 50 Centavos. 1942, 43 .... .35
53 20 Centavos. 1942, 43 .... .25
54 10 Centavos. 1942, 43 .... .15

ALUMINUM BRONZE

Type—Map of Brazil. ℞ Value.

55 5 Cruzeiros, 1942, 43 .... .75
56 2 Cruzeiros, 1942-50 .... .50
51 1 Cruzeiro. 1942-50 .... .35

Type of 1942 issue.

58 50 Centavos. 1943-47 .... .25
59 20 Centavos. 1943-48 .... .20
60 10 Centavos. 1943-47 .... .15

61 50 Centavos 1948-50.
Pres. Dutra ....

62 20 Centavos 1948-50.
Rui Barbosa ....

63 10 Centavos 1947-50.
Jose Bonifacio ....

BRITISH DOLLARS

These dollars were issued for trading purposes in the Far East by the British Government. They bear no indication of the issuing country except the standing figure of Britannia in a fret border on the obverse. The denomination is in three languages. ONE DOLLAR on the obverse, and the equivalent of one dollar in Chinese and Malay in an ornamental frame on the reverse. They were distributed chiefly through the banks at Hong Kong, Singapore, Penang and Shanghai, and were struck for the most part at the Bombay Mint, occasionally at the Calcutta Mint and a few times since 1925 at the Royal Mint, London. They were first made in 1895. In the twentieth century varying dates occur between 1901 and 1930 .... 2.50

BRITISH GUIANA AND WEST INDIES
BRITISH GUIANA

On the north shore of South America, with Venezuela on the west, Dutch Guiana on the east and Brazil on the south. A British Crown Colony.

Mint: London.

50 Pence = 1 British Guiana Dollar

SILVER

Victoria

1 4 Pence. 1901 .... .50

Edward VII

2 4 Pence. 1903, 1908-10 .... .50

George V

3 4 Pence. 1911, 1913, 1916 .... .50

Inscribed BRITISH GUIANA only.

4 4 Pence. 1917-31,36. Similar .... .35

George VI

5 4 Pence. 1938-45. Head. R̸ Value .35

BRITISH HONDURAS

Bordering on the Caribbean Sea in Central America. A British Crown Colony.
Mints: London, Birmingham (H).
100 Cents = 1 British Honduras Dollar

Victoria

SILVER

1 50 Cents. 1901. Head *l.* R
Value in circular frame 2.00

2 25 Cents. 1901. Similar 1.00

Edward VII

SILVER

3 50 Cents. 1906, 07 .... 2.00
4 25 Cents. 1906, 07 .... 1.00

COPPER-NICKEL

5 5 Cents. 1907-1909 .... .35

BRONZE

6 1 Cent. 1904, 1906, 1909 .... .50

George V

SILVER

Type of preceding reign

7 50 Cents. 1911-19 .... 2.50
8 25 Cents. 1911-19 .... .75
9 10 Cents. 1918, 19 .... .50

COPPER-NICKEL

10 5 Cents. 1911-19 .... .25

BRONZE

11 1 Cent. 1911-13 .... .50

12 1 Cent. 1914-36 .... .50

George VI

Crowned head.
Reverse types of preceding reign

SILVER

13 10 Cents. 1939-46 .... .50

COPPER-NICKEL

14 5 Cents 1939 .... .25

NICKEL-BRASS

15 5 Cents 1942-47 .... .25

BRONZE

16 1 Cent 1937-47 .... .15

With title—"KING GEORGE THE SIXTH"

17 5 Cents 1949,50. Nickel-brass ...

18 1 Cent 1949,50. Bronze ....

BRITISH NORTH BORNEO

Territory occupying the northern part of the Island of Borneo. A British Protectorate.
Mint: Birmingham.
100 Cents = 1 Straits Dollar

SILVER

1 25 Cents 1929. Arms and supporters. ℞ Value 7.50

BRONZE

5 ½ Cent 1907 .... 1.50

COPPER-NICKEL

2 5 Cents. 1903-41 .... .50

3 2½ Cents. 1903-20 .... .35

4 1 Cent. 1904-41 .... .25

BRITISH WEST AFRICA

Before 1912 Nigeria—British West Africa

In Western Africa, on the Gulf of Guinea. A British Protectorate.

Mints: London. Birmingham (H). King's Norton (KN). Pretoria.

12 Pence = 1 Shilling. 20 Shillings = 1 West African Pound

Edward VII

COPPER-NICKEL

No.	Description	Price
1	1 Penny 1907-10. In 1908 the weight reduced	.50
2	1/10 Penny 1907.10	.75

ALUMINUM

No.	Description	Price
3	1/10 Penny 1907-08	.60

George V

COPPER-NICKEL

No.	Description	Price
4	1 Penny 1911	.75
5	½ Penny 1911	.50
6	1/10 Penny 1911	.35

After 1911 changed to British West Africa

George V

SILVER

No.	Description	Price
1	2 Shillings. 1913-20	2.00
2	1 Shilling. 1913-20	1.00
3	6 Pence 1913, 14, 1916-20. Value in closed wreath	.50
4	3 Pence. 1913, 20. Similar	.25

BRASS

Same type as silver.

No.	Description	Price
5	2 Shillings. 1920-28, 1936	1.00
6	1 Shilling. 1920-28, 1936	.75
7	6 Pence. 1920-36	.35
8	3 Pence. 1920-36	.35

NICKEL

Type of preceding reign

No.	Description	Price
9	1 Penny. 1911-34	.50

No.	Description	Price
10	½ Penny. 1912-34-36	.50
11	1/10 Penny. 1912-34	.25

Edward VIII
NICKEL

12 1 Penny. 1936 .... .75

13 ½ Penny. 1936 .... .50

14 1/10 Penny. 1936 .... .25

15 1 Penny 1936 (Error). The reverse of the above combined with the obverse of the East Africa 10 cent piece, making the piece read 10 CENTS. Rare 5.00

George VI
ALUMINUM BRONZE OR NICKEL-BRASS

Type—Crowned head. ℞ Palm.

16	2 Shillings 1938-48	1.25
17	1 Shilling 1938-48	.75
18	6 Pence 1938-48. Value in wreath	.35

19 3 Pence. 1938-48 .... .25

NICKEL-BRONZE OR COPPER-NICKEL

20	1 Penny. 1937-48	.25
21	Halfpenny. 1937-48	.15
22	1/10 Penny. 1938-48	.10

Without title—IND. IMP.

23 2 Shillings 1949 ....

24 1 Shilling 1949 ....

BULGARIA

(Narodna Republika Bulgaria)

Situated in southeastern Europe, bordering on the Black Sea. A Balkan Monarchy until 1946. A People's Republic proclaimed by the National Assembly on Sept. 15, 1946.

Mints: Vienna, Kremnitz, Brussels, Paris, Budapest (BP), London, Belgrade.

100 Stotinki = 1 Leva.

Ferdinand 1887-1918

GOLD

1	100 Leva 1912. 25 Year Jubliee. Very minute date. Vienna Mint	250.00
2	20 Leva 1912. Jubilee	35.00

SILVER

Type — Head *r.* ℞ Value in wreath

3	2 Leva 1910	2.00
4	1 Leva 1910	1.25
5	50 Stotinki 1910	.75

Type — Head *l.* ℞ Value in wreath

6	2 Leva 1912-16	2.00
7	1 Leva 1912-16	1.25
8	50 Stotinki 1912-16	.75

MINOR METALS

Type — Arms. ℞ Value in wreath

9	20 Stotinki 1906,12,13. Cop.-nickel	.25
10	10 Stotinki 1906,12,13. Cop.-nickel	.20
11	5 Stotinki 1906,12,13. Cop.-nickel	.15
12	20 Stotinki 1917. Zinc	.50
13	10 Stotinki 1917. Zinc	.50
14	5 Stotinki 1917. Zinc	.35
15	2 Stotinki 1901,12. Bronze	.25
16	1 Stotinki 1901,12. Bronze	.25

Boris III 1918-1943

SILVER

Type — Head *l.* ℞ Value in wreath

17	100 Leva 1930	5.00
18	50 Leva 1930	2.50
19	20 Leva 1930	1.00

Type — New head *l.* ℞ Value between sprays

20 100 Leva 1934,37. .... 5.00
21 50 Leva 1934 .... 2.50

MINOR METALS

Type — Cavalier of Madara

22 10 Leva 1930. Copper-nickel 1.25
23 5 Leva 1930. Copper-nickel .... .75

Type — Arms on mantle

24 2 Leva 1923. Aluminum 1.00
25 1 Leva 1923. Aluminum .... .75
26 2 Leva 1925. Copper-nickel .... .35
27 1 Leva 1925. Copper-nickel .... .25

28 50 Stotinki 1937.
Aluminum bronze .... .25

Type — Bare head. ℞ Value in wreath

29 50 Leva 1940. Copper-nickel 1.00
30 20 Leva 1940. Copper-nickel .... .75

IRON

31 10 Leva 1941. Type of No. 22 ...... .50
32 5 Leva 1941. Type of No. 23 ...... .25
33 2 Leva 1943-45. Type of No. 24 .15
34 1 Leva 1941. Type of No. 25 ...... .15

BURMA

(Pyee-Daung-Su Myanma-Nainggan)

Separated from India in 1937. Occupied by Japanese in 1942.

Republic of Burma formed on Jan. 4, 1948. Admitted to the United Nations April 19, 1948.

Currency Standard — Same as India

NICKEL

Type — A chinthe (lion). ℞ Value in wreath

1 8 Annas (1/2 rupee) 1949 ....
2 4 Annas (1/4 rupee) 1949 ....

COPPER-NICKEL

3 2 Annas 1949. Square ....
4 1 Anna 1949. Scalloped ....
5 1/2 Anna 1949. Square ....

CAMEROONS

Situated north of the Equator on the west coast of Africa. French Mandate.

Mints: Paris, Pretoria

100 Centimes = 1 Franc

ALUMINUM BRONZE

Type—Liberty head. R Value between sprays

1	2 Francs 1924,25	1.50
2	1 Franc 1924-27	1.00
3	50 Centimes 1924-27	.50

Type—Cock. R Cross of Lorraine

Legend—"Cameroun Francais"

4	1 Franc 1943	1.25
5	50 Centimes 1943	.75

Legend—"Cameroun Francais Libre"

6	1 Franc 1943	1.25
7	50 Centimes 1943	.75

ALUMINUM

8	2 Francs 1949	
9	1 Franc 1949	

GEORGIVS V REX ET IND: IMP:
20a
GEORGIVS V DEI GRA: REX ET IND: IMP:
15
50 CENTS CANADA 1917
20
18
ONE CENT CANADA 1911
16
16
17
10 CENTS CANADA 1936
19
CANADA FIVE 5 CENTS
21
CANADA ONE CENT 1922
GEORGIVS V REX IMPERATOR ANNO REGNI XXV
13
14
GEORGIVS VI D: G: REX ET IND: IMP:
22
CANADA 1935 DOLLAR
CANADA 1936 DOLLAR
CANADA 1937 DOLLAR
CANADA 25 cents 1937
24
50 CENTS CANADA 1937
23
CANADA 10 CENTS
25
5 CENTS CANADA 1937
26
1 CENT 1937 CANADA
27

C A N A D A

CANADA

(Dominion of Canada)

With the exception of Alaska, Canada occupies the entire northern part of the North American Continent. A self-governing Dominion in the British Commonwealth of Nations.

Mints: London, Birmingham, Ottawa since 1908.

100 Cents=1 Dollar.

British Sovereigns were struck at Ottawa from 1908-11, 1913-14, 1916-19, and bear the Mint Mark C on ground under St. George.

Victoria—1837-1901

SILVER

1 50 Cents. 1870-1901. Head to *l.* ℞ Value in wreath 2.00
2 25 Cents. 1870-1901 .... 1.50
3 10 Cents. 1870-1901 .... .50
4 5 Cents. 1870-1901 .... .30

The last two without diadem.

BRONZE

5 1 Cent. 1901. Head *l.* ℞ Value in leaf circle .... .25

Edward VII—1901-1910

SILVER

6 50 Cents. 1902-10 .... 2.00
7 25 Cents. 1902-10 .... 1.50
8 10 Cents. 1902-10 .... .50
9 5 Cents. 1902-10 .... .30

BRONZE

10 1 Cent. 1902-1910 .... .25

George V—1910-1936

GOLD

11 10 Dollars. 1912-14 .... 35.00
12 5 Dollars. 1912-14. .... 20.00

SILVER

13 1 Dollar. 1935. Jubilee year. Bust *l.* ℞ Voyageurs in canoe........ 2.50
14 1 Dollar. 1936. Regular issue 3.00
15 50 Cents. 1911-36 .... 1.50
16 25 Cents. 1911-36 .... .50
17 10 Cents. 1911-36 .... .25
18 5 Cents. 1911-1921 .... .25

All of the silver struck in 1911 are without DEI GRA in inscription. This was rectified in 1912.

NICKEL

19 5 Cents. 1922-1936 .... .15

BRONZE

20 1 Cent. 1911-20. Bust *l.* Similar 1911 without DEI GRA .25
21 1 Cent. 1920-36. (Reduced size) .... .10

George VI—1936-47

With title—D. G. REX ET IND. IMP.

SILVER

22 1 Dollar. 1937-38, 45-47. Voyageurs in Canoe 2.00
23 50 Cents. 1937-47. Arms of Canada between supporters 1.00
24 25 Cents. 1937-47. Caribou head... .50
25 10 Cents. 1937-47. Fishing schooner .... .20

NICKEL

26 5 Cents. 1937-42,46,47. Beaver... .15

BRONZE

27 1 Cent. 1937-47. Maple leaves ...... .10

Commemorating the visit of King George and Queen Elizabeth to Canada and the United States

SILVER

28 Dollar. 1939. View of Parliament buildings at Ottawa 2.50

TOMBAK BRASS

29 5 Cents. 1942. Type of nickel coin, 12 sided .... .50

30 5 Cents. 1943. Large V and torch. Morse code. 12 sided...... .25

STEEL

31 5 Cents. 1944, 45. Similar .... .10

George VI 1948-

With title—DEI GRATIA REX

Types of preceding issue

SILVER

32 Dollar 1948,50. Voyageurs ....

33 Dollar 1949. Newfoundland Commemorative ....
34 50 Cents. 1948-50 ....
35 25 Cents. 1948-50 ....
36 10 Cents. 1948-50 ....

NICKEL

37 5 Cents. 1948-50 ....

BRONZE

38 1 Cent. 1948-50 ....

CAPE VERDE ISLANDS

Group of Islands off West Coast of Africa—Portuguese Colony

Mint: Lisbon.

100 Centavos = 1 Escudo

New State 1926

NICKEL BRONZE (Alpaca)

Type—Bust of Republic. ℞ Arms in Wreath over value and name of colony

1	1 Escudo 1930	2.00
2	50 Centavos 1930	1.00

BRONZE

Type—Republic head and name of colony, ℞ Value and date

3	20 Centavos 1930	1.00
4	10 Centavos 1930	.75
5	5 Centavos 1930	.50

NICKEL BRONZE (Alpaca)

Type—Arms over date. ℞ Value

6	1 Escudo 1949	.35
7	50 Centavos 1949	.25

CEYLON

An island off the southern tip of India, in the Indian Ocean. A dominion since 1948.
Mints: London, Bombay, Calcutta, Birmingham, King's Norton.
100 Cents=1 Rupee.

Victoria

COPPER

1 1 Cent. 1901 .... .25
2 ½ Cent. 1901 .... .25
3 ¼ Cent. 1901 .... .20

Edward VII

SILVER

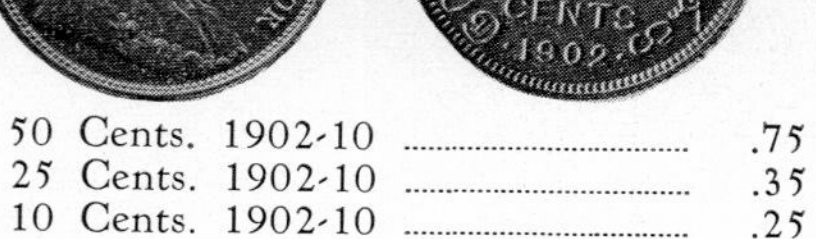

4 50 Cents. 1902-10 .... .75
5 25 Cents. 1902-10 .... .35
6 10 Cents. 1902-10 .... .25

COPPER-NICKEL

7 5 Cents. 1909, 10 .... .35

BRONZE

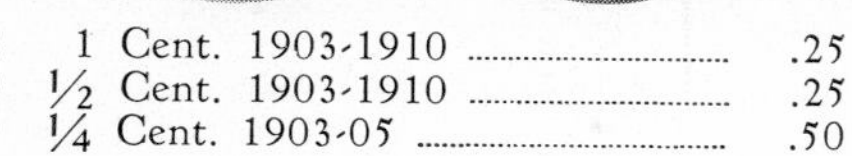

8 1 Cent. 1903-1910 .... .25
9 ½ Cent. 1903-1910 .... .25
10 ¼ Cent. 1903-05 .... .50

George V

SILVER

11 50 Cents. 1913-29 .... 1.00

12 25 Cents. 1911-26 .... .50
13 10 Cents. 1911-28 .... .25

COPPER-NICKEL

14 5 Cents. 1912-26 .... .15

COPPER

15 1 Cent. 1911-29. .... .25
16 ½ Cent. 1912-26 .... .25

George VI

SILVER

Type—Crowned head. Reverse type of preceding reign.

17 50 Cents 1942 .... 1.50
18 10 Cents 1941 .... .75

NICKEL-BRONZE

Type—Crowned head. ℞ Crowned value between leaves.

19 50 Cents 1943,45 .... .50
20 25 Cents 1943-45 .... .35

ALUMINUM-BRONZE

Crowned head ℞ Type of preceding reign.

21 10 Cents 1944. Scalloped edge ...... .15

22 2 Cents 1944. Similar .... .10

23 5 Cents 1942-45. Square .... .15

COPPER OR BRONZE

Types of preceding reign.

24 1 Cent 1937-45 .... .15
25 ½ Cent 1937,40 .... .10

The weight of the 5 Cents was reduced from 60 gr. to 50 gr. in 1945. The weight of the cent was reduced from 72.916 gr. to 36.458 gr. in 1943, 44, increased again in 1945.

CHILE

(Republica de Chile)

On the west coast of South America occupying the strip of land between the Andes and the South Pacific, south from Peru.

Mint: Santiago (S).

100 Centavos = 1 Peso. 10 Pesos = 1 Condor.

GOLD

No.	Description	Price
1	20 Pesos 1907, 1910-11, 1913-17. Bust of Republic to *l.* ℞ Arms	25.00
2	10 Pesos 1901. Similar	12.50
3	5 Pesos 1911. Similar	7.50

No.	Description	Price
4	100 Pesos or 10 Condores 1926. Head of Republic with coiled hair *l.* ℞ Arms	40.00
5	50 Pesos or 5 Condores 1926. Similar	20.00
6	20 Pesos or 2 Condores 1926. Similar	7.50

No.	Description	Price
7	100 Pesos 1932, 46, 47. Similar	40.00

SILVER

All of the silver and nickel coins are of the same type. Condor on rock *l.* ℞ Value in wreath. The special characteristic of the Chilean coinage is the frequent change of alloy (the fineness generally indicated on the pieces), and the change in size.

No.	Description	Price
8	Peso 1902-05. Fineness 0.7	1.00
9	50 Centavos 1902-05. Same	.50
10	20 Centavos 1906, 07. Fineness 0.5	.25
11	10 Centavos 1901-07. Same	.15
12	5 Centavos 1901-07. Same	.10
13	Peso 1910, 15. Fineness 0.9. Size 31.5 m.	.75
14	50 Centavos 1910. Same	.35
15	40 Centavos 1907, 08 (0.4)	.35
16	20 Centavos 1908-20. Same	.25
17	10 Centavos 1908-21. Same	.15
18	5 Centavos 1908-19. Same	.10
19	Peso 1915. Fineness 0.9. Size 27.5 m.	.50
20	20 Centavos 1916. Fineness 0.45	.25
21	10 Centavos 1915-19. Same	.15
22	5 Centavos 1915-17. Same	.10
23	Peso 1915, 17. Fineness 0.72. Size 28 m.	.50
24	Peso 1921-31. Fineness 0.5. Size 29 m.	.50

25	5 Pesos 1927. Fineness 0.9	6.00
26	2 Pesos 1927. Fineness 0.5	2.00
27	Peso 1932. Fineness (0.4)	.35

* When figures are in parenthesis the fineness is not given on the coins.

COPPER-NICKEL

28	1 Peso 1933-34,40 Same type as silver	.50
29	20 Centavos 1920-41	.15
30	10 Centavos 1920-41	.10
31	5 Centavos 1920-37	.10

COPPER

35	2½ Centavos 1904, 07, 08. Head *l.* ℞ Value in wreath	.25
36	2 Centavos 1919. Similar	.15
37	1 Centavo 1904, 1908, 1919. Similar	.10

Type—Bust of Bernardo O'Higgins
℞ Value

38	1 Peso 1942-49	.35
39	50 Centavos 1942,43	.25
40	20 Centavos 1942-49	.15
41	10 Centavos 1947	.15

CHINA. PLATE I

CHINA

Occupies a territory in the eastern part of Asia about one-third larger than continental United States. Formerly a great empire. Republic since 1911.

10 Cash = 1 Cent. 100 Cents = 1 Dollar. 1 Dollar = Tael 0.72 or 7 Mace and 2 Candareens. 10 Candareens = 1 Mace. 10 Mace = 1 Tael.

Emperor Kuang Hsu 1875-1908—Emperor Hsuan T'ung 1909-1911

Imperial Government Issues

Mint: Tientsin, Pei Yang Arsenal, 1896-1908.

Gold

A Gold tael 1906, 07. Chinese legend. ℞ dragon 300.00

---

3 Tael 1903. Chinese and Manchu legend. ℞ 29th YEAR OF KUANG HSU, dragon, HU POO. Rare. **Pl. I. No. 2** 40.00
4 5 Mace. Similar 10.00
5 2 Mace. Similar 5.00
6 1 Mace. Similar 5.00
7 ½ Mace. Similar 2.50
8 20 Cash 1905. Similar to Anhwei No. 21, but without incused center char. .... .35
9 10 Cash. Similar .... .25
10 5 Cash. Similar .... .25
11 2 Cash. Similar .... .25
12 Tael 1906. Similar to No. 20, with 32 lined triangle border. ℞ KUANG HSU NIEN TSAO, dragon, TAI-CH'ING-TI-KUO SILVER COIN 35.00
13 5 Mace. Similar, without border 10.00
14 2 Mace. Similar 7.50
15 1 Mace. Similar 5.00
16 20 Cash. Similar to No. 8, with CHIH incused at center .... .35
17 10 Cash. Similar .... .25
18 5 Cash. Similar .... .25
19 2 Cash. Similar .... .25
20 Dollar 1907. Similar to No. 12. **Pl. I. No. 3** 10.00
21 50 Cents. Similar, without border 7.50
22 20 Cents. Similar 4.00
23 10 Cents. Similar 2.00
24 20 Cash. Similar to No. 8, without HU PU .... .30
25 10 Cash. Similar .... .25
26 5 Cash. Similar .... .25
27 2 Cash. Similar .... .25
28 Dollar. Similar to CHEKIANG No. 5. ℞ Similar to No. 12. **Pl. I. No. 1** 7.50
29 20 Cents 1909. Similar 1.50
30 10 Cents. Similar 1.50
31 1 Cash. KUANG HSU, TSUNG, I WEN, date at sides. ℞ dragon .... .25
32 1 Cash undated, holed, brass, Chinese legends on both sides .25
33 Dollar (1910). Chinese and Manchu legend similar to No. 20, but without border. ℞ HSUAN T'UNG NIEN TSAO, dragon, flowers and $1. **Pl. I. No. 4** 10.00
34 ½ Dollar. Similar 2.00
35 ¼ Dollar. Similar 2.00
36 1/10 Dollar. Similar 2.00
37 Dollar 1911. Similar to No. 33, with larger flowers and date at bottom. ℞ 2 char. of value within dragon; ONE DOLLAR, varieties. **Pl. I. No. 5** 4.00
38 ½ Dollar. Similar. ℞ Dragon coiled to right about 2 char. of value 2.50
39 20 Cents. Similar 1.50
40 10 Cents. Similar .... .50
41 10 Cash. Similar. ℞ Dragon in small circle .... .35

Note—The various "Cash" denominations and 1 Cent pieces are in copper and brass. Denominations 5 Cents to dollar in silver.

CHINA. PLATE II

Provincial Issues during the Empire

ANHWEI

Mint: Anking, 1897-1899, 1902-1909, 1919-1926

19 1 Cen(t) or SEN, Chinese legend. ℞ AN-HWEI, dragon, value .50
20 10 Cash. Similar, 2 char. of value at bottom and Manchu at sides .20
21 20 Cash 1906. Chinese legend with HU PU at sides and incused HUAN at center. ℞ KUANG HSU NIEN TSAO, dragon, TAI-CH'ING-TI-KUO COPPER COIN 1.50
22 10 Cash. Similar. **Pl. II. No. 4** .75
23 20 Cash 1909. Similar to no. 21, but inscribed HSUAN T'UNG NIEN TSAO 1.50
24 10 Cash. Similar. **Pl. II. No. 5** .75

CHEKIANG

Mint: Hangchow, 1896-1906, 1919-1932

5 Dollar, no date (1902). Chinese legend. ℞ CHEH-KIANG PROVINCE, dragon, 7 MACE AND 2 CANDAREENS. Rare 150.00
6 50 Cents. Similar. ℞ 3 MACE AND 6 CANDAREENS. Rare
7 20 Cents. Similar. ℞ 1 MACE AND 4.4 CANDAREENS 1.00
8 10 Cents. Similar. ℞ 7.2 CANDAREENS .75
9 5 Cents. Similar. ℞ 3.6 CANDAREENS .75
10 20 Cash 1906. Similar to Anhwei No. 21, with CHE incused at center .35
11 10 Cash. Similar .25
12 5 Cash. Similar .50
13 2 Cash. Similar. ℞ Dragon only .50

PEI YANG

23 Dollar 1903. Chinese and Manchu legend. ℞ 29th YEAR OF KUANG HSU, dragon, PEI YANG 3.00
24 1 Cash undated. Chinese legend. ℞ 4 Chinese char. within 2 dragons .35
25 20 Cents 1905. Similar to No. 23. ℞ 31st YEAR OF KUANG HSU .75
26 Tael 1907. Chinese legend. ℞ 33rd YEAR OF KUANG HSU. dragon, PEI YANG 30.00
27 Dollar 1907. Similar. ℞ 33th YEAR OF KUANG HSU 4.00
28 Dollar 1908. Similar. ℞ 34th YEAR OF KUANG HSU 4.00
29 20 Cash. Chinese and Manchu legend. ℞ PEI YANG, dragon, TWENTY CASH .35
30 10 Cash. Similar .25

FUKIEN

Mint: Foochow, 1900—, Changchow, Moiting, Mamoi (Makiang) 1905—, Amoy, Shahsien, Yenping, Yuki, 1925—.

16 20 Cash 1906, 08. Similar to Anhwei No. 21, with incused MIN .75
17 10 Cash. Similar .50
18 2 Cash. Similar .25
19 10 Cash 1909. Similar to Anhwei No. 24 .50
20 20 Cents undated. Chinese and Manchu legend with lower chars. inverted. ℞ FOO-KIEN PROVINCE, dragon, 1 MACE AND 4.4 CANDAREENS .50
21 10 Cents. Similar. ℞ 7.2 CANDAREENS .50
22 5 Cents. Similar. ℞ 3.6 CANDAREENS .50

HONAN

Mint: Kaifeng, 1901-1914; Chengchow 1926—.

1 10 Cash 1906. Similar to Anhwei No. 22, with PIEN incused at center .25
2 10 Cash 1909, 11. Similar to Anhwei No. 24 .25

HUNAN

Mint: Changsha, 1896-1906, 1912-1926.

5 10 Cash (1906). Similar to Anhwei No. 22 with SIANG incused at center .25

HUPEH

Mint: Wuchang, 1893-1909, 1911-1938.

11 Tael 1904. Chinese and Manchu legend. ℞ HU-PEH PROVINCE, double dragons about Chinese char. of value, ONE TAEL, 2 Manchu char. at sides. 2 varieties. **Pl. II. No. 1** 10.00

Dies for these pieces were made at Osaka Mint, coins were struck at Wuchang.

12 20 Cash (1906). Similar to Anhwei No. 21 with 0 incused at center .75
13 10 Cash. Similar .50
14 5 Cash. Similar .35
15 1 Cash. Similar .25
16 Dollar (1909) undated. Chinese legend including HSUAN T'UNG. ℞ HU-PEH PROVINCE, dragon, 7 MACE AND 2 CANDAREENS 3.50
17 20 Cents. Similar. ℞ 1 MACE AND 4.4 CANDAREENS .75
18 10 Cents. Similar. ℞ 7.2 CANDAREENS .50
19 1 Cash 1908, brass. Chinese legend with 0 at center. ℞ Dragon .35
20 20 Cash (1911). Similar to Anhwei No. 23 .75
21 10 Cash. Similar .50
22 5 Cash. Similar .35

KIANGSI

Mint: Nanchang, 1901-1924, 1926-.

1 10 Cash, Chinese legend. ℞ KIANG-SI, dragon, 10 CASH, many varieties .25
2 10 Cash (1906). Similar to Anhwei No. 22, with KUNG at center .25

KIANGSU

2 10 Cash 1902, 03, 05. Chinese and Manchu legend. ℞ KIANG - SOO, dragon, TEN CASH, varieties .25
3 20 Cash (1906). Similar to Anhwei No. 21 with SU at center .35
4 10 Cash. Similar .25
5 2 Cash. Similar. ℞ dragon only .35

Mint: Tsingkiang (Chingkiang) 1905-07.

7 10 Cash (1905). Chinese legend. ℞ TSING-KIANG, dragon, TEN CASH, many varieties, some spelled CHING KIANG. **Pl. II. No. 6** 35
8 10 Cash (1906). Similar to Anhwei No. 22 with HUAI at center 35

KIANGNAN (Anhwei and Kiangsu)

Mint: Nanking, 1897-1929.

29 Dollar 1901. Chinese and Manchu legend. ℞ KIANG NAN PROVINCE, dragon, 7 MACE AND 2 CANDAREENS 2.00
30 20 Cents. Similar. ℞ 1 MACE AND 4.4 CANDAREENS .50
31 10 Cents. Similar ℞ 7.2 CANDAREENS .35
32 5 Cents. Similar. ℞ 3.6 CANDAREENS .35
33 Dollar 1901, 02, 03, 04, 05. Similar with initials HAH on obverse. **Pl. I. No. 6** 3.00
34 20 Cents. Similar 1.50
35 10 Cents. Similar .75

1904 issue has HAH combined with CH or TH. 1905 issue with and without initials YS inverted.

36 10 Cash 1902, 03, 04, 05. Chinese and Manchu legend. ℞ KIANG-NAN, dragon, TEN CASH, many varieties .25
37 10 Cash 1906, 07, 08. Similar to Anhwei No. 22 with NING at center .25
38 5 Cash. Similar .25
39 20 Cash (1909). Similar to Anhwei No. 23 .35
40 10 Cash. Similar .25

KWANGTUNG

Mint: Canton, 1889-1931, 1936-.

18 10 Cash 1906, 07. Similar to Anhwei No. 22 with YUEH at center .25
19 10 Cash 1908, 09. Similar to Anhwei No. 24 .25
20 Dollar (1909). Chinese legend. ℞ KWANG-TUNG PROVINCE, dragon, 7 MACE AND 2 CANDAREENS 3.50
21 20 Cents. Similar. ℞ 1 MACE AND 4.4 CANDAREENS .50

SHANTUNG

Mint: Tsinan, 1905-06.

3 10 Cash (1906). Similar to Anhwei No. 22 with TUNG at center .25
4 2 Cash. Similar .25

German occupation

Mint: Berlin, Germany.

5 10 Cents 1909 cu-ni. KIAUTSCHOU DEUTSCH-GEBIET surrounding imperial eagle and value. ℞ Chinese legend 2.50

6 5 Cents. Similar 2.00

SZECHUAN

Mints: Chengtu, 1898—, Chungking, 1913—, Yachow, Kangting, 1926—, Tachienlu, 1902—.

7 Rupee (1902). Head of mandarin. ℞ 4 Chinese char. in wreath, varieties 3.00

8 ½ Rupee. Similar 15.00

9 ¼ Rupee. Similar 15.00

10 20 Cash (1906). Similar to Anhwei No. 21 with CHUAN at center .... .35

11 10 Cash. Similar .... .25

12 Dollar (1909). Chinese legend. ℞ SZECHUEN PROVINCE, dragon, 7 MACE AND 2 CANDAREENS 5.00

13 50 Cents. Similar. ℞ 3 MACE AND 6 CANDAREENS. Rare ....

14 10 Cents. Similar. ℞ 7.2 CANDAREENS. Rare ....

15 5 Cents. Similar. ℞ 3.6 CANDAREENS. Rare ....

16 20 Cents. Similar to rev. on No. 12. ℞ Lion standing on peak, 3 clouds below 1.50

17 20 Cash 1909. Similar to Anhwei No. 23, with CHUAN at center .... .35

18 10 Cash. Similar .... .25

19 5 Cash. Similar .... .35

YUNNAN

Mint: Kunming (Yunnanfu) 1905—.

1 20 Cash (1906). Similar to Anhwei No. 21 with TIEN CHUAN at center .... .35

2 10 Cash. Similar .... .25

Also issued with TIEN or YUN at center.

3 Dollar (1907). Chinese legend. ℞ YUN-NAN PROVINCE, dragon, 7 MACE AND 2 CANDAREENS 3.50

4 50 Cents. Similar. ℞ 3 MACE AND 6 CANDAREENS 3.00

5 20 Cents. Similar. ℞ 1 MACE AND 4.4 CANDAREENS 1.00

6 Dollar. Similar with smaller inner circle and characters. ℞ dragon within beaded circle. No legend **Pl. II. No. 3** 3.50

7 50 Cents. Similar 2.00

8 20 Cents. Similar 1.00

9 10 Cents. Similar .... .75

10 Dollar (1909). Similar to No. 3, but HSUAN T'UNG 3.50

11 50 Cents. Similar 3.00

12 Dollar 1910. Similar to No. 10 but with KENG HSU above 4.00

MANCHURIAN VICEROYALTY FENGTIEN

Mint: Mukden, 1898-1909.

8 Dollar 1903. Chinese and Manchu legend. ℞ FUNG-TIEN PROVINCE, dragon, 7 MACE AND 2 CANDAREENS 2.00

9 20 Cents 1904. Similar. ℞ 1 MACE AND 4.4 CANDAREENS... .75

Two varieties differing in diameter and thickness.

10 20 Cash 1904, 05, brass. Chinese and Manchu legend. ℞ FUNG-TIEN PROVINCE, dragon, 20 CASH .... .35

11 10 Cash 1903, 04, 05, 06, brass. Similar. ℞ FEN-TIEN or FUNG-TIEN. **Pl. II. No. 7** .... .25

12 20 Cash 1905, 06, 07, 09. Similar to Anhwei No. 21 with FENG at center .... .35

13 10 Cash 1905, 07. Similar .... .25

14 10 Cash 1909. Similar to Anhwei No. 24 .... .25

KIRIN

Mint: Kirin Arsenal, 1882-1911.

25 Dollar 1901, 02, 03, 04, 05, 06, 07, 08. Chinese legend with Yin-Yang symbol at center. ℞ KIRIN PROVINCE, dragon, 7 . CAINDARINS . 2. **Pl. II. No. 2** ... 3.50

26 50 Cents. Similar. ℞ 3 . CAINDARINS . 6 ... 2.50

27 20 Cents. Similar. ℞ 1 MACE AND 4.4 CANDAREENS ... 1.50

28 10 Cents. Similar. ℞ CANDARINS . 72 ... 1.50

29 5 Cents. Similar. ℞ 36 CANDAREENS ... 1.50

30 Dollar 1906, 07, 08. Similar, but with potted plant at center ℞ 7 . CAINDARINS . 2 ... 4.00

31 50 Cents. Similar. ℞ 3 . CANDARINS . 6 ... 2.00

32 20 Cents. Similar. ℞ 1 MACE AND 4.4 CANDAREENS ... 1.00

33 10 Cents. Similar. ℞ CANDARINS 72 ... .50

34 5 Cents. Similar. ℞ 36 CANDARINS ... .50

35 Dollar 1908. Similar with 2 Manchu char. at center. ℞ 7 . CAINDARINS . 2 ... 10.00

36 50 Cents. Similar. ℞ 3 . CANDARINS . 6 ... 1.50

37 20 Cents. Similar. ℞ 1 MACE AND 4.4 CANDAREENS ... 1.00

38 Dollar 1908. Similar, but with figure 11 at center. ℞ 7 . CAINDARINS . 2 ... 17.50

39 20 Cents. Similar, with figure 2 at center. ℞ 1 MACE AND 4.4 CANDAREENS ... 3.50

40 2 Cash. KUANG HSU T'UNG PAO and 2 Manchu char. at center. ℞ Chinese legend with CHI at center within circle ... 1.00

41 20 Cents (1909). Similar to Chinese legend with CHI at center. ℞ HSUAN T'UNG NIEN TSAO, dragon, TAI-CH'ING-TI-KUO SILVER COIN ... 5.00

42 20 Cash. Similar ... .35

43 10 Cash. Similar ... .25

MANCHURIAN PROVINCES

Shingking, Kirin, and Heilungkiang.

44 Dollar 1907. Chinese and Manchu legend. ℞ 33rd YEAR OF KUANG HSU, dragon, MANCHURIAN PROVINCES ... 5.00

45 50 Cents. Similar ... 2.50

46 20 Cents. Similar, varieties ... 2.00

47 10 Cents. Similar ... 1.50

48 20 Cents 1909. Chinese and Manchu legend. ℞ FIRST YEAR OF HSUAN T'UNG, dragon, MANCHURIAN PROVINCES, varieties ... 1.50

49 20 Cents 1909. Similar. ℞ 1st YEAR OF HSUAN TUNG ... 1.25

50 20 Cents. Similar. ℞ MANCHURIAN PROVINCES, dragon, 1 MACE AND 4.4 CANDAREENS, varieties ... .50

Republic of China
1911-1949

GENERAL ISSUES

Mints: Shanghai, Tientsin, Hankow, Nanking.

Gold

B 20 Dollars 1916. Chinese legend of HUNH HSIEN, dragon. ℞ Bust of Yuan Shih-kai facing left 100.00

C 20 Dollars 1919. Chinese legend above and within wreath. ℞ Similar bust of Yuan Shih-kai surrounded by an ornamental border. **Pl. V. No. 1** 75.00

D 10 Dollars 1919. Similar 35.00

Silver

1 Dollar 1912. Small bust of Sun Yat-sen to l. surrounded by a Chinese legend. ℞ MEMENTO, value, BIRTH OF REPUBLIC OF CHINA. **Pl. III. No. 6** 3.00

2 Dollar. Similar. ℞ THE REPUBLIC OF CHINA, value ONE DOLLAR. **Pl. III. No. 7** 3.50

3 20 Cents. MEMENTO, bust of Dr. Sun, BIRTH OF REPUBLIC OF CHINA. ℞ Crossed flags within Chinese legend. **Pl. V. No. 20** 1.25

4 10 Cents. Similar to No. 1, rare ....

5 Dollar. Bust of Li Yuan-hung in uniform and military cap within Chinese legend. ℞ Similar to No. 2. **Pl. III. No. 8** 10.00

6 Dollar. Similar but without cap. **Pl. III. No. 9** 5.00

7 Dollar 1914. Bust of Yuan Shih-kai nearly facing. ℞ Value within wreath 15.00

8 Dollar 1914, 17, 18, 20, 21. Bust of Yuan Shih-kai to l. ℞ Similar. **Pl. IV. No. II** 1.50

9 50 Cents 1914. Similar 1.00

10 20 Cents 1914, 16, 20. Similar. **Pl. V. No. 13** .... .75

11 10 Cents 1914, 16. Similar .... .50

12 5 Cents 1914, nickel. Similar .75

13 Dollar. Chinese legends, value within wreath, ONE DOLLAR. ℞ Yuan Shih-kai in military uniform with plumed cap. **Pl. III. No. 10** 5.00

14 Dollar 1916. Winged dragon with Chinese legends above and below. ℞ Similar to No. 13. **Pl. III. No. 10a** 5.00

15 Dollar 1923. Chinese legend above dragon and phoenix. ℞ Similar to No. 8. **Pl. IV. No. 15** 7.50

16 20 Cents 1926. Chinese legend. ℞ Similar to obv. No. 15 .... .75

17 10 Cents. Similar .... .50

18 Dollar 1927. Chinese legend, Sun Yat-sen facing. Rare ....

19 Dollar 1929. Chinese legend, Sun Yat-sen facing. ℞ Similar to No. 8. Rare ....

20 Dollar 1929. THE REPUBLIC OF CHINA, crossed flags above hemisphere, value. ℞ Similar to obv. of No. 19. Rare

21 20 Cents 1929. Similar to No. 19 .... 2.50

22 Dollar 1932. Chinese legend, Sun Yat-sen in profile to l. ℞ 3 birds, junk, sun and value. **Pl. IV. No. 18** 7.50

23 Dollar 1933, 34. Similar. ℞ birds and sun omitted. **Pl. IV. No. 19** 2.00

Reduced standard

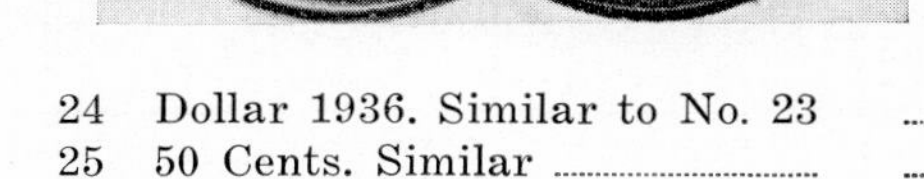

24 Dollar 1936. Similar to No. 23 ....

25 50 Cents. Similar ....

CHINA. PLATE III

CHINA. PLATE IV

CHINA. PLATE V

Copper or Brass

26 10 Cash (1912). Crossed flags, Chinese legend. ℞ THE REPUBLIC OF CHINA. TEN CASH. Value in Chinese in wreath. Many varieties. **Pl. V. No. 50** .... .25

27 10 Cash (1912). Similar. ℞ Value in Chinese. Wreath in outer circle. **Pl. V. No. 51** .25

28 10 Cash (1912). Crossed flags. ℞ THE REPUBLIC OF CHINA. TEN CASH. Wreath and sun in circle .... .25

29 5 Cash (1912). Similar .... .50

30 20 Cash 1920, 22. Crossed flags. Chinese legend. ℞ Value in Chinese in wreath. Varieties. **Pl. V. No. 49** .... .35

Nickel

31 20 Cents 1935, 36, 37, 38, 39 40, 41, 42. Bust of Sun Yat-sen to l. with Chinese legend above. ℞ Ancient pu (spade) and value .... .50

32 10 Cents 1935, 36, 38, 39, 40, 41, 42. Similar .... .35

33 5 Cents 1935, 36, 37, 38, 39, 40, 41, 42. Similar .... .25

34 50 Cents 1936, 42, 43. Similar

35 Dollar 1936. Similar ....

Aluminum

36 5 Cents 1940. .... .15

37 1 Cent 1940. .... .15

Brass or Bronze

38 2 Cents 1917. Wreath of barley around four sided panel. ℞ Circle. Center hole ....

39 1 Cent 1917. Similar .... .25

40 ½ Cent 1917. Similar .... .15

41 1 Cent 1936. Spade design. ℞ Sun in circle .... .20

42 ½ Cent 1936. Similar .... .15

43 1 Cent 1939, 40. Similar. Brass .... .20

44 ½ Cent 1939, 40. Similar. Brass .... .15

FORMOSA

Nationalist China Issue

Type — Bust of Sun Yat Sen
℞ — Map of Formosa

1 5 Chiao 1949. Silver ....

2 2 Chiao 1950. Aluminum ....

3 1 Chiao 1949. Bronze ....

CHINA. PLATE VI

Provincial Issues during the Republic

CHEKIANG

14 20 Cents 1924. Chinese legend. ℞ CHE-KIANG PROVINCE, large 20 at center, TWENTY CENTS 1.00
15 20 Cents 1924. Similar, but with crossed flags. ℞ 4 Chinese char. at center .75
16 10 Cents. Similar 1.00

HOPEI

Japanese puppet state.

Mint: Osaka, Japan.

Copper-Nickel

1 20 Cents 1937. Pagoda. ℞ Value in grain wreath .50

2 10 Cents 1937. Similar .35

3 5 Cents 1937. Stars and bars in circle .25

Bronze

Type of nickel 5 Cents

4 1 Cent 1937 .25
5 ½ Cent 1937 .20

FUKIEN

23 20 Cents 1911. Chinese legend. ℞ FOO-KIEN, incused MIN at center of 9 pairs of line-connected balls. **Pl. V. No. 27** .75
24 2 Cash (1911) cast brass, Chinese legend. ℞ Flags at sides of center round hole 1.50
25 1 Cash. Similar 5.00
26 20 Cents (1912). Similar to No. 23 with stars replacing date. ℞ MADE IN FOO-KIEN MINT, 3 flags, 1 MACE AND 4.4 CANDAREENS 1.25
27 10 Cents. Similar. ℞ 7.2 CANDAREENS 1.00
28 10 Cash. Similar. ℞ FOO-KIEN COPPER COIN, TEN CASH .50
29 20 Cents. Chinese legend. ℞ FOO-KIEN PROVINCE, large 20, 1 MACE AND 4.4 CANDAREENS .50
30 10 Cents. Similar. ℞ 7.2 CANDAREENS .50
31 20 Cents 1923. Similar to No. 26 1.50
32 20 Cents 1924. Similar 1.50
33 10 Cents. Similar .75
34 20 Cents 1924. Similar to No. 31. ℞ Similar to No. 26 .50
35 20 Cents 1927. Chinese legend over bust of Sun Yat-sen. ℞ Crossed flags with value between. **Pl. V. No. 21** 2.00
36 10 Cents. Similar 1.50
37 20 Cents 1927. Chinese legend with figures 2 at sides. ℞ Crossed flags inside Chinese legend 2.00
38 20 Cents 1927. Similar to No. 37 but with date below 2.00
39 20 Cents 1928, 31. Chinese legend surrounding sun with 20 at center. ℞ Memorial monument below Chinese legend, varieties. **Pl. V. No. 28** 1.50
40 10 Cents. Similar 1.00
41 20 Cents. Crossed flags inside Chinese legend. ℞ Similar to No. 39 1.50
42 10 Cents. Similar .75

HONAN

3 200 Cash 1912. Chinese legend above ears of grain and flowers. ℞ HO-NAN, crossed flags, 200 CASH 1.50
4 100 Cash. Similar. **Pl. VI. No. 65** 1.25
5 50 Cash. Similar 1.00
6 20 Cash. Similar 1.00
7 10 Cash. Similar .35
8 10 Cash. Similar, with Chinese char. of value at center .35
9 50 Cash. Similar. ℞ CHINA replacing HO-NAN 1.00

10 20 Cash. Similar 1.00

11 100 Cash 1931. Sun inside Chinese legend. ℞ Value in wreath. **Pl. VI. No. 66** 2.00

12 50 Cash. Similar 1.25

HUNAN

6 10 Cash (1914). Chinese legend. ℞ HU-NAN, 9-pointed star, TEN CASH .... .35

7 10 Cents 1915. HUNG HSIEN Chinese legend. ℞ Dragon facing left surrounding 2 char. of value 1.50

8 10 Cash 1915. Similar. ℞ FIRST YEAR OF HUNG SHUAN, sheaf of grain, TEN CASH 1.50

9 20 Cash. Chinese legend about crossed flags, ℞ REPUBLIC OF CHINA, grain, TWENTY CASH .35

10 20 Cash. Similar. ℞ 20 CASH .35

11 Dollar 1922. PA KUA inside wreath surrounded by Chinese legend. ℞ THE REPUBLIC OF CHINA, crossed flags and flowers, ONE DOLLAR. **Pl. IV. No. 31** 7.50

12 20 Cash. Similar. **Pl. V. No. 70** .... .75

13 10 Cash. Similar .... .50

HUPEH

23 20 Cents 1920. Yuan Shih-kai in profile with 2 Chinese char. at sides, 9th year. ℞ Wreath with Chinese legend of value 1.00

KANSU

Mint: Lanchow

2 Dollar 1914. Yuan Shih-kai in profile with KAN SU at sides. ℞ Value in Chinese inside wreath of rice 20.00

3 Dollar 1928. 12-rayed sun at center, Chinese legend above, Manchu below. ℞ Bust of Sun Yat-sen with date in Chinese 20.00

KIANGSI

3 10 Cash (1912). Chinese republican legend. ℞ KIANGSEE, 9-pointed star, TEN CASH .25

KIANGSU

6 Dollar 1912. Chinese legend above and below bust of Chen Teh-chien. ℞ THE REPUBLIC OF CHINA, 2 Chinese char. of value and sprays of rice, ONE DOLLAR 5.00

KWANGSI

Mints: Kweilin, 1905-, Nanning, 1919-21.

1 1 Cent 1919, brass. Chinese legend. ℞ KWANG-SI PROVINCE, large 1, ONE CENT, varieties. Rare ....

2 20 Cents 1919, 20, 22, 23, 24, 25. Chinese legend. ℞ KWANG-SI PROVINCE, large 20, TWENTY CENTS .... .50

3 10 Cents 1920. Similar .... .35

4 20 Cents 1926, 27. Similar with stalks of rice added on both sides .... .35

KWANGTUNG

22 20 Cents 1912-15, 17-24. Chinese legend. ℞ KWANG-TUNG PROVINCE, large 20, TWENTY CENTS .... .50

23 10 Cents 1913-14, 22. Similar........ .35

24 1 Cent 1912, 14-16, 18. Chinese legend. ℞ KWANG-TUNG PROVINCE, large 1 in circle, ONE CENT .... .25

25 2 Cents 1918. Similar .... .75

26 5 Cents 1919, 23 nickel. Similar. ℞ Large 5 and wreath .50

27 5 Cents 1912 nickel. Similar. ℞ Flag .... .50

28 20 Cents 1924. Similar. ℞ Bust. **Pl. V. No. 38** 2.50

29 20 Cents 1928-29. Chinese legend and wreath. ℞ Bust 2.00

30 10 Cents. Similar 1.00

31 1 Cent 1936. Chinese legend over 5 rams. ℞ Value and stalks of rice .... .75

KWEICHOW

3 Dollar. Chinese legend. ℞ Chinese legend above and below automobile within beaded circle 12.50

SHANTUNG

Gold

7 20 Dollars 1926. Chinese legend and wreath. ℞ dragon and phoenix ....

8 10 Dollars. Similar ....

SHANSI

Mint: Taiyuan, 1919—.

1 20 Cents (1912). Chinese legend. ℞ Crude dragon and poorly lettered MANCHURIAN PROVINCES, 1 MACE AND 4.4 CANDARINS. Rare ....

2 10 Cash. Crossed flags inside Chinese legend, SHAN SI at sides. ℞ 2 Chinese char. within wreath of rice and barley. Rare ....

SZECHUAN

20 Dollar 1912, 13, 14. Chinese legend with poppy at center. ℞ Chinese legend over circle of 18 small circles with HAN at center. **Pl. IV. No. 42** 3.50

21 50 Cents. Similar 2.00

22 20 Cents. Similar 1.50

23 10 Cents. Similar 1.00

24 100 Cash brass, Similar. **Pl. VI. No. 80** 1.50

25 50 Cash. Similar .... .50

26 20 Cash. Similar .... .75

27 10 Cash. Similar .... .35

28 5 Cash. Similar .... .25

29 200 Cash 1913. Chinese legend surrounding circle with value and grain inside. ℞ THE REPUBLIC OF CHINA, crossed flags, 200 CASH. **Pl. VI. No. 77** 4.00

30 100 Cash. Similar 1.50

31 200 Cash 1926. Chinese legend surrounding circle with CHUAN at center. ℞ 4-sided panel surrounding heads of grain. **Pl. VI. No. 78** 2.50

32 100 Cash. Similar 1.50

33 50 Cash. Similar .... .75

YUNNAN

13 50 Cash 1912, brass. Similar to No. 22, varieties. **Pl. VI. No. 84** 4.00

Gold

14 10 Dollars. Single Chinese char. intended for TIEN (Yunnan) within wreath of 4 rice stalks. ℞ 4 char. of value. Rare ....

15 5 Dollars. Rare 25.00

16 10 Dollars (1917). 5 Chinese chars. in vertical line, 5 dots at sides. ℞ Plain. Rare ....

17 5 Dollars. Similar. Rare ....

18 10 Dollars (1919). Chinese legend encircling crossed flags and star. ℞ Bust T'ang Chi-yao with Chinese legend above, 2 varieties 40.00

19 10 Dollars. Similar, with figure 1 below flags, varieties. **Pl. V. No. 4** 35.00

20 5 Dollars. Similar, with figure 2 below flags varieties. **Pl. V. No. 5** 20.00

---

21 50 Cents (1915). Chinese legend above and below beaded circle enclosing crossed flags. ℞ T'ang Chi-yao facing right, varieties 12.50

22 50 Cents (1916). Similar obv. ℞ T'ang Chi-yao nearly facing, varieties. **Pl. V. No. 46** 3.50

23 10 Cents 1923, nickel. Chinese legend. ℞ YUN-NAN PROVINCE, flag, 10 CENTS .... .75

24 5 Cents. Similar .... .50

25 50 Cents 1932. Chinese legend above crossed flags 3.00

26 20 Cents. Similar 1.00

CHINESE SOVIET

Hupeh Anhwei Honan Provinces

Silver

1 Dollar 1932. Globe with sickle and hammer superimposed. ℞ Chinese insc.: "Come and unite the Proletariat of the whole World." Value "One Dollar" in circle 35.00

2 Dollar 1932. Similar but part of reverse inscription in outer circle in Russian 100.00

Szechuan and Shensi Provinces

Silver

3 Dollar 1934. Similar but date below. ℞ Chinese insc. Value in inner circle 25.00

Copper

5 500 Cash 1934. Hammer and sickle on star. ℞ Chinese insc. Value 500 in circle 5.00

6 200 Cash 1934. Date in figures 1934. ℞ Similar. Value 200 in circle 4.00

All rare.

Kiangsi Province

Silver

4 20 Cents 1932, 33. Globe in wreath. ℞ Chinese inscription 5.00

Copper

7 5 Cents 1932. Map of China surrounded by Chinese legend, hammer and sickle superimposed. ℞ Star and value 2.50

8 1 Cent 1932. Large 1 with hammer and sickle. ℞ Type of No. 7 .... 2.00

CHINESE CHARACTERS FOR CYCLICAL DATES

辛丑	1901 27th year of Kuang Hsü Hsin-ch'ou
壬寅	1902 28th year of Kuang Hsü Jen-yin
癸卯	1903 29th year of Kuang Hsü Kuei-mao
甲辰	1904 30th year of Kuang Hsü Chia-ch'en
乙巳	1905 31st year of Kuang Hsü I-ssu
丙午	1906 32d year of Kuang Hsü Ping-wu
丁未	1907 33d year of Kuang Hsü Ting-wei
戊申	1908 34th year of Kuang Hsü Wu-shen
己酉	1909 1st year of Hsuan T'ung Chi-yu
庚戌	1910 2d year of Hsuan T'ung Keng-hsu
辛亥	1911 3d year of Hsuan T'ung Hsin-hai
壬子	1912 1st year of the Republic Jen-tzu
癸亥	1923 12th year of the Republic Kuei-hai
甲子	1924 13th year of the Republic Chia-tzu

These dates, and no others, appear on 20th century coins.

No reference is made to other dates which are shown numerally under the republic.

See also Chinese Turkestan No. 35

CHINESE TURKESTAN

CHINESE TURKESTAN
(Sinkiang)

Comprises all Chinese dependencies lying between Mongolia on the north and Tibet on the south.

Local Mints: Kashgar, Urumchi and Aksu.

10 Miscals = 1 Tael. Legends in Chinese and Turki.

Empire 1901-1911

GOLD

A 2 Mace 1902. Ration coin ....

B 1 Mace 1902. Similar. ....
Minted in Sinkiang. Very rare.

General Issue

Struck in China for circulation in Sinkiang

SILVER

1	Tael. varieties **(1)**	25.00
2	5 Miscals. Varieties **(2)**	5.00
3	4 Miscals. Varieties **(3)**	10.00
4	2 Miscals. Varieties	
5	1 Miscal. Varieties	

6	Tael. Sungarei	
7	2 Miscals. Sungarei	
8	1 Miscal. Sungarei	

Kashgar Mint

9	5 Miscals 1901-1904	7.50
10	3 Miscals 1901-1904	5.00
11	2 Miscals 1901-1904	3.50
12	5 Miscals 1905. **(7)**	7.50
13	3 Miscals 1905. Similar	
14	Tael 1907, 1908	
15	5 Miscals 1908,1909. Similar **(8)**	7.50
16	2 Miscals 1908, 1909. Similar	
17	5 Miscals 1909-1911 **(22)**	12.50

18	5 Miscals 1911. Rations	
19	3 Miscals 1911. Rations	
20	2 Miscals 1911. Rations	

Urumchi Mint

21	5 Miscals 1902-1907 **(17)**	6.50
22	3 Miscals Similar **(18)**	5.00
23	2 Miscals Similar **(19)**	3.50
24	1 Miscal. Similar	

COPPER

25 5 Cash Kuang Hsu ....

The bold faced numbers in brackets refer to the numbers on plate.

Empire

Hsuan T'ung

26 10 Cash Hsuan T'ung 1910, 1911

Republic 1911-1949

SILVER

27 Tael 1912. **(12)** 30.00
28 5 Miscals 1912, similar 7.50
29 5 Miscals 1913, 1914. Kashgar **(13)** ....
30 Tael 1917, 1918. Urumchi **(20)**... 20.00

31 Dollar, 1949 (see CCJ Sept.-Oct. 1950) ....

The bold faced numbers in brackets refer to the numbers on plate.

COPPER

32 20 Cash (1912). Varieties **(14)** 3.50

33 10 Cash (1912), 1913, 1914.
Kashgar. Similar. Varieties **(15)** 2.50

33a 10 Cash Cast. Aksu ....

34 5 Cash (1912), 1913. Kashgar.
Similar. Varieties 2.00

35 10 Cash 1930 (see CCJ Sept.-Oct. 1950). This coin has the cyclical date for 1930............

The bold faced numbers in brackets refer to the numbers on plate.

COLOMBIA

(Republica de Colombia)

Situated in the extreme northwest of South America extending up the Isthmus of Panama to the Republic of Panama.

Mints: Bogota, Medellin, Philadelphia, San Francisco, Denver, Birmingham, Brussels.

100 Centavos = 1 Peso.

GOLD

1 5 Pesos 1913-19. Workman cutting stone. ℞ Arms 15.00

2 2½ Pesos 1913-19. Similar 7.50

3 10 Pesos 1919-24. Large head of Bolivar *r*. ℞ arms 30.00

4 5 Pesos 1919-24. Similar 15.00

5 2½ Pesos 1919-20. Similar 7.50

6 5 Pesos 1922-30. Smaller head of Bolivar *r*. ℞ Arms 15.00

7 2½ Pesos 1924, 28. Similar 15.00

SILVER

8 50 Centavos 1902-08. Head of Liberty. ℞ Arms 1.50

9 5 Centavos 1902. Similar .... .25

Type: Head of Bolivar. ℞ Arms.

10 50 Centavos 1912-34 .... 1.00

11 20 Centavos 1911-38,41 .... .35

12 10 Centavos 1911-42 .... .25

COPPER-NICKEL

Type: Head of Liberty. ℞ Value.

13	5 Pesos paper money 1907-14	.25
14	2 Pesos paper money 1907-14	.20
15	1 Peso paper money 1907-14	.15

Type: Head of Liberty. ℞ Value.

16	5 Centavos. 1918-41, 46, 47	.15
17	2 Centavos. 1918-40, 46, 47	.10
18	1 Centavo. 1920-40, 46, 47 48	.10

BRONZE

Type: Liberty Cap in wreath. ℞ Value.

19	5 Centavos. 1942-45	.15
20	2 Centavos 1948	.10
21	1 Centavo. 1942-48	.10

NEW SILVER COINAGE

22	50 Centavos 1947, 48. Head of Bolivar. ℞ Value	1.50
23	20 Centavos 1945-48 Head of Santander. ℞ Value	.50
24	10 Centavos 1945-48. Similar	.25

SANTANDER

Issued during a revolt by General Rammon Gonzales Valencia.

BRASS

26 50 Centavos 1902. 50 in large C. above SANTANDER. 1902

27 20 Centavos 1902. Similar

28 10 Centavos 1902. Similar but 10 above C.

These were made from the brass from old cartridges and are in relief on one side and intaglio on the other.

COSTA RICA

(Republica de Costa Rica)

In the southern part of Central America with Nicaragua on the north and Panama on the south.

Mints: San José, Philadelphia, London

100 Centimos = 1 Colon.

100 Centavos = 1 Colon.

GOLD

1 5 Colones 1901. Head of Columbus *r.* ℞ Arms 7.50
2 2 Colones 1901-28. Similar 3.00

SILVER

3 50 Centimos 1902-18. Arms ℞ Value. Fineness .900 ..... 1.25
4 10 Centimos 1905-14. Similar ..... .25
5 5 Centimos 1905-14. Similar ..... .10
6 10 Centimos 1917, 22. Small letters. Fineness .500 ..... .25

7 1 Colon 1923. Stamped on 50 Cent. of 1903 and other dates... 1.50
8 50 Centimos 1923. Stamped on 25 Cent. of 1893 and other dates 1.25
9 25 Centimos 1924. Fineness .650 .75

MINOR COINS

Type: Arms of the Republic.
℞ Value in wreath.

10 2 Centimos. Copper-Nickel 1903 .10
11 10 Centavos. Brass 1917-19 ..... .25
12 5 Centavos. Brass 1917-19 ..... .15
13 10 Centimos. Brass or Bronze 1920-22, 1929, 1936, 1938, 1940-43, 1946, 47 ..... .25
14 5 Centimos. Brass or Bronze. 1920-22, 1929, 1936, 1941-43, 1946, 47 ..... .15

(Varying proportions of copper, tin and zinc were used in the alloys from which the last two pieces were made).

COPPER-NICKEL

Banco Internacional de Costa Rica (B.I.C.R.)

Philadelphia Mint

15 1 Colon 1935 ..... .35

16 50 Centimos 1935 ..... .25
17 25 Centimos 1935 ..... .15

Banco Nacional de Costa Rica (B.N.C.R.)

London Mint

18 2 Colones 1948 ..... .50
19 1 Colon 1937,48 ..... .35
20 50 Centimos 1937,48 ..... .25
21 25 Centimos 1937,48 ..... .15

BRASS

San Jose Mint

22 25 Centimos 1944-46 ..... .15

CRETE

An island in the Mediterranean Sea south of Greece. A Department of Greece.

Mint: Paris.

100 Lepta = 1 Drachma.

Prince George of Greece as High Commissioner—1898-1906

SILVER

1 — 5 Drachmas 1901. Head of Prince George *r.* ℞ Arms on mantle 10.00

2 — 2 Drachmas 1901. Similar 4.00

3 — 1 Drachma 1901. Similar 2.00

4 — 50 Lepta 1901. Similar. ℞ Arms 1.00

COPPER-NICKEL

5 — 20 Lepta 1900. Crown. ℞ Value in wreath .... .25

6 — 10 Lepta 1900. Similar .... .20

7 — 5 Lepta 1900. Similar .... .15

BRONZE

8 — 2 Lepta 1900-01. Similar .... .15

9 — 1 Lepton 1900-01. Similar .... .10

CUBA

(Republica de Cuba)

The largest island of the West Indies group, lying about 90 miles south of Florida.

Mint: Philadelphia.

100 Centavos = 1 Peso.

GOLD

Type — Head of Marti. ℞ Arms

1	20 Pesos 1915-16		60.00
2	10 Pesos 1915-16		25.00
3	5 Pesos 1915-16		12.50
4	4 Pesos 1915-16		12.50
5	2 Pesos 1915-16		5.00
6	1 Peso 1915-16		3.00

SILVER

Type: Star. ℞ Arms.

7	1 Peso 1915-16, 1932-34	2.00

8	40 Centavos 1915-21	.75
9	20 Centavos 1915-32,48,49	.50
10	10 Centavos 1915-20,48,49	.25

MINOR COINS

Type: Value on Star. ℞ Arms.

11	5 Centavos. Copper-nickel 1915, 16, 20. (a) Aluminum bronze 1943. (b) Brass 1946	.15
12	2 Centavos. Copper-nickel 1915, 16	.10
13	1 Centavo. Copper-nickel 1915, 16, 20. (a) Aluminum bronze 1943. (b) Brass 1946	.10

SILVER

14	1 Peso 1934-39. Head of Liberty. ℞ Arms	3.50

CURACAO

Two groups of islands in the West Indies north of the coast of Venezuela. Netherlands Colony.

Mints: Utrecht, Philadelphia, Denver

100 Cents = 1 Guilder.

SILVER

No.	Description	Price
1	¼ Guilder 1900. Head of Queen Wilhelmina *l.* ℞ Arms	.75
2	1/10 Guilder 1901. Similar	.50

New coinage with head of Queen Wilhelmina as on current Dutch coins. Denver mint 1944, Utrecht 1947.

No.	Description	Price
3	1 Rixdollar 1944. Crowned arms	5.00
4	1 Guilder 1944. Arms	1.00
5	¼ Guilder 1944, 47	.50
6	1/10 Guilder 1944, 47	.25
7	1/10 Guilder 1948	.25

MINOR COINS

No.	Description	Price
8	5 Cents 1948. Copper-nickel	.15
9	5 Cents 1948. Bronze	.15
10	2½ Cents 1944,47,48. Bronze	.15
11	1 Cent 1944, 47, 48. Bronze	.10

During the war 1, 5, 10, 25 cent pieces were struck in Philadelphia for use in Curacao and Surinam. They are of the regular Dutch type with palm tree mint mark.

CYPRUS

An island in the Mediterranean Sea off the coast of Turkey. A British Crown Colony.
Mint: London.
9 Piastres=1 Shilling.

Victoria

SILVER

1	18 Piastres.	1901.	2.50
2	9 Piastres.	1901.	1.50
3	4½ Piastres.	1901.	1.00
4	3 Piastres.	1901.	.75

BRONZE

5	1 Piastre.	1901.	.65
6	½ Piastre.	1901.	.50
7	¼ Piastre.	1901.	.35

Edward VII

SILVER

8	18 Piastres.	1907.	2.00
9	9 Piastres.	1907.	1.25

BRONZE

10 1 Piastre. 1908. .25
11 ½ Piastre. 1908. .25
12 ¼ Piastre. 1902, 1905, 1908. .15

George V
SILVER

13 45 Piastres. 1928. 12.50
14 18 Piastres. 1913, 1921. 2.50
15 9 Piastres. 1913, 1919, 1921. 1.50
16 4½ Piastres. 1921. 1.00

COPPER-NICKEL

17 1 Piastre. 1934. .25
18 ½ Piastre. 1934. .15

These pieces have a scalloped edge.

BRONZE

19 1 Piastre. 1922, 1927, 1930-31. .25
20 ½ Piastre. 1922, 1927, 1930-31. .20
21 ¼ Piastre. 1922, 1926. .15

George VI
SILVER

Type—Crowned head *l.* ℞ Lions.

22 18 Piastres 1938, 40 2.00
23 9 Piastres 1938, 40 1.00
24 4½ Piastres 1938 .50

COPPER-NICKEL

25 1 Piastre 1938, 41 .15
26 ½ Piastre 1938 .10

27 2 Shillings 1947 .75
28 1 Shilling 1947 .50

BRONZE

29 1 Piastre 1942-46 .15
30 ½ Piastre 1942-45 .10

With title—
"GEORGIVS SEXTVS DEI GRATIA REX"

COPPER-NICKEL

31 2 Shillings 1949
32 1 Shilling 1949

BRONZE

33 1 Piastre 1949
34 ½ Piastre 1949

CZECHOSLOVAKIA

CZECHOSLOVAKIA

(Ceskoslovenska Republika)

A Central European country. Occupied by Germany in 1938. Reestablished in 1945.
Mint: Kremnica.
100 Haleru = 1 Korona.

GOLD

Commemorative Medals

1 4 Ducat size 1928. Commemorating tenth anniversary of republic. Saint above arms. ℞ Saint guiding plow drawn by demon... 35.00

2 2 Ducat size 1928. Similar.............. 20.00

Commemorative Coins

3 2 Ducats 1923, 1929-38. Lion on shield. ℞ Half figure of St. Wenzeslaus facing 20.00

4 1 Ducat 1923-38. Similar 10.00
The first thousand 1 ducat pieces of 1923 show the date thus 28-x-1923, and were numbered consecutively. They were issued to commemorate the fifth anniversary of the Republic.

5 10 Ducats 1929-38. Lion on shield. ℞ St. Wenzeslaus on horse 125.00

6 5 Ducats 1929-38. Similar 60.00

SILVER

7 20 Korona 1933, 34. Arms. ℞ Three standing figures 4.00

8 10 Korona 1928. Bust of Pres. Masaryk r. ℞ Arms. 2.50
Issued to commemorate the 10th anniversary of the Republic.

9 10 Korona 1930-33. Arms. ℞ Seated female figure and linden branch 2.00

10 5 Korona 1928-32. Lion. ℞ Smelting furnace and large 5 (27 mm) 1.50

11 20 Korona 1937. Bust of Masaryk. ℞ Arms 3.50
Commemorating the death of Masaryk founder and first President.

COPPER NICKEL

15 5 Korona 1925-27. Similar to 10 but 30 mm .... .50

16 1 Korona 1922-38. Lion. ℞ Kneeling female with sheaf of wheat .... .35

17 50 Haleru 1921, 22, 1924-27, 1931. Lion. ℞ 50 over wreath of linden and wheat .... .25

18 25 Haleru 1933. Lion. ℞ Large 25 .20

19 20 Haleru 1921-38. Lion. ℞ Sheaf of wheat .... .15

BRASS OR BRONZE

25 10 Haleru 1922-38. Lion. ℞ Bridge .... .15

26 5 Haleru 1923-39. Similar .... .10

ZINC

27 2 Haleru 1923-25. Similar .... .10

NICKEL

28 5 Korona 1938-39. Lion. ℞ Smelting furnace and large 5 (27 mm) .... .75

SLOVAKIA

SILVER

30 50 Korona 1944. Tiso 7.50

31 20 Korona 1939. Tiso 10.00

32 20 Korona 1941. Saints Cyril and Methodius 5.00

33 10 Korona 1944. Three figures—Pribena 3.00

NON PRECIOUS METALS

34 5 Korona. Nickel 1939. Head of Father Hlinka 2.00

35 1 Korona. Copper Nickel 1940-42. Arms (22 mm) .... .50

36 50 Haleru. Brass 1941; (a) Aluminum 1943; (b) Zinc 1943. Plough in field .... .35

37 20 Haleru. Brass 1940; (a) Aluminum 1942; (b) Zinc 1943. Nitra Castle .... .25

38 10 Haleru. Brass 1939. (a) Aluminum 1942. Bratislava Castle........ .15

39 5 Haleru. Brass 1942. (a) Aluminum 1942. Value 5 .... .15

PROTECTORATE OF BOHEMIA-MORAVIA

40 1 Korona. Zinc 1940-44. Value between branches .... .25

41 50 Haleru. Zinc 1940-44. Two Sheaves. Type of No. 17 .... .20

42 20 Haleru. Zinc 1940-44. Wheat Ears. Type of No. 19 .... .15

43 10 Haleru. Zinc 1940-43. Charles Bridge .... .10

REPUBLIC OF CZECHOSLOVAKIA

(Restored)

SILVER

44 50 Korona 1947. Female standing 2.50

45 100 Korona 1948. Six hundredth anniversary of Charles Univ. Prague 5.00

46 50 Korona 1948. Third anniversary of liberation from Nazis ... 2.50

47 100 Korona 1948. Thirtieth anniversary of liberation from Austria 5.00

48 100 Korona 1949. Seven hundredth anniversary of granting of mining privileges of Jihlava ....

49 100 Korona 1949. Stalin 70th birthday ....

50 50 Korona 1949. Stalin ....

MINOR COINS

51 2 Korona 1947,48. Copper-nickel. Janosik **(45)** ...... .50

52 1 Korona 1946,47. Copper-nickel. 1950 Aluminum. Similar to No. 16 but 21 m.m...... .35

53 50 Haleru 1947-50. Bronze Similar to No. 17 but 20 mm ...... .25

54 20 Haleru 1948. Bronze. Type of No. 19 .... .15

5 Gulden
1
10
1932
Freie
Stadt Danzig
1/2 Gulden
1927
4
6
2
1923
7
11
8
9
14
15
16
17
13
12
NEC
TEMERE
NEC TIMIDE

DANZIG

DANZIG

(Die Freie Stadt Danzig)

Situated on the Baltic Sea, with the Polish corridor on the west, Poland on the south, and East Prussia (of which it was formerly a part) on the east. Now a part of Poland pending a peace treaty with Germany.

Mints: Berlin, Utrecht.

100 Pfennigs = 1 Gulden.

GOLD

One thousand gold pieces of 25 Gulden denomination were struck in Berlin in 1923 and 1930 bearing the design of Neptune and a trident. These however were in the nature of souvenirs rather than a circulating medium.

SILVER

1 5 Guldens 1923, 24, 27, Church. ℞ Arms between lions 7.50

2 2 Guldens 1923, 24. Small Galley and inscription. Utrecht Mint... 2.50

3 1 Gulden 1923, 24. Small Galley and inscription. Utrecht Mint... 1.50

4 ½ Gulden 1923, 24, 27. Conventional brig. ℞ Inscription. Utrecht and Berlin (1927) .... .75

5 5 Guldens 1932. Similar. Reduced size. Utrecht Mint 6.00

6 5 Guldens 1932. Grain Elevator. ℞ As above. Berlin Mint 8.00

7 2 Guldens 1932. Large Galley. Berlin Mint 2.50

COPPER-NICKEL

8 10 Pfennigs 1923. Arms in hexagonal frame. ℞ Inscription...... 20

9 5 Pfennigs 1923, 1927, 28. Similar .... .15

All struck at Berlin.

NICKEL

10 1 Gulden 1932. Large 1. ℞ Crowned Crosses .... .50

11 ½ Gulden 1932. Similar .... .35

12 10 Guldens 1935. City Hall. ℞ Arms between lions 6.00

13 5 Guldens 1935. Ship. ℞ Similar 2.50

ALUMINUM BRONZE

14 10 Pfennigs 1932. Cod fish. ℞ Inscription .... .25

15 5 Pfennigs 1932. Flounder. ℞ Similar .... .15

BRONZE

16 2 Pfennigs 1923, 1926, 1937. Crowned crosses. ℞ Inscription .... .15

17 1 Pfennig, 1923, 1926, 27, 1929-30, 1937. Similar .... .10

ZINC

18 10 Pfennigs 1920. Arms. ℞ Value in panel .... .35

7
16
10 KRONER
15
20 KRONER
1
CHRISTIAN IX KONGE AF DANMARK
MED GUD FOR ÆRE OG RET
9
2 KRONER
17
18
2 KRONER
19
20
1870-1930
21
KONGE AF DANMARK
25
2 KRONER
DANMARK

DENMARK

DENMARK

(Kongeriget Danmark)

Occupies the peninsula of Jutland between the North Sea and the Baltic Sea. A constitutional monarchy.

Mint: Copenhagen.
100 Ore = 1 Krone.

Christian IX—1863-1906

SILVER

1 2 Kroner 1903. (40 years reign). Bust *r.* ℞ Seated figure *l.* 2.00
2 25 Ore 1904-05. Head *r.* ℞ Value between dolphin and wheat ear .... .25
3 10 Ore 1903-05. Similar .... .15

BRONZE

4 5 Ore 1902, 1904, 1906. Crowned C IX. ℞ as above........ .20
5 2 Ore 1902, 1906. Similar .... .15
6 1 Ore 1902, 1904. Similar .... .10

Frederik VIII—1906-1912

GOLD

7 20 Kroner 1908-12. Head *l.*........ 20.00
8 10 Kroner 1908-09. Similar 10.00

SILVER

9 2 Kroner 1906. (On the succession). Bust of Frederik VIII *l.* ℞ Bust of Christian IX *l.* 1.50
10 25 Ore 1907, 1911. Head *l.* ℞ Value in ornamental circle .... .25
11 10 Ore 1907, 1910-12. Similar .10

BRONZE

12 5 Ore 1907-08, 1912. Crowned F 8 in monogram. ℞ Value in circle .... .20
13 2 Ore 1907, 1909, 1912. Similar .15
14 1 Ore 1907, 1909-10, 1912. Similar .... .10

Christian X 1912-1947

GOLD

15 20 Kroner 1913-31. Head r. ℞ Arms 20.00
16 10 Kroner 1913-17. Similar 10.00

SILVER

17 2 Kroner 1912 (On the Succession) 1.50
18 2 Kroner 1915-16 .... 1.25
19 2 Kroner 1923 (Silver Wedding) 1.50
20 2 Kroner 1930 (60th Birthday) 1.25
21 2 Kroner 1937 (25 Years of Reign) 1.50

21a 2 Kroner 1945 (75th Birthday)... 1.50
22 1 Krone 1915-16. Similar to 18...... .75
23 25 Ore 1913-20. Crowned CX. ℞ Value .... .25
24 10 Ore. 1914-19. Similar .... .10

MINOR METALS

Type: Crowned CX. ℞ Crown

25 2 Kroner. Aluminum bronze 1924-38 .... 1.00
26 1 Krone. Aluminum bronze 1924-38 .... .50
27 ½ Krone. Aluminum bronze 1924-26 .... .25

27a 1 Krone. Aluminum bronze. 1942. Head. ℞ Value .... .50

Type: Crowned CX. ℞ Value

28 25 Ore. Copper-nickel 1920-23 .... .25

30 10 Ore. Copper-nickel 1920-23 .... .15

32 5 Ore. Bronze 1913-23; (A) Iron 1918-19 .... .25

33 2 Ore. Bronze 1913-23; (A) Iron 1918-19 .... .15

34 1 Ore. Bronze 1913-23; (A) Iron 1918-19 .... .10

Type: Crown above hole. CX-R at sides

29 25 Ore. Copper-nickel 1924-41; (A) Zinc 1944 .... .25

31 10 Ore. Copper-nickel 1924-41; (A) Zinc 1942-44 .... .10

Type: Crowned CX. ℞ Value—holed

35 5 Ore. Bronze 1927-41; (A) Aluminum 1941; (B) Zinc 1943 .15

36 2 Ore Bronze 1926-41; (A) Aluminum 1941; (B) Zinc 1942-45 .... .10

37 1 Ore. Bronze 1926-41; (A) Aluminum 1941; (B) Zinc 1944 .10

Frederik IX 1947-

Type—Head r. ℞ Arms

41 2 Kroner. Aluminum Bronze 1947,48

42 1 Krone. Aluminum Bronze 1947,48

43 25 Ore 1948. Copper-nickel ....

44 10 Ore 1948. Copper-nickel ....

45 5 Ore 1948-50. Zinc ....

46 2 Ore 1948-50. Zinc ....

47 1 Ore 1948-50. Zinc ....

DANISH WEST INDIES

A group of islands in the West Indies, east of Puerto Rico. Former Danish Colony, purchased by the United States in 1917.

Mint: Copenhagen.

500 Bits = 100 Cents = 5 Francs = 1 Daler.

Christian IX—1863-1906

GOLD

1 50 Francs or 10 Dalers 1904. Christian IX to *l.* ℞ Seated figure ... 75.00

2 20 Francs or 4 Dalers 1904, 05. Similar ... 20.00

SILVER

3 2 Francs or 40 Cents 1905. Bust to *l.* ℞ Three female figures ... 2.00

4 1 Franc or 20 Cents 1905. Similar ... 1.00

5 50 Bits or 10 Cents 1905. Similar. ℞ Olive branch or value ... .50

NICKEL

6 25 Bits or 5 Cents 1905. Crowned C9 in monogram. ℞ Trident, caduceus and sickle ... .25

BRONZE

7 10 Bits or 2 Cents 1905. Similar to above ... .15

8 5 Bits or 1 Cent 1905. Similar .10

9 2½ Bits or ½ Cent 1905. Similar .10

Frederik VIII—1906-1912

SILVER

10 2 Francs or 40 Cents 1907. Frederik to *l.* ℞ Three female figures ... 4.00

11 1 Franc or 20 Cents 1907. Similar ... 2.00

Christian X—1912-1917

BRONZE

12 5 Bits or 1 Cent 1913. Crowned CX in monogram. ℞ Trident, caduceus and sickle ... .10

DOMINICAN REPUBLIC

(Republica Dominicana)

Occupies about two-thirds of the Island of Santo Domingo in the West Indies, situated between Cuba and Puerto Rico.

Mints: Philadelphia, Ottawa
100 Centavos = 1 Peso.

SILVER

Type—Liberty head ℞ Arms

1 Peso 1939 .... 3.50

2 Half Peso 1937, 47 .... 1.25
3 25 Centavos 1937, 39, 42-47 .... .50
4 10 Centavos 1937, 39, 42 .... .35

COPPER-NICKEL

Same type as silver

5 5 Centavos 1937, 39, 45 .... .15

BRONZE

Type—Palm tree ℞ Arms.

6 1 Centavo 1937, 39, 41, 42, 47, 49 .10

EAST AFRICA AND UGANDA PROTECTORATE

(After 1920 East Africa)

Mints: London, Birmingham (H). King's Norton Metal Co. (KN).
100 Cents = 1 Shilling.

Edward VII
SILVER

1 50 Cents. 1906, 1909-10. King's head *r.* ℞ Lion and mountains 1.00

2 25 Cents. 1906-10. Similar .... .65

COPPER-NICKEL

3 10 Cents. 1907, 1910. Central hole, crown and ornaments. ℞ Elephant's tusks .... .75
4 5 Cents. 1908. Similar .... .50

5 1 Cent. 1907, 09, 10. Similar........ .60
6 ½ Cent. 1909. Similar .... .35

ALUMINUM

7 1 Cent. 1907, 08. Similar .... .60
8 ½ Cent. 1908. Similar 2.00

George V
SILVER

9 50 Cents 1911-19. King's bust *l.* ℞ Lion and mountains........ 1.00
10 25 Cents. 1911-18. Similar........ .50

NICKEL

11 10 Cents. 1911-13, 1918. Crown and ornaments around central hole. ℞ Elephant's tusks........ .50
12 5 Cents. 1913-19. Similar........ .35
13 1 Cent. 1911-18. Similar........ .25

EAST AFRICA

(After 1920)

All territory in East Africa under British control. British Protectorates—Kenya, Uganda, Tanganyika, Nyasaland.

Mints: London, Birmingham (H), King's Norton Metal Co. (KN), Bombay, Calcutta

1 Florin= 1 Rupee. 100 Cents=1 Shilling.

George V

SILVER

1 1 Florin. 1920-21. King's bust *l.* ℞ Lion and mountains 3.50

2 1 Shilling. 1920-21. Similar 2.00

2a 25 Cents. 1920, 21. Similar 1.25

New Standard

3 Shilling 1921-26. Similar........ 1.25

4 50 Cents [½ Shilling] 1921-24........ .75

COPPER-NICKEL

5 10 Cents. 1920-21. Crown and ornaments around central hole. ℞ Elephant's tusks .... .50

6 5 Cents. 1921. Similar .... .35

7 1 Cent. 1921 .... .25

COPPER

8 10 Cents. 1921-35, 1933-35. Similar to nickel pieces........ .50

9 5 Cents. 1921-35. Similar........ .35

10 1 Cent. 1922-31. Similar........ .25

Edward VIII

COPPER

11 10 Cents. 1936. Similar .... .25

12 5 Cents. 1936. Similar .... .25

George VI

SILVER

13 1 Shilling. 1937-46 .... 1.00

14 50 Cents. 1937-44 .... .50

COPPER OR BRONZE

Type of preceding reigns.

15 10 Cents. 1937-45 .... .35

16 5 Cents. 1937-43 .... .25

17 1 Cent. 1942. Bronze .... .15

With title—"GEORGIVS SEXTVS REX"

COPPER-NICKEL

18 1 Shilling 1948 ....

19 50 Cents 1948 ....

ECUADOR

(Republica del Equador)

On the Pacific coast in northwest South America, bounded by Colombia on the north and Peru on the east and south.

Mints: Philadelphia, Lima, Birmingham, Gorham Mfg. Co. of New York, Mexico City.

100 Centavos = 1 Sucre.
25 Sucres = 1 Condor.

GOLD

1 1 Condor. 1928. Bust of Bolivar ℞ Arms. Birmingham Mint 30.00

SILVER

Type: Head of Sucre. ℞ Arms.

2 2 Decimos de Sucre (20 Centavos) 1912, 1914-16 .... .50
3 1 Decimo de Sucre (10 Centavos) 1902-16 .... .25
4 ½ Decimo de Sucre (5 Centavos) 1902-15 .... .15

COPPER-NICKEL

Type: Arms. ℞ Value.

5 5 Centavos 1909-18 .... .15
6 2 Centavos 1909 15
7 1 Centavo 1909 .... .10
8 ½ Centavo 1909 .... .10
9 10 Centavos 1917-18. ℞ DIEZ CENTAVOS .... .25
10 10 Centavos 1919. ℞ 10 CENTAVOS .... .25
11 5 Centavos 1919 .... .15
12 2½ Centavos 1917 .... .15

Type: Head of Bolivar in wreath. ℞ Arms.

13 10 Centavos 1924-25 .... .25
14 5 Centavos 1924-25 .... .15

Law of March 4, 1927

SILVER

Type: Head of Sucre. ℞ Arms.

15 2 Sucres 1928, 30 .... 1.00
16 1 Sucre 1928, 30, 34 .... .50
17 5 Decimos de Sucre (50 Centavos) 1928, 30 .... .35

NICKEL

Type: Head. ℞ Arms.

18 10 Centavos 1928, 29 .... .25
19 5 Centavos 1928, 29 .... .15
20 2½ Centavos 1929 Arms. ℞ Value .... .15

BRONZE

21 1 Centavo 1928 Arms. ℞ Value... .10

Laws of 1937-42

NICKEL

22 1 Sucre 1937. Head of Sucre. ℞ Arms .... .35

MINOR COINS

Type: Arms. ℞ Value.

23 20 Centavos. Nickel 1937; (a) Bronze 1942-44 .... .20

24 10 Centavos. Nickel 1937; (a) Bronze 1942, 43 .... .15

25 5 Centavos. Nickel 1937; (a) Bronze 1942-44 .... .10

SILVER

26 5 Sucres 1943. Head of Sucre. ℞ Arms 2.50

27 2 Sucres 1944. Similar 1.00

COPPER-NICKEL

30 1 Sucre 1947 ....

31 20 Centavos 1947 ....

32 10 Centavos 1947 ....

33 5 Centavos 1946-47 ....

44
45
6
37
24
25
20
PIASTRES
1916
10
PIASTRES
1916
1929
1917
28
10
TEN
MILLIEMES
65
56
23
100
PIASTRES
66

E G Y P T

EGYPT

Under Turkey

(Misr)

Occupies the northeast corner of Africa with the Mediterranean Sea on the north and the Red Sea on the east. A Kingdom.

Mints: Berlin, Brussels, Birmingham (H), Vienna.
1 Ochr-el-Guerche = 1/10 Guerche or Piastre.
100 Milliemes = 1 Guerche or Piastre.
100 Piastre = 1 Pound Egyptian.

All of the coins for Egypt under Turkish rule have the Toughra, or peculiar emblem of the Sultan, generally within a wreath, and on the silver with quivers at the bottom, and an Arabic inscription within a wreath or circle of stars on the reverse. The coins are similar to the Turkish coins and can be distinguished from the Turkish piece by the name MISR written in Arabic.

Abdul Hamid II—1876-1909

All of the coins for this ruler bear the accession date in Turkish figures (1293 of the Hegira) or 1876, with the year of the reign at the top of the reverse, and in this case the denomination is under the Toughra; or under the Toughra when the value is expressed elsewhere. The regnal year for 1901 is 27 and for 1909 is 34.

SILVER

1 20 Guerche 1901-07. Toughra in wreath. ℞ Insc. in wreath 3.00
2 10 Guerche 1901-07 .... 1.50
3 5 Guerche 1901-07 .... .75
4 2 Guerche 1901-07 .... .35
5 1 Guerche 1901-07 .... .15

NICKEL

6 10 Ochr-el-Guerche (1 Piastre). 1901, 1903-05, 1907. Toughra in wreath. ℞ Insc. in circle of stars .... .25
7 5 Ochr-el-Guerche 1901, 1903-5, 1907. Toughra in closed wreath. ℞ Value and insc. .... .20
8 2 Ochr-el-Guerche 1901-02, 1904, 1906-07. Similar .... .15
9 1 Ochr-el-Guerche 1901-02, 1904-07. Similar .... .10

BRONZE

10 ½ Ochr-el-Guerche (1/20 Piastre). 1901-02, 1904-07, 1909. Toughra. ℞ Inscription .10
11 ¼ Ochr-el-Guerche (1/40 Piastre). 1902-04, 1906-07, 1909. Similar .... .10

Mohammad V—1909-1915

The coins of this ruler are similar to those of Abdul Hamid but the date is (1327 A.H.) or 1909 A.D. and the regnal years from 1 to 6.

SILVER

12 20 Guerche 1910-12, 1915. Toughra in wreath with quivers. ℞ Insc. in wreath 3.00
13 10 Guerche 1910-12, 1915. Similar 1.25
14 5 Guerche 1910-14. Similar .... .50
15 2 Guerche 1910-11. Similar .... .25
16 1 Guerche 1910-11 .... .15
All struck at Birmingham.

COPPER-NICKEL

17 10 Ochr-el-Guerche 1910-12, 1916 (year 6). Toughra in wreath. ℞ Insc. in circle of stars .... .25
18 5 Ochr-el-Guerche 1910-12, 1916 (year 6). Toughra in closed wreath. ℞ Value and inscription .... .20
19 2 Ochr-el-Guerche 1910-12. Similar .... .15
20 1 Ochr-el-Guerche 1910-12, 1914. Similar .... .10

BRONZE

21 ½ Ochr-el-Guerche 1910-14. Toughra. ℞ Inscription .... .10
22 ¼ Ochr-el-Guerche 1910-1914. Similar .... .10

INDEPENDENT

Mints: Bombay, Birmingham, King's Norton, Calcutta, London, Budapest, Pretoria.

Sultan Husein Kamil—1915-1917

GOLD

23 100 Piastres 1916. Sultan Husein Kamil in Arabic in wreath. ℞ Value and insc. in wreath 30.00

SILVER

24 20 Piastres 1916-17. Similar to the gold 3.00
25 10 Piastres 1916-18. Similar 1.25
26 5 Piastres 1916-18. Similar .... .50
27 2 Piastres 1916-18. Similar .... .25

COPPER-NICKEL

28 10 Milliemes 1916-17. Central hole. Inscription on both sides .25
29 5 Milliemes 1916-17. Similar .... .20
30 2 Milliemes 1916-17. Similar .... .15
31 1 Millieme 1917. Similar .... .10

These pieces were struck at Birmingham and King's Norton for several years after, or into the reign of Fuad, but still bearing the date 1917.

BRONZE

32 ½ Millieme 1917. Similar to the silver .... .15

King Fuad I—1917-1936

As Sultan

SILVER

33 10 Piastres 1920. Arabic inscription. ℞ Insc. and value 3.50
34 5 Piastres 1920. Similar 2.50
35 2 Piastres 1920. Similar 1.50

As King, after 1922

GOLD

36 500 Piastres 1922. Bust *r.* ℞ Arabic insc. in circle 150.00
37 500 Piastres 1929, 1930. Bust *l.* ℞ Similar 150.00
38 100 Piastres 1922. Bust *r.* ℞ Similar 25.00
39 100 Piastres 1930. Bust *l.* ℞ Similar 25.00
40 50 Piastres 1923-24, 1926, 1928-29. Bust *r.* ℞ inscription 12.50
41 50 Piastres 1930. Bust *l.* ℞ Similar 12.50
42 20 Piastres 1923-26, 1928-29. Bust *r.* ℞ Similar 7.50
43 20 Piastres 1930. Bust *l.* ℞ Similar 7.50

SILVER

44 20 Piastres 1923, 1925. Bust *r.* ℞ Arabic insc. in circle 10.00
45 20 Piastres 1929, 1933. Bust *l.* ℞ Similar 10.00
46 10 Piastres 1923, 1925-26. Bust *r.* ℞ Similar 2.50
47 10 Piastres 1929, 1933. Bust *l.* ℞ Similar 2.50
48 5 Piastres 1923, 1925-26. Bust *r.* ℞ Similar 1.00
49 5 Piastres 1929, 1933. Bust *l.* R Similar 1.00
50 2 Piastres 1923, 24. Bust *r.* ℞ Similar .... .50
51 2 Piastres 1929. Bust *l.* ℞ Similar .... .50

COPPER-NICKEL

52 10 Milliemes 1924. Bust *r.* ℞ Value and insc. .... .25
53 10 Milliemes 1929, 1933-35. Bust *l.* ℞ Similar .... .25
54 5 Milliemes 1924. Bust *r.* ℞ Similar .... .20
55 5 Milliemes 1929, 1934-35. Bust *l.* ℞ Similar .... .20
56 2½ Milliemes 1933. Bust *l.* ℞ Similar. Octagonal .... .15
57 2 Milliemes 1924, 1929. Bust *r.* ℞ Similar .... .15
58 2 Milliemes 1929. Bust *l.* ℞ Similar .... .15

BRONZE

59 1 Millieme 1924-25. Bust *r.* ℞ Similar .... .20
60 1 Millieme 1929, 1932, 1934-35. Bust *l.* ℞ Similar .... .20
61 ½ Millieme 1924-25. Bust *r.* ℞ Similar .... .15
62 ½ Millieme 1929, 1932. Bust *l.* ℞ Similar .... .15

Farouk I—1937-

SILVER

63 20 Piastres 1937. Bust *l.* ℞ Value and dates 7.50

64 10 Piastres. 1937 .... 3.00
65 5 Piastres. 1937 .... 1.25
66 2 Piastres. 1937 .... .50
66a 2 Piastres. 1944. Hexagonal .... .50
Errata—No. 63 appears on the plate as No. 6

GOLD

Commemorating the Royal wedding.

Similar type to silver.

67 500 Piastres 1938 .... 225.00
68 100 Piastres 1938 .... 35.00
69 50 Piastres 1938 .... 12.50
70 20 Piastres 1938 .... 7.50

COPPER-NICKEL

Type—Bust to *l.* ℞ Value and dates.

71 10 Milliemes 1938 .... .25
72 5 Milliemes 1938 .... .20
73 2 Milliemes 1938 .... .15
74 1 Millieme 1938. Center hole.......... .10

BRONZE

Type of preceding.

75 1 Millieme 1938 .... .15
76 ½ Millieme 1938 .... .10

77 10 Milliemes 1943. Scalloped edge .25
78 5 Milliemes 1943. Scalloped edge .20
79 2 Milliemes 1943 .... .15
80 1 Millieme 1943,46 .... .10

ERITREA

On the northeast African coast of the Red Sea. Formerly an Italian Colony. Occupied by British Colonial Forces in 1940.

Mint: Rome.

SILVER

1 1 Talari 1918...... Female bust *r.* ℞ Crowned eagle 20.00

ESTONIA

(Eesti Vabariik)

Borders on the Baltic Sea and the Gulf of Finland in northern Europe. Now part of the USSR.
Mints: Reval, Copenhagen, Hirsch of Berlin, Tallinn.
100 Penni = 1 Mark.
100 Senti = 1 Kroon.

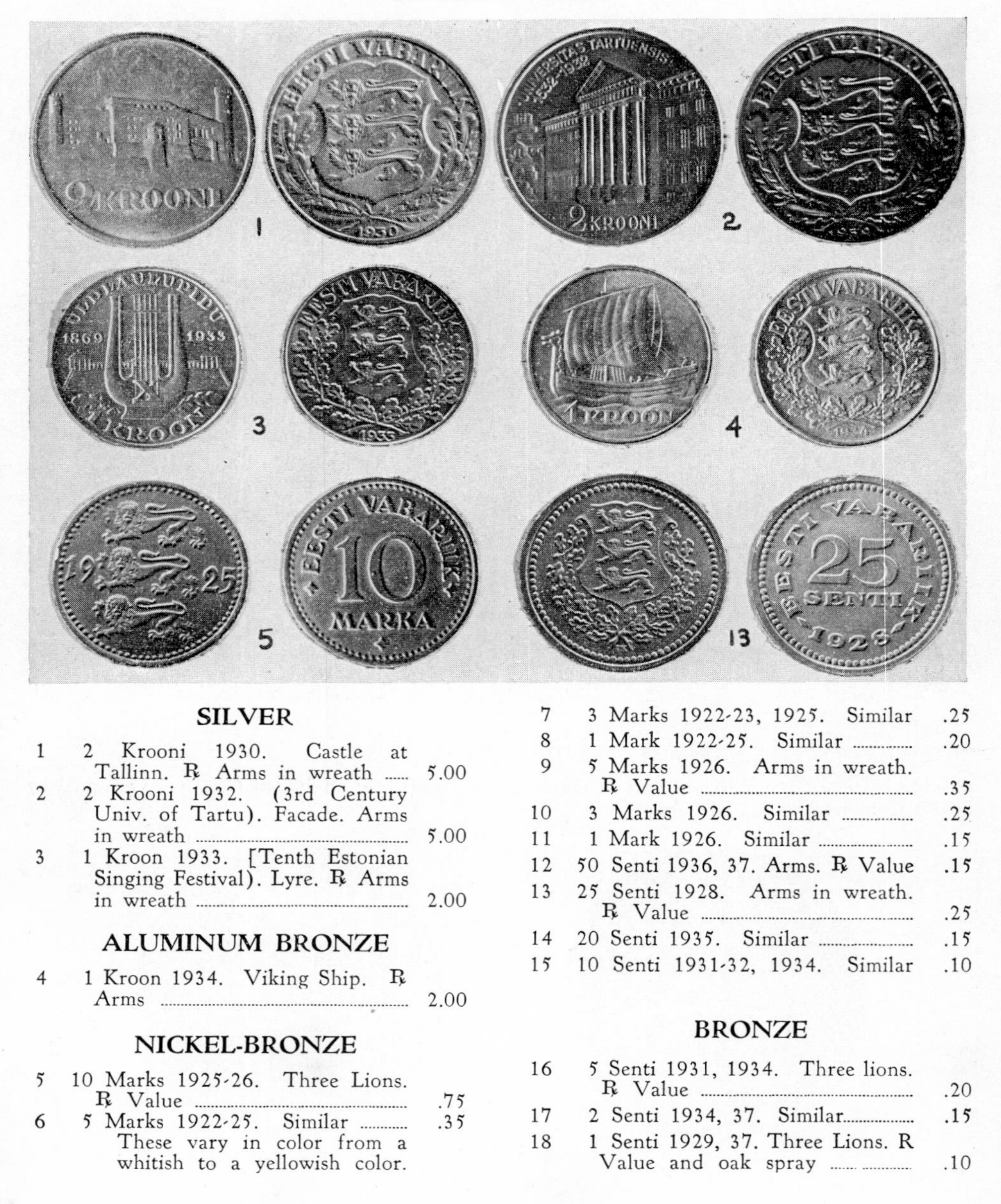

SILVER

1	2 Krooni 1930. Castle at Tallinn. ℞ Arms in wreath	5.00
2	2 Krooni 1932. (3rd Century Univ. of Tartu). Facade. Arms in wreath	5.00
3	1 Kroon 1933. [Tenth Estonian Singing Festival). Lyre. ℞ Arms in wreath	2.00

ALUMINUM BRONZE

4	1 Kroon 1934. Viking Ship. ℞ Arms	2.00

NICKEL-BRONZE

5	10 Marks 1925-26. Three Lions. ℞ Value	.75
6	5 Marks 1922-25. Similar	.35
	These vary in color from a whitish to a yellowish color.	
7	3 Marks 1922-23, 1925. Similar	.25
8	1 Mark 1922-25. Similar	.20
9	5 Marks 1926. Arms in wreath. ℞ Value	.35
10	3 Marks 1926. Similar	.25
11	1 Mark 1926. Similar	.15
12	50 Senti 1936, 37. Arms. ℞ Value	.15
13	25 Senti 1928. Arms in wreath. ℞ Value	.25
14	20 Senti 1935. Similar	.15
15	10 Senti 1931-32, 1934. Similar	.10

BRONZE

16	5 Senti 1931, 1934. Three lions. ℞ Value	.20
17	2 Senti 1934, 37. Similar	.15
18	1 Senti 1929, 37. Three Lions. R Value and oak spray	.10

ETHIOPIA
(Abyssinia)

In northeast Africa, bounded by Eritrea, French and British Somaliland on the northeast, Italian Somaliland on the southeast, Kenya Colony on the south and the Anglo-Egyptian Soudan on the west. Emperor Haille Selassie fled at the time of the Italian invasion. Upon the re-occupation by British forces in 1941 Selassie was declared ruler again.

Mints: Paris (A), Addis Ababa.
16 Guerche = 1 Menelik Talari.
100 Cents or Matoñas = 1 Talari.

Menelik II—1889-1913
GOLD

Gold coins were struck at Addis Ababa on various occasions from the dies of silver coins. They bear the head of Menelik and have the lion of Judah on the reverse. They were probably not for general circulation but were gift or presentation pieces used by royalty, and were mostly struck after Menelik's death.

Gold coins of three denominations but of varying weights bearing the head of Menelik with a wreath at bottom and with the lion of the Addis Ababa type were said to have been struck to commemorate the crowning of the Empress Zauditu in 1916. Their denominations were 1 Wark, ½ Wark and ¼ Wark. The dies were undoubtedly made in Paris at an earlier date.

Paris Mint.

SILVER

1 — 1 Talari or Ber 1901-04. Head *r.* ℞ Lion. Designed by Chaplain, no mint letter but marks of cornucopia and torch 5.00

2 — ½ Talari or Agod 1915, 1925. Similar but by Lagrange. The design of the 1894 issue. Mint Mark A 2.00

3 — ¼ Talari or Roob 1915-1925. Similar 1.00

4 — 1/16 Talari or Gersh. 1903-28. Similar .... .50

Addis Ababa Mint. Since 1896.

The dies were made in Paris but bear no mint marks. The striking does not compare with those struck in Paris.

SILVER

5 — ½ Talari. *Obv.* of the Lagrange type. ℞ Similar to Chaplain type 1.50

6 — ¼ Talari. Similar 1.00

7 — 1/16 Talari. Similar .... .50

COPPER

8 — Besa. From dies of the unused ⅛ Talari but with value obliterated. Most of these pieces were struck after Menelik's death .... .35

8a — ½ Besa. From dies of 1/16 Talari 3.00

Empress Zauditu—1916-1930

GOLD

9 — 3½ Warks. Crowned head of Zauditu *l.* ℞ Die of ½ Talari, 31 mm. ....

10 — 1 Wark. Similar. ℞ Die of ⅛ Talari 20 mm. The obverse dies by H. Dammann ....

Haile Selassie I—1930-1936

GOLD

During this reign a number of gold pieces of various designs were made but these seem to be more in the nature of medals than coins. The only pieces noted that seem to be in the nature of coins are as follows:

11 — 1 Wark 1931. Bust of Emperor *r.* ℞ St. George and the dragon ....

12 — ½ Wark 1931. Bust of Emperor *l.* ℞ St. George ....

NICKEL

Type—Head *r.* ℞ Lion

13 — 50 Matoña or Cents 1933 .... .75

14 — 25 Matoña or Cents 1933 .... .50

15 — 10 Matoña or Cents 1933 .... .35

COPPER

16 — 5 Matoña or Cent 1934 .... .35

17 — 1 Matoña or Cent 1934 .... .25

Dire Dawa

ALUMINUM

18 — 1 Piastre 1922. French inscription. Token issued by merchants at Dire Dawa and used extensively. Now demonetized.

Haile Selassie—Returned in 1941

Mint: Philadelphia.

Type—Bust of Haile Selassie *l.* ℞ Lion of Judah, value below

SILVER

19 — 50 Cents 1944, 45, 47. Size 25m. 1.00

BRONZE

20 — 25 Cents 1944, 45. Size 26m. .... .50

21 — 10 Cents 1944, 45, 49. Size 23m. .25

22 — 5 Cents 1944, 45-47, 49. Size 20m. .... .15

23 — 1 Cent 1944, 45. Size 17m. .... .10

FAROE ISLANDS

Danish possession lying between the Shetlands and Iceland

100 Ore = 1 Krone

Type of regular Danish Coinage, struck in London Mint. Without usual mint mark and engraver's initials.

COPPER-NICKEL

1 25 Ore 1941 ....

2 10 Ore 1941 ....

BRONZE

3 5 Ore 1941 ....
4 2 Ore 1941 ....
5 1 Ore 1941 ....

FIJI

A group of approximately 250 islands in the South Pacific due east of northern Australia. A British Crown Colony.

Mints: London, San Francisco.

George V
SILVER

Obverses with crowned bust l.

1 1 Florin (2 Shillings). 1934-36 ...... 2.50

2 1 Shilling. 1934-36. Native boat 1.25
3 6 Pence. 1934-35. Turtle .... .75

COPPER-NICKEL

4 1 Penny. 1934-36. Crown over hole. ℞ Value .... .25
5 ½ Penny. 1934. Similar .... .15

Edward VIII
COPPER-NICKEL

6 1 Penny. 1936. Similar .... .35

George VI
SILVER

Reverses same as preceding issue.

7 Florin. 1937-45. Crowned bust l. 1.50
8 Shilling. 1937-41 ...... .75
9 6 Pence. 1937-41 ...... .50

COPPER-NICKEL

10 Penny. 1937-41,45 ...... .15

11 ½ Penny. 1940,41 ...... .15

BRASS

12 Penny. 1942, 43 ...... .15
13 ½ Penny. 1942, 43 ...... .10

ALUMINUM BRONZE

14 Threepence 1947 ......

With title—"KING GEORGE THE SIXTH"

COPPER-NICKEL

15 Penny 1949 ......
16 ½ Penny 1949 ......

FINLAND
(Suomen Tasavalta)

In northern Europe bounded on the north by Norway, on the east by the USSR, on the south by the Gulf of Finland, and on the west by the Gulf of Bothnia, Sweden and Norway.
Mint: Helsinki (S).
100 Pennia = 1 Markka.

Union with Russia
Nicholas II—1894-1916
GOLD

1 20 Markkaa 1903-13. Crowned double headed eagle in circle. ℞ Value in wreath 15.00
2 10 Markkaa 1904-13. Similar 7.50

SILVER

Type of gold coins.

3 2 Markkaa 1905-07. Similar to the gold 2.00
4 1 Markka 1907, 1908, 1915. Similar 1.00
5 50 Pennia 1907, 08, 11, 15, 16. Similar but without circle ...... .50
6 25 Pennia 1901-17. Similar ...... .35

COPPER

7 10 Pennia 1905-17. Crowned N.II. ℞ Value in wreath ...... .15
8 5 Pennia 1901-17. Similar ...... .10
9 1 Penni 1901-16. Similar ...... .10

Revolutionary Period
1917, 1918
SILVER

12 50 Pennia 1917. Similar to imperial coin but crown removed 2.50
13 25 Pennia 1917. Similar 2.50

COPPER

21 10 Pennia 1917. Similar 2.50
23 5 Pennia 1917, 18. Similar 2.00
26 1 Penni 1917. Similar 1.50
25 5 Pennia 1918. Trumpets and banner in circle 10.00

REPUBLIC

Mints: Helsinki (S), Copenhagen, Birmingham (H)

GOLD

10 200 Markkaa 1926. Lion on sword *l*. ℞ Value and pine sprays 30.00

11 100 Markkaa 1926, 27. Similar 15.00

MINOR METALS

14 20 Markkaa. Aluminum Bronze 1931-39. Arms in pine wreath. ℞ Value in wreath .... .75

15 10 Markkaa. Aluminum Bronze 1928-39. Similar .... .60

16 5 Markkaa. Aluminum Bronze 1928-42; (a) Brass 1946-49 .... .35

17 1 Markka. Copper Nickel (24 mm) 1921-24. Lion on sword. ℞ Value between pine branches .35

18 1 Markka. Copper Nickel (21 mm) 1928-40; (a) Bronze 1940-43,49; (b) Iron 1943-49. Similar .25

19 50 Pennia. Copper Nickel 1921-40; (a) Bronze 1941-43; (b) Iron 1943-48. Similar. ℞ Value between wheat ears .... .20

20 25 Pennia. Copper Nickel 1921-40; (a) Bronze 1940-43; (b) Iron 1943-45 .... .15

22 10 Pennia. Copper 1918-40. Lion on sword. ℞ Value .... .25

24 5 Pennia. Copper 1918-40. Lion on sword. ℞ Value .... .15

27 1 Penni. Copper 1918-24. Lion on sword. ℞ Value .... .10

28 10 Pennia. Bronze (22 mm) 1940. Two pine branches. ℞ Value. Holed type .... .15

29 5 Pennia. Bronze (18 mm) 1940. Similar .... .10

30 10 Pennia. Bronze (18 mm) 1941-43. Similar .... .15

31 5 Pennia. Bronze (16 mm) 1941-43. Similar .... .10

32 10 Pennia. Iron (16 mm) 1943-45. Similar .... .15

FRANCE

(Republique Francaise)

Mint: Paris (A) or symbols, Cornucopia and torch 1901-30; Cornucopia and wing 1931 Emergency Mints, Castelsarrasin (C); Vincennes, same marks as Paris; Poissy, zigzag line, closed in 1927.

100 Centimes = 1 Franc.

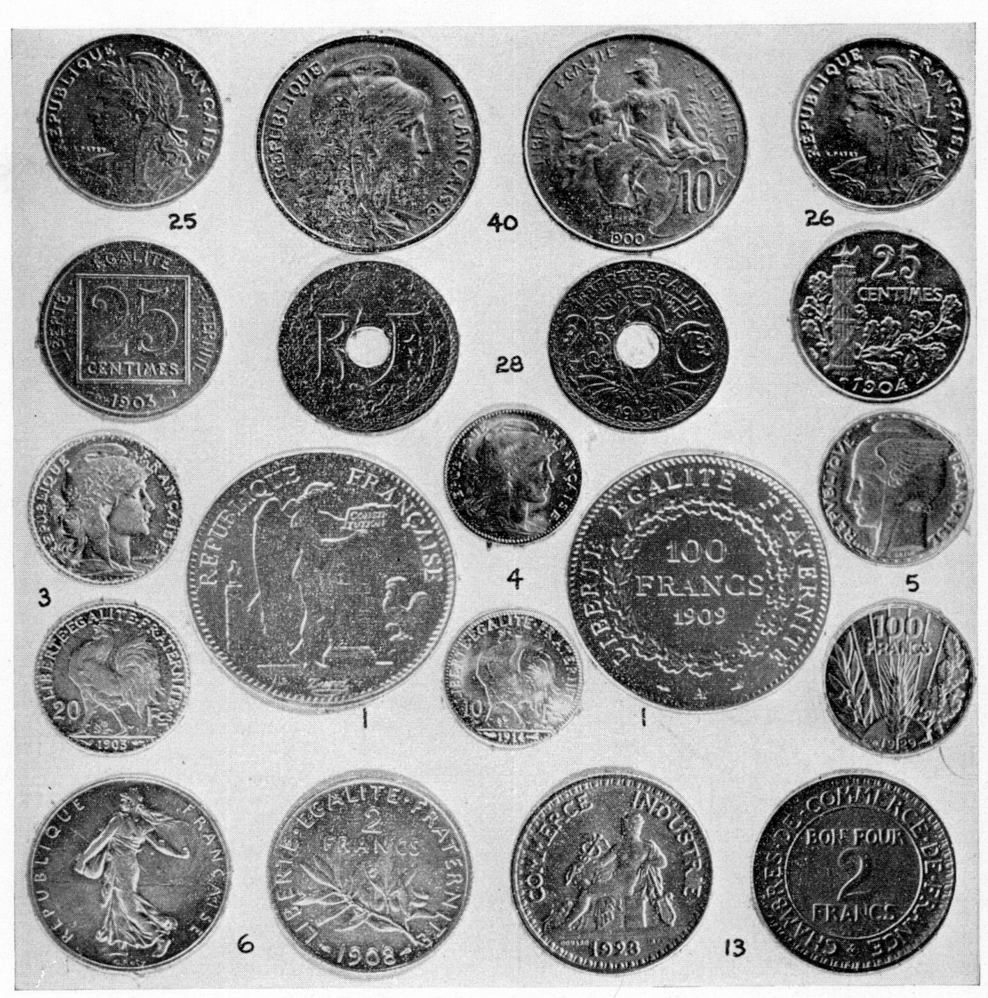

GOLD

1	100	Francs 1901-21. Dupre type	100.00
2	50	Francs 1904. Similar	100.00
3	20	Francs 1901-21. Chaplain type	12.50
4	10	Francs 1901-14. Similar	6.50
5	100	Francs 1935-36. Bazor type	50.00

SILVER

Roty type: Sower ℞ Value

6	2	Francs 1901-20	.75
7	1	Franc 1901-20	.35
8	50	Centimes 1901-20	.25

Turin type: Head r. ℞ Value

11 20 Francs 1929-38 .... 2.50

12 10 Francs 1929-39 .... .60

MINOR METALS

25 25 Centimes. Nickel 1903. Patey type (Round) .... .15

26 25 Centimes. Nickel 1904-05. Patey type, new reverse (Polygonal) .... .15

Dupuis type—Bust r.
℞ Allegorical group.

40 10 Centimes. Bronze 1901-21 .... .15

41 5 Centimes. Bronze 1901-21. .10

42 2 Centimes. Bronze 1901-20. ℞ Value .... .10

43 1 Centime. Bronze 1901-20. Same .10

Chamber of Commerce Tokens

13 2 Francs. Aluminum bronze 1920-31 .... .25

14 1 Franc. Aluminum bronze 1920-31 .... .15

15 50 Centimes. Aluminum bronze 1921-31 .... .10

35 5 Francs. Nickel 1933. Bazor type .75

34 5 Francs. Nickel 1933-39. Lavrillier type; (a) Aluminum-bronze 1939-40; (b) Aluminum 1945-50 .... .35

37 10 Francs. Turin type. Copper-nickel 1945-50. Size $25\frac{1}{2}$ mm.... .50

Guiraud Type

38 20 Francs 1950. Aluminum bronze

39 10 Francs 1950. Aluminum bronze

Morlon type: Head l. ℞ Value

16 2 Francs. Aluminum bronze 1931-44; (a) Aluminum 1941-50 .... .25

17 1 Franc. Aluminum bronze 1931-44; (a) Aluminum 1941-50 .... .15

18 50 Centimes. Aluminum bronze 1931-44; (a) Aluminum 1941-50 .10

Lindauer type, holed.

28 25 Centimes. Nickel 1914-17; (a) Copper-nickel, Nickel-brass or bronze 1917-40, 46 .... .15
30 10 Centimes. Copper-nickel, Nickel-brass or bronze 1917-39; (a) Zinc 1941 .... .10
31 10 Centimes. Zinc 1944, 45. Reduced size .... .10
32 5 Centimes. Copper-nickel 1917-20. Diam 19 mm. .... .10
33 5 Centimes. Copper-nickel, Nickel brass 1920-39. Diam. 17 mm.... .10

During World War II most coins of the regular Republican type were struck at Beaumont-le-Roger (A) and Castelsarrasin (B).

Vichy State

Type: Double Axe ℞ Value

V1 2 Francs. Aluminum 1942-44 .... .50
V2 1 Franc. Aluminum 1941-44 .... .25
V3 50 Centimes. Aluminum 1942-44 .15

Holed Type: Ears of Wheat. ℞ Value

V4 20 Centimes. Zinc 1941 VINGT .50

V5 20 Centimes. Zinc 1941-45 .... .15
V6 10 Centimes. Zinc 1941-42. Diam. 21 mm. .... .10
V7 10 Centimes. Zinc 1943-44. Reduced size .... .10

Allied Occupation Currency

O1 2 Francs. Brass 1944. Wreath ℞ Value ....

Struck at the Philadelphia mint.

FRENCH EQUATORIAL AFRICA

(Afrique Equatoriale Francaise)

Situated in the heart of Africa with a seacoast on the South Atlantic Ocean between Spanish Guinea and the Belgian Congo.

Mints: Pretoria, Paris

BRONZE

Type—Cock ℞ Cross of Lorraine.

1 Franc 1942,43 .... .75
2 50 Centimes 1942,43 .... .50

The 1942 coins are brass and the 1943 bronze.

ALUMINUM BRONZE

Type—Liberty cap above RF. ℞ Value, center hole

3 25 Centimes 1943 ....
4 10 Centimes 1943 ....
5 5 Centimes 1943 ....

These coins were never put into circulation.

ALUMINUM

Type—Bust of Republic. ℞ Antelope head.

6 2 Francs 1948 ....
7 1 Franc 1948 ....

FRENCH SOMALILAND

(Cote Francaise des Somalis)

Situated in the Gulf of Aden between British Somaliland and the former Italian East Africa.

Mint: Paris

100 Centimes = 1 Franc

ALUMINUM

Type—Bust of Republic. ℞ Antelope head.

1 5 Francs 1949 ....

2 2 Francs 1949 ....

3 1 Franc 1949 ....

FRENCH WEST AFRICA

(Afrique Occidentale Francaise)

Comprising the following colonies—Senegal, French Guinea, Ivory Coast, Dahomey, French Sudan, Mauritania, Niger and Dakar.

Mints: London, Paris

ALUMINUM BRONZE

Type of France No. 17

1 1 Franc 1944 ....

2 50 Centimes, 1944,47 ....

ALUMINUM

3 2 Francs 1948,50 ....

4 1 Franc 1948,50 ....

GERMAN EAST AFRICA COMPANY

Reached from the coast of Lake Tanganyika and from Lake Nyasa to Victoria Nyanza, bordering on the Indian Ocean. Now comprised of Tanganyika (British Mandate) Ruanda (Belgian Congo) and the "Kionga Triangle" (Portuguese Mozambique).

SILVER

1 1 Rupee 1901-02. Kaiser helmeted *l.* ℞ Arms 2.00

2 ½ Rupee 1901. Similar........ 1.25

3 ¼ Rupee 1901. Similar........ .75

GERMAN EAST AFRICA

(Deutsch Ostafrika)

Mints: Berlin (A), Hamburg (J), Tabora (T).

GOLD

4 15 Rupees 1916. Elephant and Mountains. ℞ German Eagle. Struck at Tabora during the World War 35.00

SILVER

5 1 Rupee 1904-14. Kaiser helmeted *l.* ℞ Value in wreath........ 1.50

6 ½ Rupee 1904-14. Similar........ 1.00

7 ¼ Rupee 1904-13. Similar........ .65

COPPER-NICKEL

8 10 Heller 1908-11, 1914. Central hole, crown above. ℞ Value and sprays .75

9 5 Heller 1913-14. Similar .50

BRONZE

10 5 Heller 1908-10. Crown. ℞ Value in wreath 2.50

11 1 Heller 1904-13. Similar .35

12 ½ Heller 1904-06. Similar .25

COPPER

13 20 Heller 1916. Crown date and DOA (Deutsch-Ostafrica). ℞ Value in wreath 1.50

13a 5 Heller 1916 2.00

BRASS

14 20 Heller 1916. Similar .50

15 5 Heller 1916. Similar 1.50

The above were struck at Tabora during the World War.

GERMANY

(Empire)

(Deutsches Reich)

Mints: Berlin (A), Munich (D), Muldnerhütte (E), Stuttgart (F), Karlsruhe (G), Hamburg (J).

100 Pfennigs = 1 Mark.

For the gold coins and the silver above the 1 mark piece see the various German States. The Empire, as such, struck only the minor silver and the base metal coins.

SILVER

1 1 Mark 1901-16. German Eagle. ℞ Value in wreath .35

2 50 Pfennigs 1901-03. Eagle in wreath. ℞ Value in wreath .25

3 ½ Mark 1905-09, 1911-18. Similar but change in denomination .25

NICKEL

4 25 Pfennigs 1909-12. Eagle. ℞ Value in wreath of wheat. 1909-10 .20

5 10 Pfennigs 1901-16, 1918. Eagle. ℞ Value .15

6 5 Pfennigs 1901-1915. Similar .10

IRON

7 10 Pfennigs 1915-17. Eagle in circle of dots. ℞ Somewhat similar .25

8 5 Pfennigs 1915-18. Similar to nickel issue but edge reeded. (The reeding sometimes barely shows) .20

ZINC

9 10 Pfennigs 1917-18. Similar to nickel piece but without mint marks .15

COPPER

10 2 Pfennigs 1904-08, 1910-16. Eagle. ℞ Value .10

11 1 Pfennig 1901-16. Similar .10

ALUMINUM

12 1 Pfennig 1916-18. Similar. 1916 and 1918 rare .25

GERMAN EMPIRE

THE STATES OF THE GERMAN EMPIRE

The coinage of these divisions of the Empire consist of the gold and the silver coins of 5, 3 and 2 marks.

The reverses are all alike consisting of the arms on the Imperial Eagle and DEUTSCHES REICH, date and value. Therefore only the obverses will be described.

ANHALT

Mint: Berlin (A).

GOLD

Friedrich I—1871-1904

13 20 Marks 1901. (70th birthday) 40.00
13a 10 Marks 1901. Similar 20.00

Friedrich II—1904-1918

14 20 Marks 1904. Head *l.* 30.00

SILVER

Friedrich II—1904-1918

15 5 Marks 1914. (Silver wedding). Heads of the Duke and Duchess *l.* 5.00
16 3 Marks 1909, 1911 .... 2.50
17 3 Marks 1914. (Silver wedding). Similar to the 5 Marks...... 2.50
18 2 Marks 1904. Head *l.* 1.50

BADEN

Mint: Karlsruhe (G).

GOLD

Friedrich I—1852-1907

19 10 Marks 1901. Head *l.*........ 12.50
20 10 Marks 1902-07. Head *r.*........ 10.00

Friedrich II—1907-1918

21 20 Marks 1911-14. Head *l.*........ 17.50
22 10 Marks 1909-13. Similar 12.50

SILVER

Friedrich I—1852-1907

23 5 Marks 1901-02. Head *l.*........ 6.00
24 5 Marks 1902. (50th year of reign). Head *r.* Laurel spray below and dates 1852-1902 .... 3.00
25 5 Marks 1902-04, 1907. Head *r.* 3.00
26 5 Marks 1906. (Golden wedding). Heads of Friedrich and Louise *r.* 4.00
27 5 Marks 1907. (Death of the Grand-duke). Head *r.* *1826, + 1907 .... 5.00
28 2 Marks 1901-02. Head l........ 1.00
29 2 Marks 1902. (50th year of reign). Similar to the 5 Mark piece 1.50
30 2 Marks 1902-07. Head *r.* 2.00
31 2 Marks 1906. (Golden wedding). Similar to the 5 Marks 1.25
32 2 Marks 1907. (Death of the Grand-duke). Similar to the 5 Marks 1.25

Friedrich II—1907-1918

33 5 Marks 1908, 1913. Head *l.* 3.50
34 3 Marks 1908-12, 1914-15. Head *l.* 2.00
35 2 Marks 1911, 1913. Head *l.*...... 1.50

BAVARIA

(Bayern)

Mint: Munich (D).

GOLD

Otto—1886-1913

36 20 Marks 1905, 1913. Head *l.*...... 17.50
37 10 Marks 1901-07, 1909-12. Similar 10.00

Ludwig III—1913-1918

38 20 Marks 1914. Head *l.* 25.00
39 20 Marks 1914. Larger head. Very rare ....

SILVER

Otto—1886-1913

40 5 Marks 1901-04, 1906-08, 1913. Head *l.* 3.50
41 5 Marks 1911. (90th birthday of the Prince-regent). Head of Luitpold *r.* 4.00
42 3 Marks 1908-13. Head of Otto *l.* 2.00
43 3 Marks 1911. (90th birthday of the Prince-regent). Similar to the 5 Marks 2.50
44 2 Marks 1901-08, 1912-13. Head *l.* 1.00
45 2 Marks 1911. (90th birthday). Similar to the 5 Marks 1.50

GERMAN EMPIRE

Ludwig III—1913-1918

46 5 Marks 1914. Head *l.* 2.50
47 3 Marks 1914. Head *l.* 1.00
48 3 Marks 1918. (Golden wedding). Heads of Ludwig and Marie Therese *r.* 300.00
49 2 Marks 1914. Head *l.* 1.00

BREMEN

Mint: Hamburg (J).

GOLD

50 20 Marks 1906. Arms of Bremen 25.00
51 10 Marks 1907. Similar 12.50

SILVER

52 5 Marks 1905. Arms of Bremen 150.00
53 5 Marks 1906. Arms smaller...... 4.00
54 2 Marks 1904. Similar 1.00

BRUNSWICK
(Braunschweig)

Mint: Berlin (A).

SILVER

Ernst August—1913-1918

55 5 Marks 1915. (On the receipt of the Duchy in 1913). Head of Ernst August and Victoria Luise *r.* Inscription ends with BRAUNSCHWEIG 20.00
56 5 Marks 1915. Similar but u. LUNEB added 5.00
57 3 Marks 1915. Similar to 55........ 10.00
58 3 Marks 1915. Similar to 56........ 2.50

HAMBURG

Mint: Hamburg (J).

GOLD

59 20 Marks 1905 - 06, 1908 - 10, 1912-13. Arms of Hamburg........ 15.00
60 10 Marks 1901-13. Similar 7.50

SILVER

61 5 Marks 1901 - 04, 1907 - 08, 1913. Arms of Hamburg 2.50
62 3 Marks 1908-14. Similar 1.50
63 2 Marks 1901-08, 1911-14. Similar 1.25

HESSE

Mint: Berlin (A).

Ernst Ludwig—1892-1918

GOLD

64 20 Marks 1901, 1903, 1905-6, 1908, 1910-11, 1913. Head *l.*... 20.00
The first two dates have GROSSHERZOG spelled with one S.

SILVER

65 5 Marks 1904. (400th anniv. of Philip the Magnanimous). Heads of Philip and Ernst Ludwig *l.* 4.00
66 3 Marks 1910. Head of Ernst Ludwig *l.* 2.00
67 3 Marks 1917. (25th year of reign). Head *l.* 40.00
68 2 Marks 1904. (400th anniv. of Philip). Similar to the 5 Marks 2.00

LIPPE-DETMOLD

Mint: Berlin (A).

SILVER

Leopold IV—1905-1913

69 3 Marks 1913. Head *l.* 5.00
70 2 Marks 1906. Head *l.* 1.50

LUBECK

Mint: Berlin (A).

GOLD

71 10 Marks 1901, 1904. Arms of Lubeck 17.50
72 10 Marks 1905-06, 1909-10. Arms of new design 15.00

SILVER

73 5 Marks 1904, 1907-8, 1913. Arms of Lubeck 3.00
74 3 Marks 1908-14. Similar 1.50
75 2 Marks 1901. Arms as on the 10 Marks 1.00
76 2 Marks 1904-07, 1911-12. New design 1.00

GERMAN EMPIRE

MECKLENBURG-SCHWERIN

Mint: Berlin (A).

Friedrich Franz IV—1897-1918

GOLD

Commemorating accession after coming of age.

77 20 Marks 1901. Head *r.* 60.00
78 10 Marks 1901. Similar 30.00

SILVER

79 5 Marks 1904. (On the marriage of the grand duke). Heads of Friedrich Franz and Alexandra *l.* 3.50
80 5 Marks 1915. (Centenary as a grand duchy). Busts of Friedrich Franz I and IV *l* 7.50
81 3 Marks 1915. Similar 3.50
82 2 Marks 1901. Head *r.* 1.50
83 2 Marks 1904. (Marriage commemoration). Similar to the 5 Marks 1.00

MECKLENBURG-STRELITZ

Mint: Berlin (A).

Adolf Friedrich—1904-1914

GOLD

84 20 Marks 1905. Head *l.* 60.00
85 10 Marks 1905. Similar 30.00

SILVER

86 3 Marks 1913. Head *l.* 7.50
87 2 Marks 1905. Head with beard *l.* 1.50

OLDENBURG

Mint: Berlin (A).

SILVER

Friedrich August—1900-1918

88 5 Marks 1901. Head *l.* 10.00
89 2 Marks 1900-01. Similar 3.00

PRUSSIA

Mints: Berlin (A), Hamburg (J).

Wilhelm II—1888-1918

GOLD

90 20 Marks 1901-13. Head *r.* Berlin 1901-13. Hamburg 1905-06, 1909-10, 1912 .... 15.00
91 10 Marks 1901-07, 1909-12. Similar 7.50
92 20 Marks 1913-15. Bust in uniform *r.* 17.50

SILVER

93 5 Marks 1901-04, 1906-08. Head *r.* 2.50
94 5 Marks 1901. (200th anniv. of Prussia as a kingdom). Busts of William II and Friedrich I *l.* 2.50
95 5 Marks 1913-14. Bust *r.* 2.50
96 3 Marks 1908-12. Head *r.* 1.50
97 3 Marks 1910. (Centenary of Berlin University). Heads of Frederick William III and William II *l.* 1.25
98 3 Marks 1911. (Centenary of the Univ. of Breslau). Heads of Frederick William III and William II *l.* 1.25
99 3 Marks 1913. (Centenary of the War of Liberation). King on horseback surrounded by soldiers. ℞ Eagle on snake 1.25
100 3 Marks 1913. (25th year of reign). Bust in uniform *r.* Laurel branch beneath, and 1888-1913 .... 1.25
101 3 Marks 1914. Bust as above, but dates and laurel branch removed 1.50
102 3 Marks 1915. (100th anniv. of the uniting of Mansfeld with Prussia). St. George and the Dragon 5.00
103 2 Marks 1901-08, 1911-12. Head r. 2.00
104 2 Marks 1901. (200th anniv. of Prussia as a Kingdom). Same as the 5 Marks of 1901 .... 1.00
105 2 Marks 1913. (Centenary of the War of Liberation). Similar to the 3 Marks........ 1.00
106 2 Marks 1913. (25th year of reign). Same as the 3 Marks........ 1.00

REUSS, Elder Branch

Mint: Berlin (A).

SILVER

Heinrich XXII—1859-1902

107 2 Marks 1901. Head *r.* 2.50

Heinrich XXIV—1902-1918

108 3 Marks 1909. Head *r.* 3.00

GERMAN EMPIRE

SAXONY

Mint: Muldnerhutte (E).

GOLD

Albert—1873-1902

109 10 Marks 1901-02. Head *r.* 10.00

Georg—1902-1904

110 20 Marks 1903. Head *r.* 20.00
111 10 Marks 1903-04. Similar 10.00

Friedrich August III—1904-1918

112 20 Marks 1905, 1913-14. Head *r.* 17.50
113 10 Marks 1905-07, 1909-12. Similar 10.00

SILVER

Albert—1873-1902

114 5 Marks 1901-02. Head *r.* 3.50
115 5 Marks 1902. (On the death of the King). Similar but dates * 23.IV.1828 + 19.12. 1902 .... 4.00
116 2 Marks 1901-02. Similar to the regular issue 2.00
117 2 Marks 1902. (On the death of the King). Head *r.* and dates * 1828 + 1902 .... 1.50

Georg—1902-1904

118 5 Marks 1903-04. Head *r.* 2.50
119 5 Marks 1904. (On the death of the King). Similar but *8. VIII.1832 + 15.X.1904 .... 3.50
119a 2 Marks 1903. Commemorating royal mint visit 10.00
120 2 Marks 1903-04. Similar to regular 5 Marks 1.50
121 2 Marks 1904. (On the death of the king). Similar to the 5 Marks 1.50

Friedrich August III—1904-1918

122 5 Marks 1907-08, 1914. Head *r.* 3.00
123 5 Marks 1909. (500th anniv. of Leipzig University). Busts of Frederick the Pugnacious and Frederick August *l.* 3.50
124 3 Marks 1908-13. Head *r.* 1.50
125 3 Marks 1913. (Dedication of the National Battle Monument at Leipzig). View of the monument 1.50
126 3 Marks 1917. (4th centenary of the Reformation). Bust of Frederick the Wise 350.00
126a 2 Marks 1905. Commemorating royal mint visit 12.50
127 2 Marks 1905-08, 1911-12, 1914. Head *r.* 1.00
128 2 Marks 1909. (500th anniv. of Leipzig University). Similar to the 5 Marks 1.00

SACHSEN-ALTENBURG

Mint: Berlin (A).

SILVER

Ernst—1853-1908

129 5 Marks 1901. Head *r.* 4.00
130 5 Marks 1903. (50th year of reign). Head *r.* and dates 1853, 1903 in laurel branch 5.00
131 2 Marks 1901. Head *r.* 3.50

SACHSEN-COBURG-GOTHA

Mint: Berlin (A).

Carl Eduard—1900-1918

GOLD

132 20 Marks 1905. Head *r.* 50.00
133 10 Marks 1905. Similar 25.00

SILVER

134 5 Marks 1907. Head *r.* 7.50
135 2 Marks 1905, 1911. Head *r.* 3.50
Year 1911 very rare, only 100 struck.

SACHSEN-MEININGEN

Mint: Munich (D).

George II—1866-1914

GOLD

136 20 Marks 1905. Head *l.* 50.00
137 20 Marks 1910, 1914. Head *l.* different design 50.00
138 10 Marks 1902, 1909, 1914. Similar 25.00

SILVER

139 5 Marks 1901. Head *r.* 6.50
140 5 Marks 1902, 1908. Head *l.* Different portrait 6.50
141 3 Marks 1908, 1913. Head *l.* 2.00
142 3 Marks 1915. (On the death of the Duke). Head *l.* and * 1826 + 1914 .... 2.50
143 2 Marks 1901. Head *r.* 1.50

144 2 Marks 1902, 1913. Head *l*. ... 1.50
145 2 Marks 1915. (On the death of the Duke). Similar to the 3 Marks of 1915 ... 1.50

SACHSEN-WEIMAR

Mint: Berlin (A).

Wilhelm Ernst—1901-1918

GOLD

146 20 Marks 1901. Head *l*. ... 50.00

SILVER

147 5 Marks 1903. (On the marriage of the Grand-duke). Heads of Wilhelm Ernst and Caroline *l*. ... 4.50
148 5 Marks 1908. (350th anniv. of the University of Jena). Facing bust of Johann Friedrich holding sword, and 1558-1908... 4.50
149 3 Marks 1910. (Second marriage of the Grand-duke). Heads of Wilhelm Ernst and Feodora *l*. Wilhelm is spelt Wilheim ... 2.50
150 3 Marks 1915. (Centenary as a Grand-duchy). Busts of Wilhelm Ernst and Carl August *r*. ℞ New design ... 2.50
151 2 Marks 1901. Head *l*. ... 2.00
152 2 Marks 1903. (Marriage of the Grand-duke). Similar to the 5 Marks of 1903 ... 2.00
153 2 Marks 1908. (350th anniv. of the University of Jena). Similar to the 5 Marks of 1908 1.50

SCHAUMBURG-LIPPE

Mint: Berlin (A).

Georg—1893-1911

GOLD

154 20 Marks 1904. Head *l*. ... 60.00

SILVER

155 5 Marks 1904. Head *l*. ... 4.50
156 3 Marks 1911. (On the death of the Prince). Head *l*. *10 X 1846 + 29 IV 1911 ... 3.00
157 2 Marks 1904. Head *l*. ... 2.00

SCHWARZBURG-SONDERSHAUSEN

Mint: Berlin (A).

SILVER

Karl Gunther—1880-1909

158 3 Marks 1909. (On the death of the Prince). Head *r*. and * 1830- + 1909 ... 3.00
159 2 Marks 1905. (25th year of reign). Head *r*., laurel branch and 1880-1905. Two minor varieties ... 2.50

WALDECK

Mint: Berlin (A).

Friedrich—1893-1918

GOLD

160 20 Marks 1903. Head *l*. ... 60.00

SILVER

161 5 Marks 1903. Head *l*. ... 17.50

WURTTEMBERG

Mint: Stuttgart (F).

Wilhelm II—1891-1918

GOLD

162 20 Marks 1905, 1912-14. Head *r*. ... 17.50
163 10 Marks 1901-1913. Similar ... 10.00

SILVER

164 5 Marks 1901-04, 1906-08, 1913. Head *r*. ... 4.00
165 3 Marks 1908-14. Head *r*. There are two minor varieties of the 1908 ... 1.50
166 3 Marks 1911. (Silver wedding). Heads of the King and Queen *r*. ... 2.50
167 3 Marks 1916. (25th year of the reign). Head *r*. 1891-1916 and laurel ... 50.00
168 2 Marks 1901-08, 1912-14. Head *r*. ... 2.00

GERMANY

Republic

Mints: As under the Empire, also Vienna (B).

Post World War I

51 50 Pfennig. Silver 1919. Similar to last Imperial coinage ... .35
52 50 Pfennig. Aluminum 1919-22. Bundle of wheat. ℞ Value ... .15
53 10 Pfennig. Zinc 1919-22. Similar to Imperial coinage ... .10
54 5 Pfennig. Iron 1919-22. Similar .10
55 3 Marks. Aluminum 1922. Eagle, no inscription. ℞ Value ... .15

No.	Description	Price
56	3 Marks. Aluminum 1922. Third Anniversary of Weimar Constitution. Eagle and inscription. ℞ Value	.25
57	500 Marks. Aluminum 1923. Eagle. ℞ Value	.25
58	200 Marks. Aluminum 1923. Similar	.25
59	100 Marks. Aluminum 1923. Similar	.50
60	20 Marks. Aluminum 1923. Similar	.50

Law of Nov. 8, 1923

No.	Description	Price
61	50 Rentenpfennig. Aluminum Bronze 1923-24. Wheat stalks. ℞ Value in lozenge	.35
62	10 Rentenpfennig. Aluminum Bronze 1923-24. Similar	.20
63	5 Rentenpfennig. Aluminum Bronze 1923-24. Similar	.15
64	2 Rentenpfennig. Bronze 1923-24. Value. ℞ Bundle of wheat	.10
65	1 Rentenpfennig. Bronze 1923-24. Similar	.10

Reform of 1924

No.	Description	Price
66	5 Marks. Silver 1927-33. Oak Tree. ℞ Eagle	3.00
67	3 Marks. Silver 1924, 25. Eagle. ℞ Value	2.00
68	3 Marks. Silver 1931-33. Eagle and Inscription. ℞ Value in oak wreath	2.00
69	2 Marks. Silver 1925-31. Eagle. ℞ Value in oak wreath	1.25
70	1 Mark. Silver 1924, 25. Eagle, no inscription. ℞ Value	.60
71	1 Mark. Silver 1925-27. Eagle, no inscription. ℞ Value in oak wreath	.60
72	50 Pfennig. Nickel 1927-36. Eagle in circle. ℞ Large 50	.30
73	10 Reichspfennig. Aluminum Bronze. 1924-26. Wheat Stalks. ℞ Value	.15
74	5 Reichspfennig. Aluminum Bronze. 1924-26, 1930, 31. Similar	.10
75	4 Pfenning. Bronze. 1932, 33. Eagle. ℞ Large 4	.15
76	2 Pfennig. Bronze 1924, 25. Similar	.10
77	1 Pfennig. Bronze 1924-36. Similar	.10

COMMEMORATIVE COINS

5 Marks Silver (36 mm)

No.	Description	Price
1	1925 1000th Year of the Rhineland. Knight in chain mail behind shield. ℞ Value	4.00
2	1927 Centenary of Bremerhaven. Ship to l. ℞ Eagle on shield	4.00
3	1927 450th Anniversary of Tuebingen. Bust of Eberhard. ℞ Eagle	4.50
5	1929 2nd Century of birth of Lessing. Head l. ℞ Eagle	4.00
6	1929 1000th Anniversary of founding of Meissen. Man holding two shields. ℞ Eagle	4.50
7	1929 10th Anniversary of the Constitution. Head of Hindenberg. ℞ Hand	4.00
8	1930 Graf Zeppelin's World Flight. Zeppelin on world. ℞ Eagle	7.50
9	1930 Evacuation of the Rhineland. Eagle on bridge. ℞ Eagle on shield	4.50
10	1932 Centenary of death of Goethe. Head l. ℞ Eagle	4.00

3 Marks Silver

No.	Description	Price
18	1925 1000th year of the Rhineland	3.00
19	1926 700th year of the freedom of Lubeck	3.00
20	1927 Centenary of Bremerhaven	3.00
21	1927 1000th Anniversary of founding of Nordhausen	3.00
22	1927 400th Anniversary of founding of Univ. of Marburg	3.00
23	1927 450th Anniversary Univ. of Tuebingen	3.00
24	1928 4th Century of death of Durer	3.00
25	1928 900th Anniversary of founding of Naumburg	3.00
26	1929 1000th Anniversary of founding of Dinkelsbuhl	3.00
27	1929 2nd century of birth of Lessing	3.00
28	1929 Union of Waldeck with Prussia	3.00
29	1929 10th Anniversary of Constitution	3.00
30	1929 100th Anniversary of founding of Meissen	3.00
31	1930 Graf Zeppelin's world flight	5.00
32	1930 700th Anniversary of death of von der Vogelweide	3.00
33	1930 Evacuation of the Rhineland	3.00

GERMAN REPUBLIC

GERMAN REPUBLIC

34 1931 3rd Centenary of rebuilding of Magdeburg 3.00
35 1931 Centenary of death of von Stein 3.00
37 1932 Centenary of death of Goethe 3.00

Law of March 18, 1933

78 5 Marks 1934, 35. Potsdam Military Church. 29 m 3.00

79 5 Marks. Silver 1935, 36. Head of Hindenburg. ℞ Eagle 3.00

80 1 Mark. Nickel 1933-36. Eagle and motto. ℞ Value in wreath .50
81 50 Pfennig. Aluminum 1935. Eagle. ℞ Value. Plain fields .... .35

COMMEMORATIVE COINS

5 Marks—Silver—29 mm

82 1933 450th Anniversary of birth of Luther. Head l. ℞ Eagle 5.00
No. 11 on the plate

83 1934 Anniversary of Nazi rule. Potsdam Military Church and date 21 Marz—1933. ℞ Eagle 4.00

84 1934 175th Anniversary of birth of Schiller 5.00

2 Marks—Silver

85 1933 450th Anniversary of birth of Luther 2.00
86 1934 175th Anniversary of birth of Schiller 2.00
87 1934 Anniversary of Nazi rule........ 1.25

TOTALITARIAN STATE

Eagle on Swastika Types

88 5 Marks. Silver 1936-38. Head of Hindenberg 3.00
89 2 Marks. Silver 1937-39. Head of Hindenberg 1.25
90 50 Pfennig. Nickel 1938, 39. Eagle on swastika .... .30
91 50 Pfennig. Aluminum 1940. Similar but without circle on reverse .... .30
92 10 Pfennig. Aluminum bronze 1936, 37; (a) zinc 1945 .... .15
93 5 Pfennig. Aluminum bronze 1936, 37; (a) zinc 1940-44 .... .10
94 2 Pfennig. Bronze 1936, 37; (a) zinc 1940-44 .... .10
95 1 Pfennig. Bronze 1936, 37; (a) zinc 1940-45 .... .10

Type without swastika

96 10 Pfennig 1945-48 ....
97 5 Pfennig 1947,48 ....
98 1 Pfennig 1945-48 ....

POSTWAR COINS

Western Occupation Zone

Bank Deutscher Lander

Law of June 18, 1948

Mints — Munchen, Stuttgart, Karlsruhe, Hamburg

101 50 Pfennig 1949. Copper-nickel

102 10 Pfennig 1949. Brass over steel
103 5 Pfennig 1949. Brass over steel
104 1 Pfennig 1948,49. Bronze ....

FEDERAL REPUBLIC

Authorized June 29, 1950

105 1 Mark 1950. Copper-nickel ......

106 50 Pfennig 1950. Copper-nickel...

107 10 Pfennig 1950. Brass over steel
108 5 Pfennig 1950. Brass over steel

109 2 Pfennig 1950. Bronze over steel
110 1 Pfennig 1950. Bronze over steel

Eastern (Soviet) Zone

Mint — Berlin

111 50 Pfennig 1950 ....

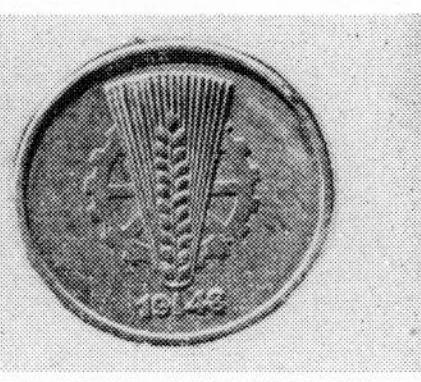

112 10 Pfennig 1948,49. Aluminum
113 5 Pfennig 1948. Aluminum ......
114 1 Pfennig 1949. Aluminum ......

GREAT BRITAIN

GREAT BRITAIN

Mints: Royal Mint, London. Supplementary—Birmingham (H), Imperial Chemical Industries Ltd. at King's Norton (K.N.). Branch mints for striking of Sovereigns and ½ Sovereigns, Bombay (I), Sydney (S), Perth (P), Melbourne (M), Pretoria (SA), Ottawa (C).

12 Pence = 1 Shilling.

20 Shillings = 1 Pound or Sovereign.

Victoria—1837-1901

With veiled bust l.

GOLD

1	1 Sovereign 1901. St. George	15.00
2	½ Sovereign 1901. Similar	7.50

SILVER

3	½ Crown 1901. Crowned shield	1.25
4	2 Shillings (Florin) 1901. Similar. ℞ Crown over 3 shields	1.00

5	1 Shilling 1901. Shields on Garter	.50
6	6 Pence 1901. Value in wreath	.30
7	3 Pence 1901. Value in wreath	.25
8	Maundy set 1901. 4, 3, 2, 1 d	2.00

BRONZE

9	1 Penny 1901. Brittania	.25
10	½ Penny 1901. Similar	.15
11	1 Farthing 1901. Similar	.10

Edward VII—1901-1910

With head to r.

GOLD

12	5 Pounds 1902. St. George	100.00
13	2 Pounds 1902. Similar	40.00
14	1 Sovereign 1902-10. Similar	15.00
15	½ Sovereign. Similar	7.50

SILVER

16	1 Crown 1902. St. George	5.00
17	½ Crown 1902-10. Crowned shield	1.50
18	1 Florin 1902-10. Britannia	1.25
19	1 Shilling 1902-10. Lion on crown	.60
20	6 Pence 1902-10. Value in wreath	.35
21	3 Pence 1902-10. Value in wreath	.25
22	Maundy Set 1902-10. 4, 3, 2, 1 d	2.00

BRONZE

23	1 Penny 1902-10. Britannia	.25
24	½ Penny 1902-10. Similar	.15
25	1 Farthing 1902-10. Similar	.10

George V—1910-1936

With head to l.

GOLD

26	5 Pounds 1911. St. George	125.00
27	2 Pounds 1911. Similar	50.00
28	1 Sovereign 1911-32. Similar	15.00
29	½ Sovereign 1911-16. Similar	7.50

SILVER

30	1 Crown 1927-1934, 1936	5.00
31	1 Crown 1935. (Silver Jubilee)	3.50
32	½ Crown 1911-27. Crowned shield	1.25
33	½ Crown 1927-36. Shield	1.25
34	1 Florin 1911-27. Four crowned shields in form of a cross	1.00
35	1 Florin 1927-33, 1935-36. Similar. ℞ Four uncrowned shields	1.00
36	1 Shilling 1911-27. Lion on crown in circle	.50
37	1 Shilling 1927-36. Without circle	.50
38	6 Pence 1911-27. Lion on crown	.30
39	6 Pence 1927-36. Acorn design	.30
40	3 Pence 1911-27. Value in wreath	.25
41	3 Pence 1927-36. Three acorns	.25
	All denominations struck between 1920-1927 were much alloyed.	
42	Maundy Set 1911-1936	2.50

GREAT BRITAIN

BRONZE

43 1 Penny 1911-22, 1926-27 Britannia .... .25
44 1 Penny 1928-32, 1934-36. Variety .25
45 ½ Penny 1911-27. Variety .... .15
46 ½ Penny 1927-36. Variety .... .15
47 1 Farthing 1911-36 .... .10

Edward VIII—1936

No coins issued bearing his portrait. Those dated 1936 bore the portrait of George V.

George VI—1936-

With head l.

GOLD

48 5 Pounds 1937. St. George 125.00
49 2 Pounds 1937. Similar 50 00
50 1 Sovereign 1937. Similar 20.00
51 ½ Sovereign 1937. Similar.... 15.00
All of these pieces have plain edges.

SILVER

56 1 Crown 1937. Crowned Arms 3.50
57 ½ Crown 1937-46. Shield 1.25
58 2 Shillings 1937-46. Crowned rose 1.00
59 1 Shilling 1937-46. English crest ... .50
60 1 Shilling 1937-46. Scottish cross... .50
61 6 Pence 1937-46. Crowned GRI... .30
62 3 Pence 1937-46. Shield on Rose .25
63 Maundy Set 1937-48 4, 3, 2, 1d ... 5.00

NICKEL BRASS

70 3 Pence 1937-48. Similar. R Thrift plant. 12 sided .... .25

BRONZE

71 1 Penny 1937-48. Britannia .... .25
72 ½ Penny 1937-48. Galleon .... .15
73 1 Farthing 1937-48. Wren .... .10

COPPER-NICKEL

Same types as in silver. Composition Cu. 75 Ni. 25.

74 ½ Crown 1947,48 .... .75
75 2 Shillings 1947,48 .... .60
76 1 Shilling 1947,48. English .... .35
77 1 Shilling 1947,48. Scottish .... .35
78 6 Pence 1947,48 .... .25

Without title — IND. IMP.

SILVER

79 Maundy set 1949,50 ....

COPPER-NICKEL

Types of preceding issue except 6 pence

80 ½ Crown 1949,50 ....

81 2 Shillings 1949,50 ....
82 1 Shilling 1949,50. English ....
83 1 Shilling 1949,50. Scottish ....

84 6 Pence 1949,50 ....

NICKEL BRASS

85 3 Pence 1949,50 ....

BRONZE

86 1 Penny 1949,50 ....
87 ½ Penny 1949,50 ....
88 1 Farthing 1949,50 ....

GREECE

(Kingdom of Hellas)

Occupies the southern peninsula of the Balkans, stretching down into the Mediterranean Sea.
Mints: London, Paris, Brussels, Vienna, Birmingham, King's Norton, Poissy.
100 Lepta = 1 Drachma.

George I—1863-1913

SILVER

1 2 Drachmai 1911. Head *l.* ℞ Thetis on sea horse 2.50
2 1 Drachma 1910-11. Similar 1.50

NICKEL

3 20 Lepta 1912-14, 1920. Holed type. Inscription and shield. ℞ Athena, value and olive .... .25
4 10 Lepta 1912-14, 1920. Holed type. Inscription and crown. ℞ Owl and value .... .20
5 5 Lepta 1912-14, 1920. Similar .15
All struck at Paris.

George II—1922-1923

NICKEL-BRONZE

6 50 Lepta 1922 .... .25

ALUMINUM

7 10 Lepta 1922. Crown. ℞ Value and olive spray .... .15

Republic

SILVER

8 20 Drachmai 1930. Head of Poseidon *r.* ℞ Prow of galley... 2.00
9 10 Drachmai 1930. Head of Demeter *l.* ℞ Wheat ear 1.25

NICKEL

10 5 Drachmai 1930. Phoenix. ℞ Value in wreath .... .25

COPPER-NICKEL

11 2 Drachmai 1926. Head of Athena *l.* ℞. Inscription .... .20

12 1 Drachma 1926-1930. Similar .15

13 50 Lepta 1926, 1930. Similar ...... .10

14 20 Lepta 1926. Similar. Mint: Vienna .... .10

The 1 Drachma and the 50 Lepta are found wth a small B above the date indicating a second striking.

Commemorating the restoration of the Greek monarchy Nov. 25, 1935.

Coinage in brackets.

GOLD

Type—Head of George II *l.* R Value in wreath.

15 100 Drachmai 1935 (300) 150.00

16 20 Drachmai 1935 (750) 25.00

SILVER

Type—Head of King *l.* ℞ Crowned arms, value.

17 100 Drachmai 1935 (2000) 10.00

The above coins were struck in England in 1940. They are purely a speculative venture being originally sold at a high premium.

GREENLAND

A large island between the Atlantic and the Polar Sea, separated from the North American continent by Baffin Bay and Davis Strait. A Danish Colony.

Mints: Copenhagen, Philadelphia.

100 Ore = 1 Krone.

ALUMINUM BRONZE

Type—Crowned arms. ℞ Polar bear

1	1 Krone 1926,49	1.25
2	50 Ore 1926,49	.75
3	5 Kroner 1944.	2.00

COPPER-NICKEL

4	25 Ore 1926	.35
	a. Reissue with center hole 1926	.35

Cryolite Mining and Trading Co.

Tokens used at Ivigtut made by the Copenhagen Mint.

COPPER NICKEL

5	10 Kroner 1922. Polar bear on shield. ℞ Value in circle	5.00
6	2 Kroner 1922. Similar	1.00
7	50 Ore 1922. Similar	.35
8	10 Ore 1922. Similar	.25

GUADELOUPE

Two large islands (Basse-Terre and Grande Terre) and smaller islands forming a group of the Windward Islands in the West Indies, between Antigua and Dominica. A French Colony.

Mint: Paris.

100 Centimes = 1 Franc.

NICKEL

1	1 Franc. 1903, 1921. Head of native *l.* ℞ Palm and value	1.00
2	50 Centimes. 1903, 1921. Similar	.50

Both pieces are 20 sided.

GUATEMALA

(Republica de Guatemala)

The northern state of Central America.

Mints: Guatemala, Philadelphia, London, Birmingham, Hamburg.

100 Centavos = 8 Reales = 1 Peso.

100 Centavos = 1 Quetzal.

COPPER-NICKEL

1	1	Real 1901	.25
2	½	Real 1901	.20
3	¼	Real 1901. Mountains	.15

BRONZE
(Provisional Issue)

4 25 Centavos 1915 ..... 1.25

5 12½ Centavos 1915 ..... 1.00

ALUMINUM BRONZE

6 5 Pesos 1923. Bust of Barrios ..... .75

7 1 Peso 1923. Bust of Granados ..... .35

8 50 Centavos 1922. Sun ..... .35

Reform of Nov. 26, 1924

Type — Arms. ℞ Quetzal on pillar

GOLD

9	20	Quetzales 1926	100.00
10	10	Quetzales 1926	40.00
11	5	Quetzales 1926	20.00

SILVER

12	1	Quetzal 1925	20.00
13	½	Quetzal 1925	1.50
14	¼	Quetzal 1925-29	.75
15	10	Centavos 1924-38, 43-48	.25
16	5	Centavos 1924-38, 43-48	.15

17 25 Centavos 1943-48. National palace .... .50

18 25 Centavos 1950. Native head ...

19 10 Centavos 1949,50. Quiriga monolith ....

20 5 Centavos 1949,50. Ceiba tree

MINOR COINS

Type: Arms. ℞ Value.

21 2 Centavos. Nickel Brass 1932...... .15
22 1 Centavo. Bronze 1925, 29, 1932, 33; (a) Nickel brass 1934-38 .... .10
23 ½ Centavo. Nickel Brass 1932, 33 .10

Type: Arms. ℞ Value.

24 2 Centavos. Bronze 1943-45 .... .15
25 1 Centavo. Bronze 1943-47 .... .10
26 ½ Centavo. Bronze 1946 .... .10

27 1 Centavo. 1949, 50. Fray Bartolome de las Casas. ....

GUERNSEY

One of the Channel Islands off the northwest coast of France. A British Crown possession.
Mint: Birmingham. 8 Doubles=1 Penny.

BRONZE

1 8 Doubles. 1902-03, 1910-11, 1914. Arms in wreath. ℞ Value in wreath .... .25
2 8 Doubles. 1918-47. Similar but plainer shield .... .25
3 4 Doubles. 1902-20,45 Arms. ℞ Value .... .25
4 2 Doubles. 1902-29. Similar.......... .15
5 1 Double. 1902-38 .... .10

The name on the coins shows the French spelling Guernesey.

HAITI

(Republique d'Haiti)

Occupies the western third of the Island of Santo Domingo, lying between Cuba on the west and Puerto Rico on the east.

Mints: Scoville Mfg. Co., Waterbury, Conn.; Philadelphia

100 Cents = 1 Gourde.

COPPER-NICKEL

1 50 Cents 1904-08. Bust of Pres. Nord. Alexis I. ℞ Arms .... .60

2 20 Cents 1904-08. Similar .... .35

3 10 Cents 1904-09. Similar .... .25

4 5 Cents 1904-08. Similar .... .20

5 5 Cents 1904. Arms. ℞ Large 5 .10

6 10 Cents 1949. Head of Pres. Dumarsais Estime ....

7 5 Cents 1949. Similar ....

HEJAZ

(After 1936 Saudi Arabia)

In western Arabia bordering on the Red Sea. A Kingdom.

Mint: Mecca. 40 Paras = 1 Garch or Piastre. 100 Garch = 5 Riyals = 1 Dinar.

Husein ibn Ali—1916-1924

GOLD

1 1 Dinar (100 Piastres) 1334 + 8 A.H. or 1923 A.D. Arabic inscription in 5 oval panels. ℞ Similar 35.00

SILVER

2 1 Riyal (20 Garch) 1334 + 8 A.H. Arabic inscription in 3 panels. ℞ Insc. in 5 panels 10.00

3 ½ Riyal. Same date. Similar 3.00

4 ¼ Riyal. Similar 2.00

BRONZE

5 40 Paras (1 Garch). 1334 + 8 A.H. Arabic inscription in circle and 4 compartments 2.00

6 20 Paras. Similar 1.50

7 10 Paras. Similar 1.25

HONDURAS

(Republica de Honduras)

In Central America bounded on the north by the Caribbean Sea, and lying between Guatemala and Nicaragua.

Mints: Tegucigalpa, Philadelphia.

100 Centavos = 1 Peso. 100 Centavos = 1 Lempira.

GOLD

1 5 Pesos 1902, 1908, 1913. Liberty head *l.* ℞ Arms 100.00

2 1 Peso 1912, 13, 1922. Similar... 15.00

SILVER

Type: Liberty stdg. ℞ Arms.

3 1 Peso 1903, 04 .... 3.50

4 50 Centavos 1908-11 .... 2.00

5 25 Centavos 1901-18 .... .75

BRONZE

Type: Arms. ℞ Value.

6 2 Centavos 1908. ℞ 2 CENTS in wreath. The reverse die was struck over the 10 cent silver die .... .25

7 2 Centavos 1910-13. ℞ 2 CENTAVOS in wreath. Many of the dies for these were converted from the old 1 cent dies .... .25

8 2 Centavos 1919-20. ℞ 2 and date in wreath .... **.25**

9 1 Centavo 1907-08. ℞ Value in closed wreath. 20 mm. The reverse die struck over the 10 cent silver dies .... .25

10 1 Centavo 1910. ℞ 1 CENTAVO 1910 in wreath .... .25

11 1 Centavo 1910-13. Size 15 mm. Reverse struck over 5 cent silver die .... .25

12 1 Centavo 1919, 20. ℞ 1 and date in wreath .... .25

Decree of April 3, 1926

SILVER

Type: Indian head. ℞ Arms and date.

13 1 Lempira 1931-37 .... 1.50

14 50 Centavos 1931-37 .... .75

15 20 Centavos 1931, 32 .... .35

MINOR COINS

Type: Arms and date. ℞ Value in wreath.

16 10 Centavos. Copper Nickel 1932 .15

17 5 Centavos. Copper Nickel 1931, 32, 49 .... .10

18 2 Centavos. Bronze 1939, 49 .... .20

19 1 Centavo. Bronze 1935, 39, 49 ... .15

HONG KONG

An island and peninsula in southeast China at the mouth of the Canton River. British Crown Colony.

Mints: London, Birmingham (H). 100 Cents=1 Dollar.

Victoria

SILVER

1 10 Cents. 1901. Crowned bust *l.* ℞ Value in circle .... .50
2 5 Cents. 1901. Similar .... .25

BRONZE

3 1 Cent. 1901. Similar .... .35

Edward VII

SILVER

4 50 Cents. 1902-05 .... 2.00
5 20 Cents. 1902-05 .... 1.00
6 10 Cents. 1902-05. Similar .... .50
7 5 Cents. 1903-05. Similar .... .25

BRONZE

8 1 Cent. 1902-05. Similar .... .35

George V

SILVER

9 10 Cents. 1935. Crowned bust *l.* ℞ Value in circle .... .25
10 5 Cents. 1932-33. Similar .... .25

COPPER-NICKEL

11 10 Cents. 1935-36. Same as the silver .... .25
12 5 Cents. 1935. Same as the silver .... .25

BRONZE

13 1 Cent. 1919, 1922-26, Crowned head *l.* ℞ Value in Chinese in circle, 28 mm. .... .35
14 1 Cent. 1931-33. Similar but size reduced to 22 mm. .... .25

George VI

NICKEL

Type of preceding reign.

15 10 Cents. 1937 .... .25
16 5 Cents. 1937 .... .20

17 10 Cents. 1938, 39. Larger head .25
18 5 Cents. 1938, 39, 41 .... .20

BRONZE

19 Cent 1941 ....

With title—"KING GEORGE THE SIXTH"

NICKEL-BRONZE

20 10 Cents 1948-50 ....
21 5 Cents 1949,50 ....

HUNGARY

(Magyar Orzag—Kingdom of Hungary)

Bounded by Czechoslovakia on the north, Yugoslavia on the south, Roumania on the east and Germany on the west.

Mint: Kormoczbanya (KB). 100 Filler = 1 Korona.

Francis Joseph—1848-1916

GOLD

1 100 Korona 1907. 40 Anniv. of the Hungarian Coronation. Head *r.* ℞ Coronation scene....100.00

2 100 Korona 1907-08. Regular issue. Standing figure of Francis Joseph *r.* ℞ Arms of Hungary with angel supporters 125.00

3 20 Korona 1900-16. Similar 12.50

4 10 Korona 1900-15. Similar 7.50

SILVER

5 5 Korona 1900, 1906-09, Head *r.* ℞ Angels holding crown, value below 3.00

6 5 Korona 1907. Jubilee issue. Similar to the 100 Korona Jubilee issue 4.00

7 2 Korona 1912-14. Similar to the regular 5 Korona .... .75

8 1 Korona 1906, 1912-16. Head *r.* ℞ Crown over value .... .60

NICKEL

9 20 Filler 1906-08, 1914. Crown. ℞ Value in wreath .... .20

10 10 Filler 1906, 1908-09. Similar.... .15

11 10 Filler 1914-16. Crown. ℞ Value above spray .... .10

This latter piece is very much alloyed and has a yellowish color.

BRONZE

12 2 Filler 1900-10, 1914-15. Similar to the 20 Filler .... .10

13 1 Filler 1900-03, 1906. Similar .10

IRON

14 20 Filler 1916. Crown. ℞ Value above sprays .... .20

15 10 Filler 1915. Similar .... .15

16 2 Filler 1916. Crown. ℞ Value in circular spray .... .10

Karl—1916-1918

IRON

17 20 Filler 1917-18. Same as the previous iron 20 Filler .... .25

18 10 Filler 1918. Similar .... .20

19 2 Filler 1917-18. Similar to previous iron 2 Filler .... .15

HUNGARY

Kingdom 1920-45. Ruled by a regent (Magyar Kiralysag).
Proclaimed a republic in 1946 (Magyar Koztarsasag).

Mints: Budapest (BP), Vienna, Bern.

100 Fillers = 1 Pengö

Post World War I Issue

IRON

1 20 Filler 1919-21. Crown. ℞ Value .... .25
2 10 Filler 1919-20. Similar .... .15

Law of Nov. 21, 1925

SILVER

3 1 Pengo 1926-38. Arms. ℞ Value .75
4 2 Pengo 1929-38. Madonna 1.00

5 5 Pengo 1930. 10th year of the Regency. Bust of Admiral Horthy r. ℞ Hungarian arms...... 7.50

6 2 Pengo 1935. Pasmany Commemorative. University of Budapest issue 2.50

7 2 Pengo 1935. Rakoczi Commemorative. Bust r. ℞ Arms 2.50

8 2 Pengo 1936. Liszt Commemorative. Head r. ℞ Arms 2.50

9 5 Pengo 1938. Commemorating 900th anniversary of death of St. Stephen. Bust r. 5.00

10 5 Pengo 1939. Bust of Horthy 6.00

COPPER-NICKEL

Type—Crown. ℞ Value.

11 50 Filler 1926-38 .... .35
12 20 Filler 1926-38 .... .30
13 10 Filler 1926-38 .... .25

BRONZE

14 2 Filler 1926-38. Crown. ℞ Value .15
15 1 Filler 1926-38. Similar .... .10

World War II Issues

18 5 Pengo. Aluminum 1943. Bust of Admiral Horthy 75th Birthday 3.00
19 5 Pengo. Aluminum 1945. Parliament 2.00
20 2 Pengo. Aluminum 1941. Arms .50
21 1 Pengo. Aluminum 1941. Arms .25
22 20 Filler. Steel 1940-44. Crown. ℞ Value centerhole .... .20
23 10 Filler. Steel 1940-44. Similar ...... .15
24 2 Filler. Steel 1940-44; (a) Zinc 1943 .... .10

Reform of 1946

25 5 Forint. Silver 1946-47. Head of Kossuth 3.50
The 1946 issue weighs 20 gr; the 1947 issue 12 gr.
26 2 Forint. Aluminum 1946 .... .50
27 1 Forint. Aluminum 1946 .... .25
31 50 Filler. Aluminum 1948 .... .35
28 20 Filler. Copper Aluminum 1946, 47 .... .20
29 10 Filler. Copper Aluminum 1946, 47 .... .15
32 5 Filler. Aluminum 1948 .... .25
30 2 Filler. Bronze 1946, 47 .... .10

Silver Commemorative Coins

33 20 Forint 1948. Tancsics Mihaly 7.50

34 10 Forint 1948. Szechenyi 4.00

35 5 Forint 1948. Petofi 3.50

Peoples Republic
(Magyar Nepkoztarsasag)

36 50 Filler 1948. Aluminum. Worker ....

37 5 Filler 1948. Aluminum. Native girl ....

38 2 Filler 1950. Aluminum ....

ICELAND

(Island)

An island close to the Arctic Circle in the North Atlantic. The Althing (Parliament) voted May, 1941 to cancel the union of Iceland with Denmark, declaring Iceland independent, and in June, 1941 proclaimed a Republic.

Mints: Copenhagen, London. 100 Aurar = 1 Krona.

Christian X of Denmark, 1912-1942

Type—Crowned arms. ℞ Value.

1 2 Kroner 1925, 29, 40. Alum. Bronze 1.00

2 1 Krona 1925, 29, 40. Alum. Bronze .... .75

3 25 Aurar 1922-40. Copper-nickel; (a) 1942 Zinc .... .40

4 10 Aurar 1922-40. Copper-nickel; (a) 1942 Zinc .... .30

Type—CX crowned. ℞ Value.

5 5 Aurar 1926, 31, 40. Bronze .... .25

6 2 Aurar 1926-38. Bronze; (a) 1942 Zinc .... .20

7 1 Eyrir 1926-38. Bronze; (a) 1942 Zinc .... .15

Commemorative Issue

1000 Anniversary of the Althing. The values are expressed on the edges.

SILVER

8 10 Kroner (1930). Seated figure l. ℞ Shield with supporters 20.00

9 5 Kroner 1930. Standing figure. ℞ Dragons interlaced 10.00

BRONZE

10 2 Kroner 1930. Seated figure facing. ℞ Icelandic Cross, designs in angles 5.00

No. 9 and 10 are transposed on the plate.

Iceland Republic

Type—Arms. ℞ Value.

ALUMINUM BRONZE

11	2 Kroner 1946	.85
12	1 Krona 1946	.50

COPPER-NICKEL

13	25 Aurar 1946	.35
14	10 Aurar 1946	.25

BRONZE

15	5 Aurar 1946	.15
16	1 Eyrir 1946	.10

INDIA

An Empire in the British Commonwealth of Nations. The name India describes the central peninsula of Southern Asia, south of the Himalayas, from Bhutan to Tibet.

Mints: Calcutta, Bombay, either B or dot, Lahore.

12 Pies=1 Anna. 3 Pies=1 Pice. 16 Annas=1 Rupee. 15 Rupees=1 Mohur.

Victoria

SILVER

1 1 Rupee. 1901. Crowned bust *l.* ℞ Value in scroll border...... 1.25

2 ¼ Rupee. 1901. Similar .... .50

3 2 Annas. 1901. Similar .... .25

COPPER

4 ¼ Anna. 1901. Similar to the silver. ℞ Value in circle .... .25

5 ½ Pice. 1901. Similar .... .20

6 1/12 Anna. 1901. Similar .... .15

Edward VII

SILVER

7 1 Rupee. 1903-10. Head *r.* ℞ Value between lotus sprays 1.25

8 ½ Rupee. 1905-10 .... .60

9 ¼ Rupee. 1903-09 .... .35

10 2 Annas. 1903-10 .... .25

COPPER-NICKEL

11 1 Anna. 1907-10. Crowned bust *r.* ℞ Value in scroll. Scalloped edge .... .15

COPPER

Type of preceding reign.

12 ¼ Anna. 1903-10 .... .15

13 ½ Pice. 1903-10 .... .15

14 1/12 Anna. 1903-10 .... .10

George V

GOLD

15 15 Rupees (1 Mohur). 1918. Crowned bust *l.* ℞ Value in ornamented circle 30.00

SILVER

16 1 Rupee. 1911-20. Crowned bust *l.* ℞ Value in floral scroll... 1.25

17 ½ Rupee. 1911-36. Similar .... .35

18 ¼ Rupee. 1911-36. Similar .... .25

19 2 Annas. 1911-16. Similar .... .20

COPPER-NICKEL

20 8 Annas. 1919. Crowned bust *l.* ℞ 8 in framework 1.25

21 4 Annas. 1919-21. Similar. ℞ 4 in square. 8 sided .... .25

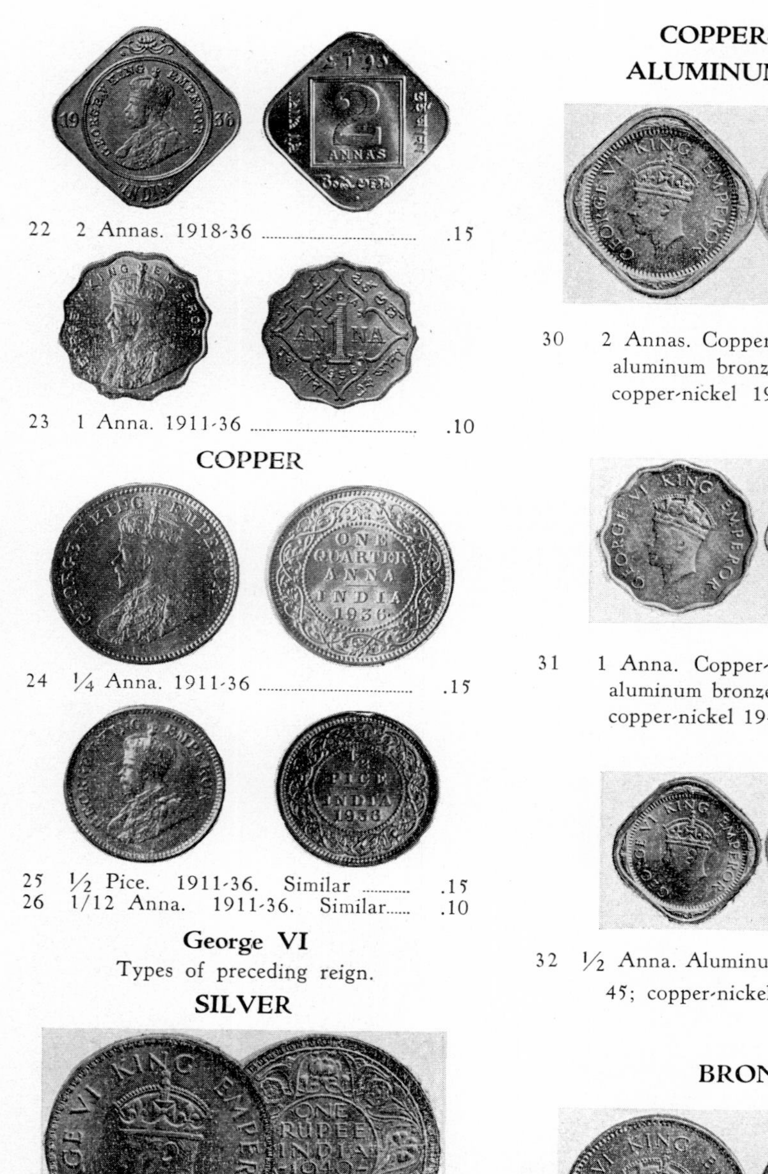

22 2 Annas. 1918-36 .... .15

23 1 Anna. 1911-36 .... .10

COPPER

24 ¼ Anna. 1911-36 .... .15

25 ½ Pice. 1911-36. Similar .... .15
26 1/12 Anna. 1911-36. Similar.......... .10

George VI

Types of preceding reign.

SILVER

27 1 Rupee 1940-46 .... 1.00
28 ½ Rupee 1937-46 .... .50
29 ¼ Rupee 1937-46 .... .30

COPPER-NICKEL ALUMINUM-BRONZE

30 2 Annas. Copper-nickel 1937-42; aluminum bronze 1942-45; copper-nickel 1946-48 .... .15

31 1 Anna. Copper-nickel 1937-42; aluminum bronze 1942-45; copper-nickel 1945-48 .... .10

32 ½ Anna. Aluminum bronze 1942-45; copper-nickel 1946-48 .... .10

BRONZE

33 ¼ Anna 1937-43 .... .15

34 ½ Pice 1937-43 .... .15
35 1/12 Anna 1937-41 .... .10
36 1/12 Anna 1941-43. Thin flan .... .10

37 1 Pice 1943-48. Holed .... .15

NICKEL

Type—Crowned head. ℞ Tiger.

38 1 Rupee 1946-48 .... 1.00
39 ½ Rupee 1946-48 .... .50
40 ¼ Rupee 1946-48 .... .25

INDIA

(Bharat)

A sovereign democratic republic within the British Commonwealth of Nations.
Mints: Calcutta, Bombay
12 Pies = 1 Anna. 3 Pies = 1 Pice
16 Annas = 1 Rupee

NICKEL

Type—The Asoka pillar, 3 lions on pedestal. ℞ Value

1 1 Rupee 1950 ....

2 ½ Rupee 1950 ....

3 ¼ Rupee 1950 ....

COPPER-NICKEL

Type—Asoka pillar. ℞ Brahman bull

4 2 Annas 1950 ....
5 1 Anna 1950. Scalloped ....

6 ½ Anna 1950 ....

BRONZE

Type—Asoka pillar. ℞ Horse

7 1 Pice 1950 ....

NATIVE INDIAN STATES

BAHAWALPUR

One of the Punjab States

Sadiq Mohammed V—1907

GOLD

1 1 Ashrafi 1343 AH = 1935 A.D.

SILVER

2 1 Rupee 1343 AH ....

COPPER

3 1 Paisa 1343 AH ....

4 ¼ Anna 1940 .... .50

5 ½ Pice 1940 .... .25

BIKANIR

Under Western Rajputana states agency.

Sri Ganga Singhji—1887-1943

GOLD

1 1 Mohur 1937 (Samvat 1994) ...

2 ½ Mohur 1937 .... 50.00

SILVER

3 1 Rupee 1937 .... 5.00
Commemorating 50 years of reign

BHUTAN

A State in the Eastern Himalaya.
Mint: Calcutta.

Maharajah Jigme Wangchuk—1926

SILVER

1 ½ Rupee 1928. Bust of ruler *l.* ℞ Nine compartments enclosing the eight lucky signs and inscription in center 10.00

BRONZE

2 1 Paisa 1928. Similar 3.50

3 1 Paisa (1930) ....

BUNDI

Raghubir Singh—1889-

SILVER

1 1 Rupee 1958 Samvat = 1901 A.D. Seated figure holding sword; around, EDWARD VII. EMPEROR. ℞ Nagari inscription 7.50

2 ½ Rupee 1909. In center dagger 3.50

3 ¼ Rupee 1909. Similar 2.00

COOCH BEHAR

Under Eastern States Agency

Jitandra Harayan—-1912-1922

GOLD

1 1 Mohur 404 (1914). Arms elephant and lion supporters. ℞ Native inscription 75.00

GWALIOR

The premier Mahratta State in Central India. *Mint:* Gwalior.

Madho Rao III—1886-1925

GOLD

1 1/3 Mohur. Samvat era 1959= 1902. Bust *r.* heavily indented bordure. ℞ Arms with supporters 50.00

SILVER

2 1 Rupee. 25th year (1911). Persian inscription ℞ Nagari *Ma* between trident and bow and arrow 3.50

3 ½ Rupee. Similar 2.00
3a ¼ Rupee. Similar 1.25
4 2 Annas. Similar .... .75

COPPER

5 ¼ Anna. Samvat date 1958 (1901). Coiled Cobra with sceptre and trident. ℞ Nagari insc. within floriated border .... .75
6 ½ Pice (1901). Similar .... .50
7 ¼ Anna. Samvat date 1970 (1913). Bust of Madho. Rao *r.* ℞ Arms with supporters...... 1.25
8 ¼ Anna. Samvat date 1974 (1917). Similar but lower relief .75

Jivaji III—1925-

COPPER BRASS

9 ¼ Anna. Samvat date 1986 (1929). Bust *l.* ℞ Similar to above .... .35
10 ½ Anna 1942. Brass .... .35
11 ¼ Anna. Copper .... .25

HYDERABAD

The Largest and most populous Indian State.

Mint: Hyderabad state mint.

Mir Mahbub Ali Khan II—1868-1911

Halli Sicca coins exist with dates after 1319 A.H. Gold 1/16, ⅛, ¼, ½ and 1 Mohur. Silver 1/16, ⅛, ¼, ½ and 1 Rupee. Type as per No. 1 on plate. Only a few of the denominations are known with 20th century dates.

New design with Char Minar

Persian M in gateway.

Dates between 1321 A.H. and 1329 A.H.

GOLD

6 1 Mohur 35.00
7 ½ Mohur 20.00
8 ¼ Mohur 10.00
9 ⅛ Mohur 7.50

SILVER

10 1 Rupee 1321-29 .... 2.50
11 ½ Rupee 1328,29 .... 1.25
12 ¼ Rupee 1323-28 .... .75
13 ⅛ Rupee 1323 .... .50

COPPER

14 ½ Anna 1324,25 .... .75
15 2 Pai 1322-29 .... .50
16 1 Pai 1327 .... .25

Mir Usman Ali Khan—1911-

GOLD

With dates between 1330 A.H. and 1362
Denominations in Persian

17	1 Mohur or Ashrafi. Similar to gold of Mir Mahbub. Persian Ain in gateway. ℞ Inscription in circles and sword panels	50.00
18	½ Mohur	30.00
19	¼ Mohur	15.00
20	⅛ Mohur	10.00

SILVER

21	1 Rupee. Similar to the silver of Mir Mahbub with Ain in gateway	1.50
22	8 Annas	1.00
22a	4 Annas	.50
22b	2 Annas	.35

COPPER-NICKEL

23	1 Anna 1338 (1919). Toughra. Value in four languages. ℞ Insc. in three parallel compartments	.35
24	1 Anna 1356 (1937). Toughra. ℞ Value. Square	.15

COPPER

Type of preceding ruler

25	2 Pai 1338	.35
26	1 Pai 1349	.20

Denominations indicated by numerals

SILVER

27 1 Rupee 1362 (1942) ....

28 ½ Rupee 1363 ....
29 ¼ Rupee 1362 ....
30 ⅛ Rupee 1362 ....

Denominations in Urdu

NICKEL

31 ½ Rupee 1366 (1947) ....

32 ¼ Rupee 1366 ....
33 ⅛ Rupee 1366 ....

BRONZE

34 1 Anna 1366. Square ....

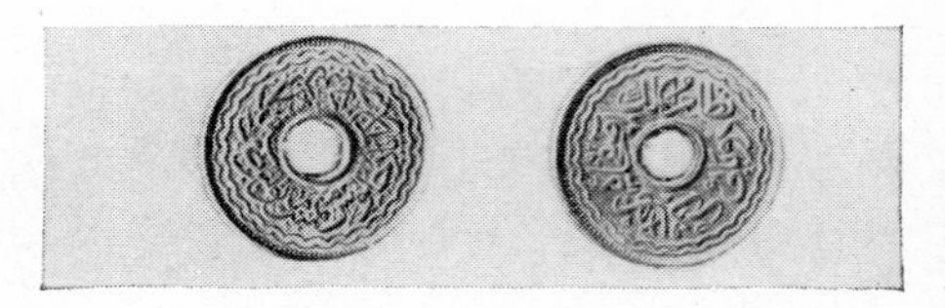

35 2 Pai 1364-68. Holed ....

INDORE

Under Central India Agency

Mint: Indore.

Shiyaji Rao—1866-1903

SILVER

1 1 Rupee. Samvat 1958 = 1902 A.D. Facing bust of the Holkar. ℞ Arms with horse and bull 7.50

COPPER

2 ½ Anna. Samvat 1958, 1959= 1901-02 A.D. Seated bull .... .50

3 ¼ Anna. Similar .... .25

Yeshwant Rao Holkar—1930-

4 ½ Anna 1992 (1935) .... .50

5 ¼ Anna 1992 (1935) .... .35

JAIPUR

Under Rajputana Agency.
Mint: Sawai Jaipur.

Madho Singh II—1880-1922

SILVER

Christian dates 1901-07 and yearly dates from 22-27 in Persian figures.

1	1 Rupee. Persian inscription and sprig. ℞ Persian insc.	2.50
2	½ Rupee. Similar	1.00
3	¼ Rupee. Similar	.75
4	⅛ Rupee. Similar	.50

COPPER

With yearly dates from 22-42

5	¼ Anna. Similar to silver	.25

All native work.

Madho Singh III—1922-

6	1 Anna 1944. Nickel-bronze	.35

JODHPUR

Largest state in the Rajputana Agency.

COPPER

(In the name of Edward VII)

1	¼ Anna 1906. Persian inscription on both sides	.35
2	½ Pice 1906. Similar	.25

(In the name of George VI)

3	¼ Anna. Undated	.25

JUNAGADH

Under Western States Agency.
Mint: Junagadh.

Rasal Mahabat Khan III—1892-

COPPER

1	1 Dokdo. Samvat 1964-65 = 1907-08 A.D. Nagari insc. in circle and around. ℞ Persian insc.	.75

Native workmanship.

KUTCH

Under Western India State Agency
Mint: Bhuj.

2 Trambiya = 1 Dokdo = 1/24 Kori.

Khengarji III—1876-1942

In the name of Edward VII

COPPER

1	1 Dokdo 1909	2.00

2	1 Trambiyo 1909	.75

In the name of George V

SILVER

3	5 Kori 1917-35	3.50
4	2½ Kori 1926-35	2.50
5	1 Kori 1923-35	1.25
6	½ Kori 1928	.75

COPPER

7	3 Dokda 1926-35	2.50
8	1½ Dokdo 1926,31	1.50
9	1 Dokdo 1920,29	1.00
10	1 Trambiyo 1920	.50

In the name of Edward VIII

SILVER

11	5 Kori 1936	
12	2½ Kori 1936	
13	1 Kori 1936	

COPPER

14	3 Dokda 1936	2.50

In the name of George VI

SILVER

15	5 Kori 1937,38	
16	1 Kori 1938-40	

Vijayaarijji 1942-1947

In the name of George VI

SILVER

17	5 Kori 1942	
18	1 Kori 1944	

COPPER

19	½ Kori 1944	
20	¼ Kori 1944	
21	⅛ Kori 1944	
22	1/16 Kori 1944	
23	1/48 Kori 1944 (Trambiyo)	

Madanasinhji—1948

COPPER

24	⅛ Kori. Samvat 2004	

Kutch formed into Chief Commissioners Province June 1st, 1948. The Kori was demonetized April 26, 1949 when Indian currency was introduced.

MEWAR UDAIPUR

(Mewar)

Under Eastern Rajputana States Agency.

Mints: Udaipur, Calcutta.

Gold mohurs, silver rupees, halves, quarters, two and one anna pieces, known as the Swarup Shahi rupees have been struck from 1851 to 1913 and have two lines of Nagari with ornament below and five Nagari characters in an eight lobed circle on the other side. The workmanship is very crude.

Bhupal Singh—1930-

SILVER

1	1 Rupee (1932). Nagari inscription and the hills of Mewar within a floral border. R̷ Four line insc. with floral border	3.00

2 ½ Rupee. Similar 1.50
3 ¼ Rupee. Similar 1.00
4 2 Annas. Similar .... .75
5 1 Anna. Similar .... .50

Well executed pieces made at the Calcutta Mint for the Durbar of the ruler of Mewar.

COPPER

6 1 Anna 1943. Octagonal .... .35
7 ½ Anna 1942. Round .... .35
8 ¼ Anna 1942. Square .... .25

PUDUKOTA

One of the three Madras States.
Mints: Calcutta, Birmingham.

BRONZE

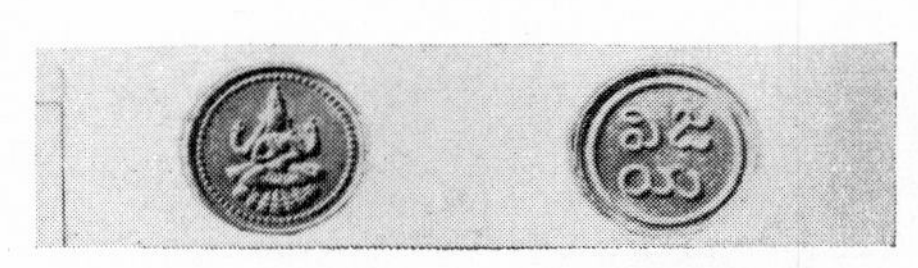

1 Amman Cash (1902-). Seated figure. ℞ Native inscription in two lines .... .35

RAJKOT STATE

GOLD

1 1 Mohur 1945 ....

RUTLAM

COPPER

1 1 Paisa 1945 (Samvat). Crude restrike of 1947 .... .35

SAILANA

Mint: Calcutta.

COPPER

1 ¼ Anna 1908. Head of Edward VII *r.* ℞ Value, etc. 7.50
2 ¼ Anna 1912. Head of George V. *l.* ℞ As above 5.00

TONK

Under Rajputana—Jaipur Agency
Mint: Calcutta.

COPPER

1 1 Pice 1329 A.H.=1911. Persian inscription on both sides. Native workmanship .... .50

Mohammad Saadat Ali Khan

2 1 Pice (1350 A.H.=1932 A.D). Ball between crossed scimitars, around, Persian insc. ℞ Peacock tail feather. Insc. and ornaments in circle .... .50

This piece comes in two sizes 21 and 26 mm. Modern work.

TRAVANCORE

One of the three Madras States.
Mint: Trivandrum, Birmingham.
16 Cash = 1 Chuckram.
4 Chuckram = 1 Fanam.
32 Chuckram = 8 Fannams = 1 Rupee.

Rama Varma—1885-1931

SILVER

1 ½ Rupee 1087-1107. Malabar Era=1911-1931 A.D. Conch shell in wreath. Malayalam inscription around. ℞ Value in wreath etc. in English 2.00

2 ¼ Rupee. Similar 1.25

3 1 Fanam. Conch shell in circle and wreath. ℞ R V and value.......... .50

4 2 Chuckrams. No date. Similar to the fanam. Two varieties, CHS 2 and 2 CHS .... .50

COPPER

5 1 Chuckram (1904). Similar to the silver fanam .... .50

6 8 Cash. Similar .... .35

7 4 Cash. Similar .... .25

8 1 Cash. Conch shell in eight pointed star. ℞ Two line native inscription .... .25

There are two varieties of each copper piece, with the value before and after the denomination.

Bala Rama Varma—1931-

SILVER

9 ½ Rupee 1937-43 .... 1.00

10 ¼ Rupee 1937-43 .... .75

11 Fanam 1937-43 .... .35

The later coins are made of the so-called Q metal.

COPPER

12 1 Chuckram 1938. Bust in plumed hat .... .50

13 8 Cash. Undated .... .25

14 4 Cash. Undated .... .20

15 1 Cash. Undated .... .15

INDO-CHINA

(Indo-Chine Francaise)

In southeastern Asia bordering on the South China Sea and the Gulf of Siam. A French Colony and Protectorate until 1946. Now a federation consisting of the Associated States of Viet-Nam, Laos and Cambodia.

Mints: Paris (A), Poissy, Birmingham (H), San Francisco, Castelsarrasin, Beaumont-le-Roger

500 Sapeques = 100 Centimes = 1 Piastre.

SILVER

Type: Seated Figure. R̷ Value.

1 — 1 Piastre 1901-28 .... 3.00

3 — 20 Centimes 1901-38 .... .50

5 — 10 Centimes 1901-38 .... .25

In 1921 the fineness of the last two pieces was reduced from 835 to 680. In 1920 fractional coins were struck at San Francisco with no weight or fineness indicated.

2 — 1 Piastre 1931, 32. Head l. R̷ Value in ornamental frame 15.00

COPPER-NICKEL

7 — 5 Centimes 1923-25, 30, 38, 39. Head and cornucopias. R̷ Value. Holed type .... .25

BRONZE

8 — 1 Centime 1900-03, 1906. Seated figures around center hole. R̷ Value in Chinese. 27 mm. .... .25

9 — 1 Centime 1908-40. Similar but thinner .... .20

10 ½ Centime 1935-40. Liberty cap and RF. ℞ Value. Holed type .20

11 1 Sapeque 1901, 02. French legend. ℞ Chinese legend. Square holed type .25

NICKEL

Type: Bust of Liberty. ℞ Rice plants and value.

12 20 Centimes 1939-41; (a) Copper-Nickel 1940. 24 mm. .35

13 10 Centimes 1939-41; (a) Copper-Nickel 1940. 18 mm. .25

NICKEL-BRONZE

Type—Bust of Liberty. ℞ Rice Plants

14 1 Piastre 1946-48 2.50

Type—Seated figure. ℞ Value

15 50 Centimes 1946,47 1.25

ALUMINUM

Same type as 1 Piastre

16 20 Centimes 1945,46. 27m. .35

17 10 Centimes 1945,46. 23m. .25

18 5 Centimes 1945,46. 18m. .20

Vichy State

ZINC

All holed type

V1 1 Centime 1941. Liberty cap. .35

V2 ½ Centime 1940. Similar to No. 10 .25

V3 ¼ Centime 1941-42. Rice Sprays .25

ALUMINUM

Type: ETAT FRANCAISE. Rice Sprays. ℞ Value

V4 5 Centimes 1943 .35

V5 1 Centime 1943 .25

INDO-CHINA

Viet-Nam

Composed of Annam, Cochin-China and Tonkin. A Republic within the Federation of Indo-China and of the French Union. Under the presidency of Ho Chi Minh 1946-1948. Now governed by former Emperor Bao Dai of Annam.

Dong = Piastre   Hao = 1/10 Piastre   Xu = Centime

1a 1 Dong. Aluminum 1946 ....

2a 5 Hao. Aluminum 1946 ....

3a 20 Xu. Aluminum 1945 ....

IRAQ

(Mesopotamia)

In Western Asia bounded on the north by Syria and Turkey.

Mint: London.

1000 Fils = 20 Dirhem = 5 Riyals = 1 Pound or 1 Dinar.

Faisal I—1921-1933

SILVER

1	200 Fils or 1 Riyal 1932. Head *r.* ℞ Arabic inscription	5.00
2	50 Fils or 1 Dirhem 1931-1933. Similar	2.00
3	20 Fils 1931-33. Similar	.50

NICKEL

4	10 Fils 1931-33. Similar but scalloped edge	.25
5	4 Fils 1931-33. Similar	.20

BRONZE

6	2 Fils 1931-33. Similar but round	.15
7	1 Fils 1931-33. Similar	.10

Ghazi I—1933-38

SILVER

8	50 Fils or 1 Dirhem 1936-38	1.50
9	20 Fils 1938	.50

NICKEL

10	10 Fils 1937. Scalloped edge	.25

COPPER-NICKEL

11	4 Fils 1938. Similar	.20

BRONZE

12	10 Fils 1938. Same as nickel	.35
13	4 Fils 1938. Similar	.25
14	1 Fils 1936-38. Round	.10

Faisal II—1938-

BRONZE

15	10 Fils 1943. Scalloped	.25
16	4 Fils 1943. Similar	.20
17	1 Fil 1947,48	.15

IRISH FREE STATE

(Eire)

An island in the Atlantic Ocean, separated from Great Britain by St. George's Channel, the Irish Sea and North Channel. A sovereign, independent state. Name officially changed to Eire in 1937.

Mint: London.
12 Pence=1 Shilling.

The obverse design of all denominations is a harp

SILVER

1 ½ Crown 1928-38. Horse 1.25

2 1 Florin 1928-38. Salmon 1.00

3 1 Shilling 1928-37. Bull .... .50

NICKEL

4 6 Pence or Reul. 1928-29, 1934. ℞ Wolfhound .... .30

5 3 Pence or Leat Reul. 1928, 1933-34. ℞ Hare *l.* .... .25

BRONZE

6 1 Penny. 1928-38. Hen and chickens .... .15

7 ½ Penny 1928-38. Sow and pigs .10

8 1 Farthing 1928-38. Woodcock... .10

Word EIRE replaces words SAORSTAT EIREANN

SILVER

9 ½ Crown 1939-43 .... 1.25

10 1 Florin 1939-43 .... 1.00

11 1 Shilling 1939-42 .... .50

COPPER-NICKEL

12 6 Pence 1939-49 .... .30

13 3 Pence 1939-49 .... .20

BRONZE

14 Penny 1939-49 .... .15

15 ½ Penny 1939-49 .... .10

16 Farthing 1939-49 .... .10

ISRAEL

(Medinat Israel — State of Israel)

An independent sovereign state established by proclamation May 1948. Formerly a British mandate.
Mints: I. C. I. Kings Norton. Legends in Hebrew and Arabic.
1000 Prutah = 1 £ Israel

1 250 Prutah 1949. Copper-nickel ...

2 100 Prutah 1949. Copper-nickel ...

3 50 Prutah 1949. Copper-nickel ...

4 25 Prutah 1949. Copper-nickel ...

5 10 Prutah 1949. Bronze ....

6 5 Prutah 1949. Bronze ....

7 1 Prutah 1949. Aluminum ....

Provisional Issue

Made in Tel-Aviv

8 25 Mils 1949. Aluminum ....

ITALY
(Regno d'Italia)

Occupies the Apennine Peninsula in southern Europe which extends into the Mediterranean Sea.
Mint: Rome.
100 Centesimi = 1 Lira.

Vittorio Emanuele III—1900-1944

All gold or silver coins with portrait head.

GOLD

1 100 Lire 1903, 1905. Crowned eagle ... 150.00

2 20 Lire 1902-03, 1905. Similar ... 35.00
1902 also comes with small anchor on obverse, indicating gold from Eritrea.

3 50 Lire 1911. (50th anniv. of Kingdom). Allegorical figures ... 50.00

4 100 Lire 1912, 1926,27. ℞ Female and plow ... 150.00

5 50 Lire 1912, 1926,27 ... 75.00

6 20 Lire 1912, 1926,27 ... 25.00

7 10 Lire 1912, 1926,27 ... 12.50

8 100 Lire 1923. Head *l.* ℞ Fasces. OCT. 1922-23 ... 100.00

9 20 Lire 1923. Similar ... 25.00

10 100 Lire 1925. Allegorical figure and flag *l.* ... 100.00

Reduced Size
New Valuation of Lira

11 100 Lire 1931-33. Italia on prow ... 35.00

12 50 Lire 1931-33. Man carrying fasces *r.* ... 20.00

13 100 Lire 1936. Man with sword walking *l.* ... 50.00

14 50 Lire 1936. Roman eagle on two medallions ... 30.00

14a 100 Lire 1937. Reduced size ... 100.00

SILVER

15 5 Lire 1901. Crowned eagle. Very rare ... 100.00

16 2 Lire 1901-07. Similar ... 1.00

17 1 Lira 1901-02, 1905-07. Similar ... .50

18 2 Lire 1908. 1910-12. Quadriga ... 1.00

19 1 Lira 1908-10, 1912-13. Similar ... .50

20 5 Lire 1911. (50th anniv. of Kingdom). Allegorical figures ... 10.00

21 2 Lire 1911. Similar ... 1.50

22 5 Lire 1914. Quadriga ... 15.00

23 2 Lire 1914-17. Quadriga ... 1.00

24 1 Lira 1915-17. Similar ... .50

Reduced Size
New Valuation of Lira

25 20 Lire 1927-28. Standing and seated figures ... 5.00

26 10 Lire 1926-30. Head *l.* ℞ Biga ... 1.25

27 5 Lire 1926-30. Head *l.* ℞ Eagle on fasces ... .75

28 20 Lire 1928. (Tenth anniversary of the World War). Helmeted head of king *l.* ℞ Architectural fasces ... 7.50

29 20 Lire 1936, 37. Head *l.* ℞ Quadriga ... 10.00

30 10 Lire 1936, 37. Head *r.* ℞ Italia on prow of galley ... 1.50

31 5 Lire 1936, 37. Head *l.* ℞ Seated mother and children ... .75

NICKEL

32 25 Centesimi 1902-03. Crowned eagle. ℞ Value in wreath ... .20

33 20 Centesimi 1908-14, 1919-22, 1926. Classical head ... .15

34 20 Centesimi 1918-20. Crowned arms. Value in hexagon. ... .15

VITTORIO EMANUELE III
4
VITTORIO EMANUELE III
2
8
VITTORIO EMANUELE III RE D'ITALIA
VITTORIO EMANUELE III
1
REGNO D'ITALIA
LIRE 100
1912
LIRE
100
OTTOBRE
1922
1923
R
REGNO D'ITALIA
L. 100
1903
R
VITTORIO EMANUELE III RE D'ITALIA
3
VITTORIO EMANUELE III RE
11
1861 1911
L. 50
3
VITTORIO EMANUELE III RE D'ITALIA
9
RE D'ITALIA
1900
1925
10
LIRE
100
12
LIRE
20
OTTOBRE
1922
1923
13
LIRE 100
14

I T A L Y

15
VITTORIO EMANUELE III
22
VITTORIO EMANVELE III RE D'ITALIA
20
VITTORIO EMANVELE III RE D'ITALIA
REGNO D'ITALIA
L 5 R 1901
1914
L 5
1861 1911
L 5
VITTORIO EMANUELE III
VITTORIO EMANVELE III RE D'ITALIA
18
1908
L 2
VITTORIO EMANVELE III RE D'ITALIA
16
21
27
REGNO D'ITALIA
1906
VITTORIO EMANVELE III RE D'ITALIA
1926
L 5
1861 1911
L 2
VITT EM III RE D'ITALIA
VITTORIO EMANVELE III RE
25
26
1927
L 10
26
VITT EM III RE
ITALIA
A VI
1928
L 20
28
ITALIA
MCMXVIII
L. 20
MEGLIO VIVERE VN GIORNO DA LEONE CHE CENTO ANNI DA PECORA
MCMXXVIII
A VI
28

ITALY

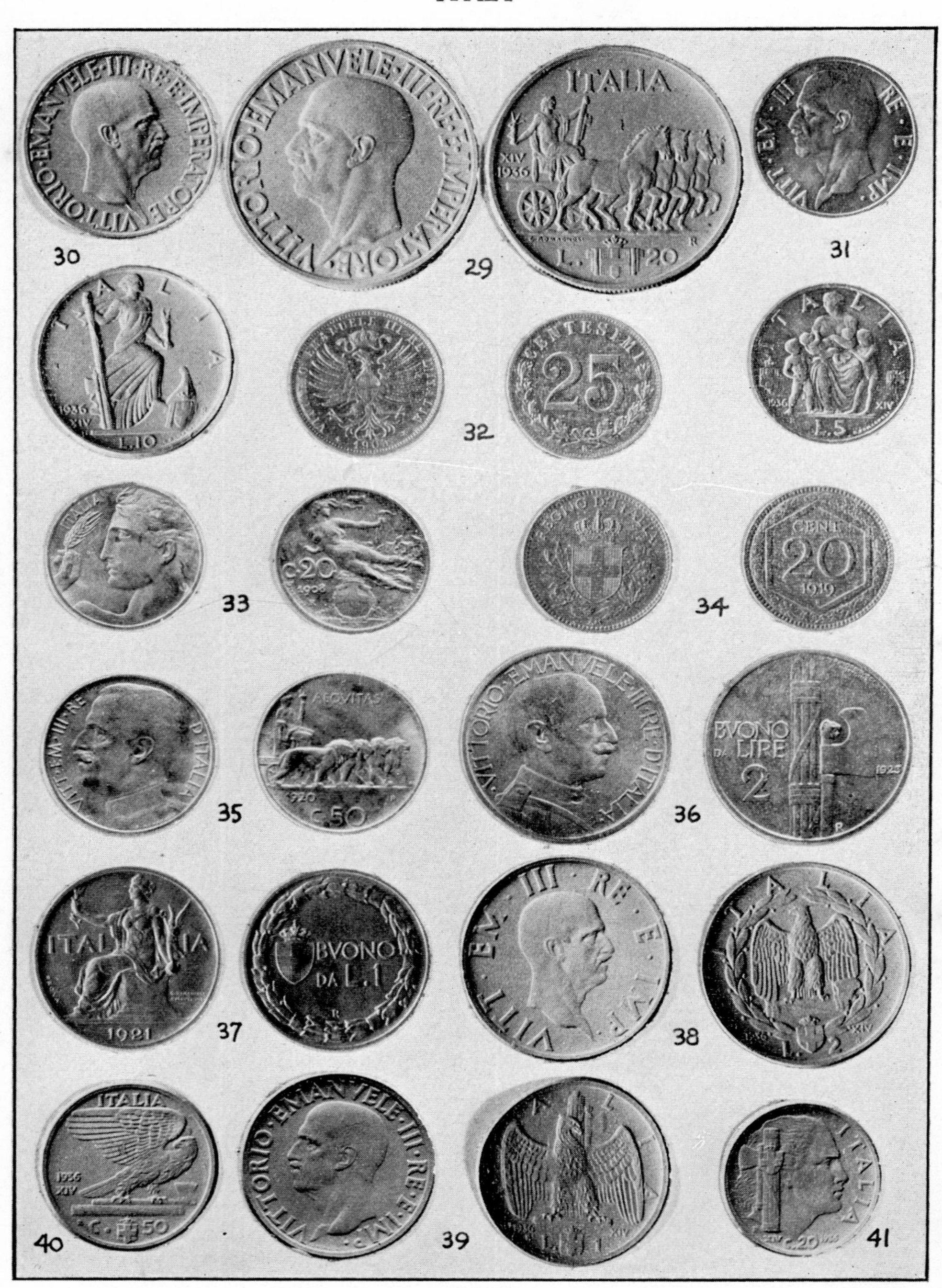
VITTORIO·EMANVELE·III·RE·E·IMPERATORE
30
VITTORIO·EMANVELE·III·RE·E·IMPERATORE
29
ITALIA
XIV
1936
L. 20
R
VITT·EM·III·RE·E·IMP
31
ITALIA
1936
XIV
L.10
CENTESIMI
25
32
ITALIA
1936
XIV
L.5
C.20
33
CENT
20
1919
34
VITT·EM·III·RE D'ITALIA
AEQVITAS
1920
C.50
35
VITTORIO·EMANVELE·III·RE·D'ITALIA
36
BVONO
DA LIRE
2
1923
R
ITAL IA
1921
37
BVONO
DA L.1
R
VITT·EM·III·RE·E·IMP
38
ITALIA
XIV
L.2
ITALIA
1936
XIV
C.50
40
VITTORIO·EMANVELE·III·RE·E·IMP·
39
ITALIA
C.20
41

ITALY

35	50 Centesimi 1919-26. Chariot drawn by lions	.25
36	2 Lire 1923-1927. Fasces	.35
37	1 Lira 1921-28 Italia seated	.25
38	2 Lire 1936-37. Eagle	.25
39	1 Lira 1936, 37. Head *l.* ℞ Eagle	.20
40	50 Centesimi 1936, 37. Eagle	.15
41	20 Cent 1936-41. Head and fasces	.10

BRONZE

42	2 Centesimi 1903, 1905-08	.20
43	1 Centesimo 1902-05, 1908	.15
44	10 Centesimi 1908. Figure on prow of galley. Very rare	
45	5 Centesimi 1908-18	.20
46	2 Centesimi 1908-17	.15
47	1 Centesimo 1908-1918. Similar	.10
48	10 Centesimi 1911. (50th anniversary of Kingdom)	.25
49	10 Centesimi 1919-37. Bee	.15
50	5 Centesimi 1919-37. Wheat ear	.10
51	10 Centesimi 1936, 38. Arms and fasces	.15
52	5 Centesimi 1936, 38. Eagle	.10

ACMONITAL (Stainless steel)

Types of 1936 issue, slight variations.

53	2 Lire 1939-43	.35
54	1 Lira 1939-43	.25
55	50 Centesimi 1939-44	.20
56	20 Centesimi 1939-45	.15

ALUMINUM BRONZE

57	10 Centesimi 1939-44	.15
58	5 Centesimi 1939-44	.10

REPUBBLICA ITALIANA —— ALUMINUM

61 10 Lire 1946-50. Pegasos ....
62 5 Lire 1946-50. Liberty ....
63 2 Lire 1946-50. Plowman ....
64 1 Lira 1946-50. Ceres ....

ITALIAN SOMALILAND

(Somalia Italiana)

On the east coast of Africa bordering on the Indian Ocean and the Gulf of Aden.
Now Somalia under Italian trusteeship.

Mint: Rome. 100 Bese = 1 Rupia. 100 Centesimi = 1 Lira.

Victor Emanuele III

SILVER

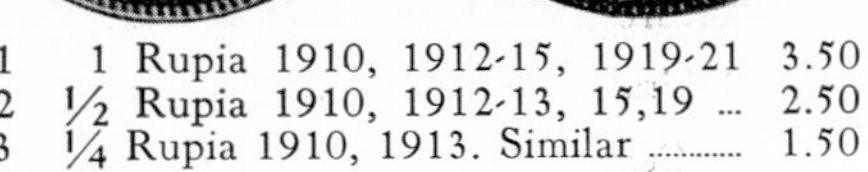

1 1 Rupia 1910, 1912-15, 1919-21 3.50
2 ½ Rupia 1910, 1912-13, 15,19 ... 2.50
3 ¼ Rupia 1910, 1913. Similar 1.50

4 10 Lire 1925 .... 7.50
5 5 Lire 1925. Similar 3.50

BRONZE

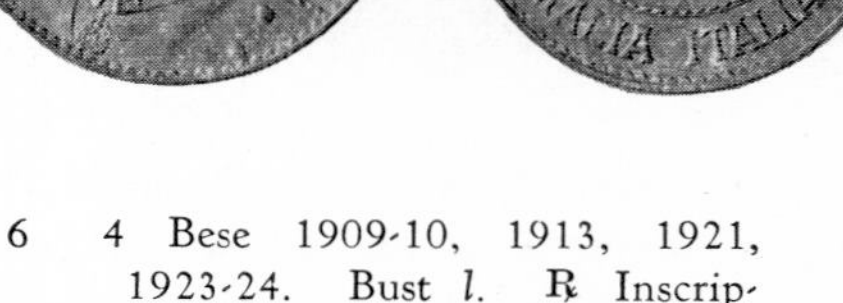

6 4 Bese 1909-10, 1913, 1921, 1923-24. Bust *l.* ℞ Inscription 2.50

7 2 Bese 1909-10, 1913, 1921, 1923-24. Similar 1.50

8 1 Besa 1909-10, 1913, 1921. Similar .... .75

JAMAICA

The largest island on the British West Indies group, in the Caribbean Sea directly south of Cuba. British Crown Colony.

Mints: London, Birmingham (H), Ottawa (C).

COPPER-NICKEL

Edward VII

1 1 Penny. 1902-04. Crowned bust *r.* ℞ Arms. Shading in cross of shield horizontal .... .50

2 1 Penny. 1905-07, 1909-10. Similar but shading vertical .... .50

3 ½ Penny. 1902 - 04. Similar. Shading horizontal .... .40

4 ½ Penny. 1904 - 07, 1909 - 10. Similar but shading vertical .... .40

5 1 Farthing. 1902 - 03. Similar but shading horizontal .... .25

6 1 Farthing. 1904 - 07, 1909 - 10. Similar but shading vertical .... .25

George V

7 1 Penny. 1914-28. Crowned bust *l.* .25

8 ½ Penny. 1914-28. Similar .... .20

9 1 Farthing. 1914-34. Similar .... .15

George VI
NICKEL BRONZE

10 1 Penny 1937-47. Crowned head .20

11 ½ Penny 1937-47. Similar .... .15

12 ¼ Penny 1937-47. Similar .... .10

With title—"KING GEORGE THE SIXTH"

13 1 Penny 1950 ....

14 ½ Penny 1950 ....

15 ¼ Penny 1950 ....

JAPAN. PLATE I

JAPAN

(Nippon)

An archipelago in the North Pacific Ocean off the coast of China and Siberia.
Mint: Osaka.
10 Rin = 1 Sen.
100 Sen = 1 Yen.

Mutsuhito—1867-1912

Meiji Era

GOLD

Type: Sun in eight lobed border.
℞ Value in wreath.

1 20 Yen. Years 37-45 (1904-12)...... 35.00
2 10 Yen. Years 34-37, 40-43 (1901-04, 1907-10) 15.00
3 5 Yen. Years 36, 44-45 (1903, 1911-12) 7.50

SILVER

Type: Dragon in circle. ℞ Value in wreath.

4 1 Yen. Years 34-40, 41-45 (1901-06, 1908-12) 2.00
5 50 Sen. Years 34-38 (1901-05)...... .75
6 20 Sen. Years 34, 37, 38 (1901, 1904-05) .... .25
7 10 Sen. Years 34, 35, 37-39 (1901, 02, 1904-06) 20

Type: Sun in circle of cherry blossoms.
℞ Value in wreath.

8 50 Sen. Years 39-45 (1906-12)...... .75
9 20 Sen. Years 39-44 (1906-11) ...... .25
10 10 Sen. Years 40-45 (1907-12) ...... .20

MINOR COINS

Type: Sun in circle. ℞ Value in wreath.

11 5 Sen. Copper nickel. Years 34-38 (1901-05) .... .10
12 1 Sen. Bronze. Years 34-35 (1901-02) .... .10

Yoshihito—1912-1926

Taisho Era

Type: Similar to last types of Meiji Era

GOLD

13 20 Yen. Years 1-9 (1912-20)........ 35.00
14 5 Yen. Years 1-2, 13 (1912-13, 1924) 10.00

SILVER

15 1 Yen. Year 3 (1914) 1.50
16 50 Sen. Years 2-6 (1913-17) .... .50
17 10 Sen. Years 1-6 (1912-17) .... .20

BRONZE

18 1 Sen. Years 2-4 (1913-15) .... .10

New Types for Taisho Era

19 50 Sen. Silver. Years 11-15 (1922-26). Rayed Sun. ℞ Value between Birds of Longevity. Size 23½ mm. .... .50
20 10 Sen. Copper-nickel. Years 9-15 (1920-26). Eight petalled flower around center hole. ℞ Value and Kiri crest .... .15
21 5 Sen. Copper-nickel. Years 6-9 (1917-20). Similar. Size 20½ mm. .... .10
22 5 Sen. Copper-nickel. Years 9-12 (1920-23). Similar. Size 19 mm. .10
23 1 Sen. Bronze. Years 5-15 (1916-26) Kiri Crest. ℞ Value in ornamental border .... .15
24 5 Rin. Bronze. Years 5-8 (1916-19). Similar .... .10

Hirohito 1926

Showa Era

Type: Similar to last types of Taisho Era

GOLD

25 20 Yen. Years 5-6 (1930-31) 35.00
26 5 Yen. Years 4-5 (1929-30) 10.00

SILVER

27 50 Sen. Years 3-12 (1928-37) ...... .50

COPPER-NICKEL

28 10 Sen. Years 2-7 (1927-32) .... .15
29 5 Sen. Year 7 (1932) .... .10

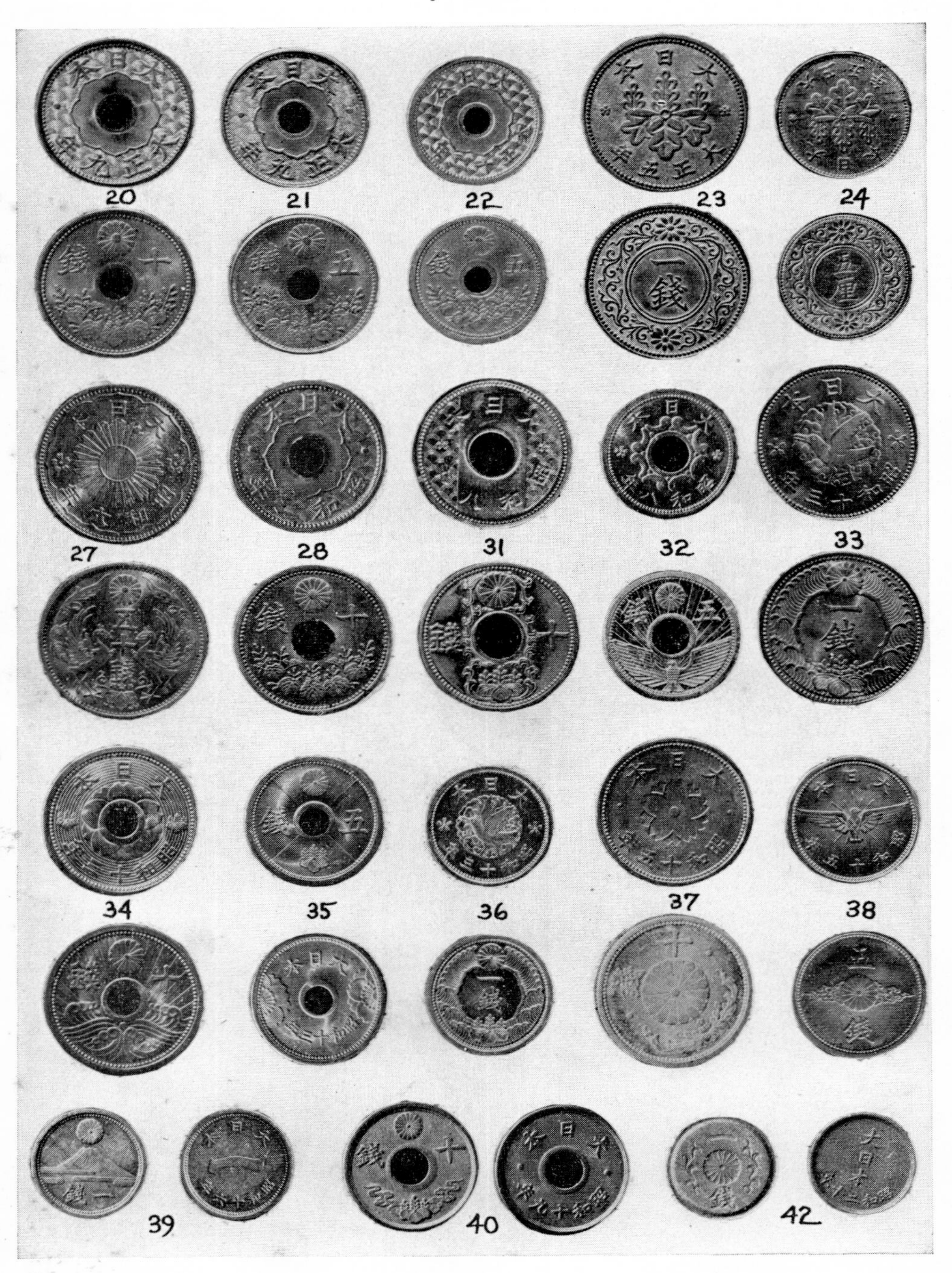

JAPAN. PLATE II

BRONZE

30 1 Sen. Years 2-12 (1927-37) .... .10

New Types for Showa Era

31 10 Sen. Nickel. Years 8-12 (1933-37) Holed. Inscription on three vertical panels. ℞ Symbols and value .... .15

32 5 Sen. Nickel. Years 8-11 (1933-36) Holed. Ornamental frame. ℞ Value above, Eagle below ...... .10

33 1 Sen. Bronze. Year 13 (1938) Gull .... .10

34 10 Sen. Aluminum Bronze. Years 13-15 (1938-40) .... .15

35 5 Sen. Aluminum Bronze. Years 13-15 (1938-40) .... .10

36 1 Sen. Aluminum. Years 13-15 (1938-40). Gull type .... .15

37 10 Sen. Aluminum. Years 15-18 (1940-43). Chrysanthemum .... .25

38 5 Sen. Aluminum. Years 15-17 (1940-42). Black Kite. ℞ Chrysanthemum and clouds .... .15

39 1 Sen. Aluminum. Years 16-18 (1941-43). Mt. Fuji. Diam 16 mm. .... .25

40 10 Sen. Tin. Years 19-20 (1944-45). Pawlownia Crest and clouds. Holed type .... .15

41 5 Sen. Tin. Years 19-20 (1944-45). Similar .... .10

42 1 Sen. Tin. Year 19 (1944). Chrysanthemum crest .... .10

43 5 Sen Tin. Year 20 (1945). Flying Black Kite. ℞ Large 5 .... .15

44 50 Sen. Bronze. Year 21 (1946). Phoenix and clouds. ℞ Rice and wheat plants .... .25

45 10 Sen. Aluminum. Year 21 (1946). Rice plants. ℞ Large 10 .15

46 50 Sen Bronze. Year 21 (1946). Cherry blossoms. ℞ Large 50 (reduced size) .... .15

47 50 Sen 1947. Brass ....

48 5 Yen 1948. Brass ....

49 1 Yen 1948. Brass ....

50 5 Yen 1949. Brass ....

51 10 Yen 1950. German Silver ....

JERSEY

One of the Channel Islands off the northwest coast of France. British Crown possession. *Mint:* London.

BRONZE

Edward VII

1 1/12 Shilling. 1909. Crowned bust *r.* ℞ Pointed shield .... .35

2 1/24 Shilling. 1909. Similar .... .25

George V

3 1/12 Shilling. 1911, 1913, 1923. Crowned bust *l.* ℞ As above ...... .35

4 1/24 Shilling. 1911, 1913, 1923. As above for same years .... .25

5 1/12 Shilling. 1923, 1926. Similar. ℞ Lettering on ribbon, blunter shield .... .25

6 1/24 Shilling. 1923, 1926. As above for same years .... .15

7 1/12 Shilling. 1931, 1933, 1935. New design. ℞ Blunt shield. Inscription not on ribbon .... .25

8 1/24 Shilling. 1931, 1933, 1935. As above for same years .... .15

George VI

9 1/12 Shilling. 1937,46,47 Crowned head *l.* ℞ Blunt shield .... .25

10 1/24 Shilling. 1937,46,47. Similar .15

Without title—IND. IMP.

11 1/12 Shilling (1949) ....
Liberation penny.

JORDAN

(Al-Mamlaka al-Hashimiya al-Urduniya)

A kingdom in northern Arabia separated from the Mediterranean by Israel

Mint: London

1000 Fils = 1 Dinar = £ 1 Sterling.

COPPER-NICKEL

1 100 Fils 1949 ....

2 50 Fils 1949 ....

3 20 Fils 1949 ....

BRONZE

4 10 Fils 1949 ....

5 5 Fils 1949 ....

6 1 Fil 1949 ....

KIAO CHAU

A district in China on the south side of the Promontory of Shantung. A former German possession, now part of the Chinese Republic.

Mint: Berlin.

100 Cents = 1 Dollar (Mexican).

COPPER-NICKEL

1 10 Cents 1909-11, 1913. Eagle on anchor. ℞ Chinese inscription 2.50

2 5 Cents 1909-11, 1913. Similar 2.00

KOREA

(Chosen or Tyosen)

A peninsula in northeastern Asia dividing the Yellow Sea from the Sea of Japan. Annexed by Japan in 1910. Occupied by American and Russian armies in 1945.

North and South Korea now have separate governments.

Mints: Ryu-zan, Korea before 1905. Osaka, Japan 1905-10.

100 Fun = 1 Yang.

100 Chon = 1 Won.

Many ¼ Yang nickel pieces of the dragon and inscription in wreath type were struck at the Ryu-zan Mint with the date of the second year of Kwo-bu (1898) until 1905 when the mint was closed.

Osaka Mint

GOLD

1 20 Won 10th year of Kwang Wu. 2nd, 3rd, 4th year of Lung Hsi (new era) = 1906, 1908-10. Dragon in circle. ℞ Value in wreath ....

2 10 Won 10th year, 1906. Similar

3 5 Won 2nd year 1908. Similar

All the gold is very rare.

SILVER

4 ½ Won 9th, 10th years = 1905, 06. Size 31m. 20.00

5 20 Chon 1905, 06. Similar 22m. 10.00

6 10 Chon 1905, 06. Similar 18m. 6.50

Reduced Standard

7 ½ Won 11th year, 2nd year = 1907, 08. Size 26m. 15.00

8 20 Chon 11th, 2, 3, 4 years = 1907-10. Size 20m. 10.00

9 10 Chon 1907-10. Similar. Size of preceding issue but reduced weight 5.00

NICKEL

10 5 Chon 9th, 11th, 3rd years, 1905, 1907, 1909. Phoenix. Value in wreath 4.00

BRONZE

11 5 Fun 6th year, 1902. Dragon type. 28 mm. Ryu-zan Mint... 3.00

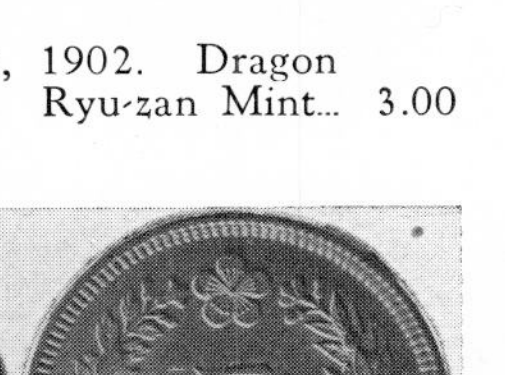

12 1 Chon 9th, 10th years, 1905-06. Phoenix type. 28 mm. Osaka Mint 2.00

13 ½ Chon 10th year, 1906. Similar. 22 mm. 1.25

14 1 Chon 11th, 1st, 2nd, 3rd, 4th years. 1907-10. 24 mm. 1.50

15 ½ Chon 11th, 1st, 2nd, 3rd, 4th years. 1907-10. 19 mm. 1.00

Silver ½ Wons and 20 Chons, nickel 5 Chons and bronze Chons bearing the 5th and 6th year (1901-02) were struck in Corea during the Russian influence. They bore a crowned eagle instead of the dragon. None of this type were put in circulation on account of the Russo-Japanese war and all were later melted down at the Osaka Mint.

LATVIA

(Latvijas Republika)

One of the Baltic states of northeastern Europe. Occupied by the USSR in 1940 and incorporated into the Soviet Union.

Mints: London, Birmingham, King's Norton, Huguenin Freres & Co. Switzerland.

100 Santimi = 1 Lats.

SILVER

1 5 Lati 1929, 1931-32. Woman's bust in native costume *r.* ℞ Arms with supporters 5.00

2 2 Lati 1925-26. Arms with supporters. ℞ Value in wreath...... 1.00

3 1 Lats 1924. Similar .... .50
Silver struck at London.

NICKEL

4 50 Santimi 1922. Figure at tiller of boat. ℞ Arms .... .40

5 20 Santimi 1922. Arms. ℞ Value above wheat ear .... .25

6 10 Santimi 1922. Similar .... .15

BRONZE

7 5 Santimi 1922. Arms ℞ Value... .25

8 2 Santimi 1922-32. Similar .... .15

9 1 Santims 1922-35. Similar .... .10

10 2 Santimi 1937-39 .... .15

11 1 Santims 1937-39 .... .10

LEBANON

(Lubnan)

Under French Mandatory Regime 1921 to 1941. Now an independent sovereign state bordering on the Mediterranean Sea in Asia Minor.

Mint: Paris

100 Piastres = 1 Lira or Pound

SILVER

Type—Cedar of Lebanon.
℞ Cornucopiae and value

1	50 Piastres 1929,33,37	2.00
2	25 Piastres 1929,33,37	1.25
3	10 Piastres 1929	.75

ALUMINUM BRONZE

Type—Cedar. ℞ Value

4	5 Piastres 1924	.35
5	2 Piastres 1924	.25

Type—Cedar. ℞ Galley

6	5 Piastres 1925-40	.25
7	2 Piastres 1925	.15

VARIOUS METALS

8	1 Piastre 1925-37. Cop. Nickel. 1940 Zinc.	.20
9	½ Piastre 1934, 36. Cop. Nickel. 1941 Zinc.	.15
10	2½ Piastres 1940. Aluminum bronze	.25

The 1 and 2 ½ piastres have center holes

Local Provisional Coinage World War II

P1 2½ Piastres. Aluminum ....

P2 1 Piastre. Aluminum ....

P3 ½ Piastre. Aluminum ....

LIBERIA

Lies on the southwest (Guinea) coast of Africa between British Sierra Leone and the French Ivory Coast Colony, with a south Atlantic coastline. Republic.

Mints: Brussels, Philadelphia.

100 Cents = 1 Dollar.

SILVER

1	50 Cents 1906. Female head *l.* ℞ Value in wreath	5.00
2	25 Cents 1906. Similar	2.50
3	10 Cents 1906. Similar	1.50

BRONZE

4	2 Cents 1906. Female head *l.* ℞ Palm tree	1.50
5	1 Cent 1906. Similar	.75

6	2 Cents 1937. Elephant *l.* ℞ Palm tree	.50
7	1 Cent 1937. Similar	.35
8	½ Cent 1937. Similar	.25

COPPER-NICKEL

Philadelphia mint. From original Brussels dies.

9	2 Cents 1941	.35
10	1 Cent 1941	.25
11	½ Cent 1941	.15

LIECHTENSTEIN

On the upper Rhine in Central Europe between Germany and Switzerland. Principality.

Mints: Vienna, Berne.

100 Heller = 1 Krone.

100 Rappen = 1 Franken.

Prince John II—1858-1929

SILVER

Kronen Values

1 5 Kronen 1904, 1910, 1915. Head *l.* ℞ Arms and value......... 7.50

2 2 Kronen 1912, 15. Similar 2.50

3 1 Krone 1900, 1904, 1910, 1915. Similar 1.50
Struck at Vienna.

Franken Values

4 5 Franken 1924. Similar to above 10.00

5 2 Franken 1924. Similar 3.00

6 1 Franken 1924. Similar 2.00

7 ½ Franken 1924. Similar 1.00
Struck at Berne.

Prince Franz I—1929-1938

GOLD

8 20 Franken 1930. Head *r.* ℞ Arms and value 35.00

9 10 Franken 1930. Similar 17.50

Prince Franz Joseph II—1938

GOLD

10 20 Franken 1946 ....

11 10 Franken 1946 ....

LITHUANIA

(Lietuva)

A Baltic State in northern Europe. Occupied by the USSR in 1940 and incorporated into the Soviet Union.

Mints: London, King's Norton, Kaunas.

100 Centu = 1 Litas.

SILVER

No.	Description	Price
1	5 Litai 1925. Lithuanian horseman. ℞ Value in wreath	7.50
2	2 Litu 1925. Similar	1.25
3	1 Litas 1925. Similar. ℞ Value and oak spray. Struck at London	.75

No.	Description	Price
4	10 Litu 1936, 37. Head of Vitatas *l.* ℞ Lithuanian horseman	8.00

No.	Description	Price
5	5 Litai 1936, 37. Dr. Jonas Basanivicius. *l.* ℞ Horseman	4.00

No.	Description	Price
6	10 Litu 1938. Head of Pres. Smetona Commemorating the 20th anniversary of the founding of the state.	8.00

ALUMINUM BRONZE

No.	Description	Price
10	50 Centu 1925. Horseman. ℞ Value. Wheat and oat ears	.35
11	20 Centu 1925. Similar	.20
12	10 Centu. 1925. Similar	.15
13	5 Centai 1925. Similar ℞ Value in circle, floral spray above	.10
14	1 Centas 1925. Similar. Struck at King's Norton	.10

BRONZE

No.	Description	Price
20	5 Centai 1936, 37. ...Horseman. ℞ Value in wreath	.15
21	2 Centai 1936, 37. Similar. ℞ Value in closed wreath	.10
22	1 Centas 1936-38. Similar. ℞ Value and wheat ear	.10

For coins under German occupation see Poland.

LUXEMBURG

In Central Europe bounded by Belgium on the west, France on the south and Germany on the east. Grand Duchy.

Mints: Stuttgart, Brussels.
100 Centimes = 1 Franc.

Adolphe—1890-1905

COPPER-NICKEL

1 10 Centimes 1901. Head *r.* ℞ Value in wreath .... .35
2 5 Centimes 1901. Similar .... .20

BRONZE

3 2½ Centimes 1901, 03. Crowned arms. ℞ Value in wreath. Minted at Brussels .... .25

William IV—1905-12

COPPER-NICKEL

5 5 Centimes 1908. Head *r.* ℞ Value in wreath .... .25

BRONZE

6 2½ Centimes 1908. Crowned arms. ℞ Value in wreath. Minted at Brussels .... .25

Marie Adelaide—1912-1919

ZINC

7 25 Centimes 1916. Inscription around hole. ℞ Value and wreath .... .35
8 10 Centimes 1915. Similar .... .25
9 5 Centimes 1915. Similar .... .20

IRON

10 25 Centimes 1919. Arms. ℞ Value in wreath .... .35
11 10 Centimes 1918. Similar .... .25
12 5 Centimes 1918. Similar Minted at Stuttgart .... .15

Charlotte 1919—

SILVER

Type: Head l. ℞ Arms.

13 10 Francs 1929 .... 2.50
14 5 Francs 1929 .... 1.25

MINOR COINS

Type: Crowned Monogram. ℞ Man puddling iron.

15 2 Francs. Nickel 1924 .... .50
16 1 Franc. Nickel 1924, 1928, 1935 .35

Type: Arms. ℞ Value in wreath.

17 10 Centimes. Iron 1923 .... .25
18 25 Centimes. Iron 1920 .... .30
19 5 Centimes. Iron 1923 .... .20

Type: Crowned Monogram. ℞ Value in wreath.

20 10 Centimes. Copper Nickel 1924 .15
21 5 Centimes. Copper Nickel 1924 .10
22 25 Centimes. Copper Nickel 1927. Arms. ℞ 25 Cts .... .20
23 50 Centimes. Nickel 1930-41. Man puddling iron. ℞ Value .... .25
24 25 Centimes. Bronze 1930, 1938 Arms. ℞ 25 Cmes .... .20

Type: Head l. ℞ Value

25 10 Centimes. Bronze 1930 .... .15
26 5 Centimes. Bronze 1930 .... .10

27 1 Franc. Copper Nickel 1939. Reaper stg. ℞ Crowned Monogram .... .50

28 50 Centimes. Nickel 1939. Man puddling iron (Letzeburg). ℞ Value .... .25

29 1 Franc. Copper Nickel, 1946-47. Man puddling iron. ℞ Value...... .35

30 25 Centimes. Bronze 1946-47. Arms. ℞ Value .... .15

31 5 Francs Nickel. 1949 ....

SILVER

600th Anniversary of John the Blind

Type: King John mounted. ℞ Head of Prince John.

C1 100 Francs 1946 .... 3.50
C2 50 Francs 1946 .... 2.00
C3 20 Francs 1946 .... 1.50

MADAGASCAR

An island off the east coast of Africa. French Colony.
Mints: Pretoria, Paris
100 Centimes = 1 Franc

BRONZE

Type: French coq to l. ℞ Cross of Lorraine

1 1 Franc 1943 .... 2.00
2 50 Centimes 1943 .... 1.00

ALUMINUM

3 2 Francs 1949,50 ....
4 1 Franc 1949 ....

MALAYA

Straits Settlements—includes Singapore, Penang, Malacca and Labuan. In southeastern Asia on the Malay Peninsula. See Straits Settlements.

George VI

SILVER

Type—Crowned head *l.* ℞ Value.

1 20 Cents 1939-45 .... 2.00
2 10 Cents 1939-45 .... 1.00
3 5 Cents 1939-45 .... .75

COPPER

Type—Head ℞ Value. Square.

4 1 Cent 1939-42 .... .25
5 ½ Cent 1939, 40 .... .15

6 1 Cent 1945. Reduced size .... .15

With title—"KING GEORGE THE SIXTH"

COPPER-NICKEL

Type of silver coins

7 20 Cents 1948-50 ....
8 10 Cents 1948-50 ....
9 5 Cents 1948 ....

MALDIVE ISLANDS

A group of thirteen coral atolls southwest from Ceylon in the Indian Ocean. Dependency of Ceylon.

Mohammad Imad-ed-Din 1900-1904

SILVER

1 4 Lari 1320 A.H. = 1902. Arabic inscription on both sides 7.50

COPPER

2 1 Lari 1320 A.H. From same dies as Silver coin. Also in brass. 16 mm. 2.00

3 ½ Lari 1319 A.H. Similar 13 mm. .... .75

4 ¼ Lari. Similar. 11 mm. .... .50

Mohammad Shams-ed-Din Iskandar 1904-

COPPER

5 4 Lari 1331 A.H. = 1913. Similar .... .50

6 1 Lari 1331 A.H. Similar .... .40
Both of these pieces are nicely struck.

MALTA

An island 58 miles due south of Sicily in the Mediterranean Sea and about 180 miles from the African coast. A British Crown Colony and important naval base.

Mint: London.

British money used on the island. One-third farthings of the British type are made especially for Malta.

BRONZE

Edward VII

1 1/3 Farthing. 1902 .... .50

George V

2 1/3 Farthing. 1913 .... .50

MANCHUKUO

In northeastern China bordered on the north by Siberia. Formerly an independent state under Japanese influence.

Mint: Osaka.
100 Fen = 1 Yuan. 10 Fen = 1 Chiao.

COPPER-NICKEL

Type—Lotus flower.

℞ Value between dragons

No.	Description	Price
1	1 Chiao. Years 2 and 3 (1933, 34) of Ta Tung	.50
2	5 Fen. Similar	.35

BRONZE

Type—Flag. ℞ Value in wreath

No.	Description	Price
3	1 Fen. Years 2 and 3	.35
4	5 Li. Similar	.25

AS AN EMPIRE

Types of preceding. Years 1 to 6 of Kang Teh.

No.	Description	Price
5	1 Chiao. Copper-nickel	.50
6	5 Fen. Copper-nickel	.35
7	1 Fen. Bronze	.35
8	5 Li. Bronze	.25

New Types. Copper-nickel or composition

No.	Description	Price
9	1 Chiao. Year 7 (1940)	
10	1 Chiao. Year 9 (1942)	
11	1 Chiao. Year 10 (1943)	
12	5 Fen. Years 9 and 10	
13	1 Fen. Years 7 to 10	
14	1 Fen. Year 11	

MARTINIQUE

One of the Windward Islands in the West Indies. French Colony.
Mint: Paris.
100 Centimes = 1 Franc.

COPPER-NICKEL

No.	Description	Price
1	1 Franc 1922. Bust of native woman *l.* ℞ Value in wreath	1.00
2	50 Centimes 1922. Similar. Same type as issued in 1897.	.50

MAURITIUS

An island in the Indian Ocean east of Madagascar. British Crown Colony.
Mints: London, Pretoria. 100 Cents=1 Rupee.

George V
SILVER

1 1 Rupee. 1934. Crowned bust *l.* 3.00

2 ½ Rupee. 1934. Similar. ℞ Stag 2.00
3 ¼ Rupee. 1934, 36. Rose, etc. ... 1.50

BRONZE

4 5 Cents. 1917, 1920-24 .... .75

5 2 Cents. 1911-12, 1917, 1920-24 .50
6 1 Cent. 1911-24 .... .25

George VI

Type—Crowned head. ℞ Types of preceding reign.

SILVER

7 1 Rupee. 1938 .... 3.50
8 ½ Rupee. 1938,46 .... 2.00
9 ¼ Rupee. 1938,46 .... 1.50

COPPER-NICKEL

10 10 Cents 1947 Scalloped .... .35

BRONZE

11 5 Cents. 1942-45 .... .25
12 2 Cents. 1943-47 .... .20
13 1 Cent. 1943-47 .... .15

With title—"KING GEORGE THE SIXTH"

COPPER-NICKEL

Types of silver coins

14 1 Rupee 1950 ....
15 ½ Rupee 1950 ....
16 ¼ Rupee 1950 ....

BRONZE

17 2 Cents 1949 ....
18 1 Cent 1949 ....

MEXICO

(Republica Mexicana)

The southernmost part of the North American continent, bounded on the north by the United States.

Mints: Mexico M or $\overset{o}{M}$, Culiacan C^{N} or C, closed 1905, Zacatecas Z^{S}. Closed 1905.
Before 1905 REPUBLICA MEXICANA.
After 1905 ESTADOS UNIDOS MEXICANOS.
100 Centavos = 1 Peso.

GOLD

1 50 Pesos 1921-31, 43-45 (Centenary of Independence) 60.00

2 20 Pesos 1916-21. Calendar stone 25.00

3 10 Pesos 1906-20. Hidalgo 12.50
4 5 Pesos 1905-20. Similar 7.50
5 2½ Pesos 1918-20. Similar 3.50
6 2 Pesos 1919-20. Eagle 2.50
7 1 Peso 1902-05. Similar 2.50

SILVER

9 Peso 1901-05, 08, 09. Eagle. ℞ Liberty cap and rays 1.50
11 20 Centavos 1901-05. Eagle ℞ Value .... .25
12 10 Centavos 1901-05. Similar .... .15
13 5 Centavos 1901-05. Similar .... .15
10 Peso 1910-14. Liberty on horse. ℞ Eagle 3.00
16 50 Centavos 1905-17. Eagle ℞ Liberty cap .... .75
17 20 Centavos 1905-18. Similar .... .25
18 10 Centavos 1905-17. Similar .... .15
19 Peso, 1918, 19. Eagle ℞ Liberty cap and value in wreath. Fineness 902.7 .... 1.25
14 50 Centavos 1918, 19. Eagle ℞ Cap. Size reduced .... .50
20 20 Centavos 1919. Similar .... .25
21 10 Centavos 1919. Similar .... .15
8 2 Pesos 1921. Centenary of Independence. Winged Victory. ℞ Eagle 3.50
22 Peso 1920-45. Similar to No. 19. Fineness 0.720 .... .75
15 50 Centavos 1919-45. Similar .... .35
23 20 Centavos 1920-43. Similar .... .25
24 10 Centavos 1925-34. Similar .... .15
25 50 Centavos 1935. Very base silver. Phila., Denver and San Francisco .... .35

26 5 Pesos 1947, 48. Head of Cuauhtemoc 2.00

27 1 Peso 1947-49. Head of Morelos .75

NICKEL

28 5 Centavos 1905-14, 1916-17. Eagle. ℞ Value .15

COPPER-NICKEL

29 10 Centavos 1936-45. Eagle *l.* ℞ Value within outer border of the Aztec Calendar stone .15

30 5 Centavos 1936-42. Similar .10

BRONZE

31 20 Centavos 1920, 1935. Eagle. ℞ Value in wreath .15

32 10 Centavos 1919-21, 1935. Similar .10

33 5 Centavos 1914-21, 1924-30, 1933-35. Similar .10

34 2 Centavos 1905-06, 1920-21, 1924-29, 1935. Similar. Size 25 mm. .10

35 2 Centavos 1915. Similar. Size 20 mm. .25

36 1 Centavo 1900-05. Eagle. ℞ Value in wreath. Ins. REPUBLICA MEXICANA .10

37 1 Centavo 1905-45. Similar, but UNIDOS ESTADOS MEXICANOS. Size 20 mm .10

38 1 Centavo 1915. Size 16 mm .25

39 5 Centavos 1942-46. Head of Dominquez .... .15

40 20 Centavos 1943-46. Temple of Sun .... .25

Decree of December 29, 1949
SILVER

41 5 Pesos 1950. Inauguration of Southern Railroad ....

42 1 Peso 1950. Gen. Morelos ....

43 50 Centavos 1950. Cuauhtemoc ...

44 25 Centavos 1950. Balance ....

COPPER-NICKEL

45 10 Centavos 1950. Benito Juarez. Authorized ....

46 5 Centavos 1950. Josefa Ortiz de Dominguez ....

BRASS

47 2 Centavos 1950. Corn ear ....

48 1 Centavo 1950. Wheat ear ....

ESTADOS UNIDOS MEXICANOS
14
50 CENTAVOS 1919
ESTADOS UNIDOS MEXICANOS
15
50 CENTAVOS 1920
91
TRANSITORIO
20 CENTAVOS
60
61
REPUBLICA MEXICANA
1915
81
REPUBLICA MEXICANA
64
REPUBLICA MEXICANA
65
71
1914
1
CENT
75
REPUBLICA MEXICANA
77
ESTADO DE DURANGO
5
CENTAVOS
REPUBLICA MEXICANA
78
ESTADO DE DURANGO
1
CENTAVO
83
20
CENTAVOS
REPUBLICA MEXICANA
99
ORO: 0.300

MEXICO

MEXICO

REVOLUTIONARY COINAGE—1913-1916

PARRAL, CHIHUAHUA

Villa Coinage

56 1913 Peso. Name. ℞ Value 3.00
60 1913 50 Centavos. Radiate cap ℞ Value 1.50

COPPER

61 1913 2 Centavos .... .50

CUÉNCAME, DURANGO

70 1914 Peso. Muera Huerta 4.00

DURANGO CITY

COPPER

71 1914 5 Centavos 1.00
73 1914 V Centavos 2.00
75 1914 Centavo 1.50
77 1914 5 Centavos. Brass .... .50
78 1914 Centavo. Aluminum .... .50

CHIHUAHUA

62 1915 Peso. Army of the North ... 2.00

COPPER

64 1915 10 Centavos 2.00
65 1914, 15 5 Centavos .... .25

JALISCO

COPPER

80 1915 5 Centavos 2.00
81 1915 2 Centavos 2.00
82 1915 1 Centavo 2.00

AGUASCALIENTES

Villa Coinage

83 1915 20 Centavos 2.00
84 1915 5 Centavos 2.00
85 1915 5 Centavos. Large 5 C 2.00
86 1915 2 Centavos 5.00
87 1915 1 Centavo 5.00

CHICONCUAUTLA

Madero Brigade

91 1915 20 Centavos 1.25
92 1915 10 Centavos 2.50

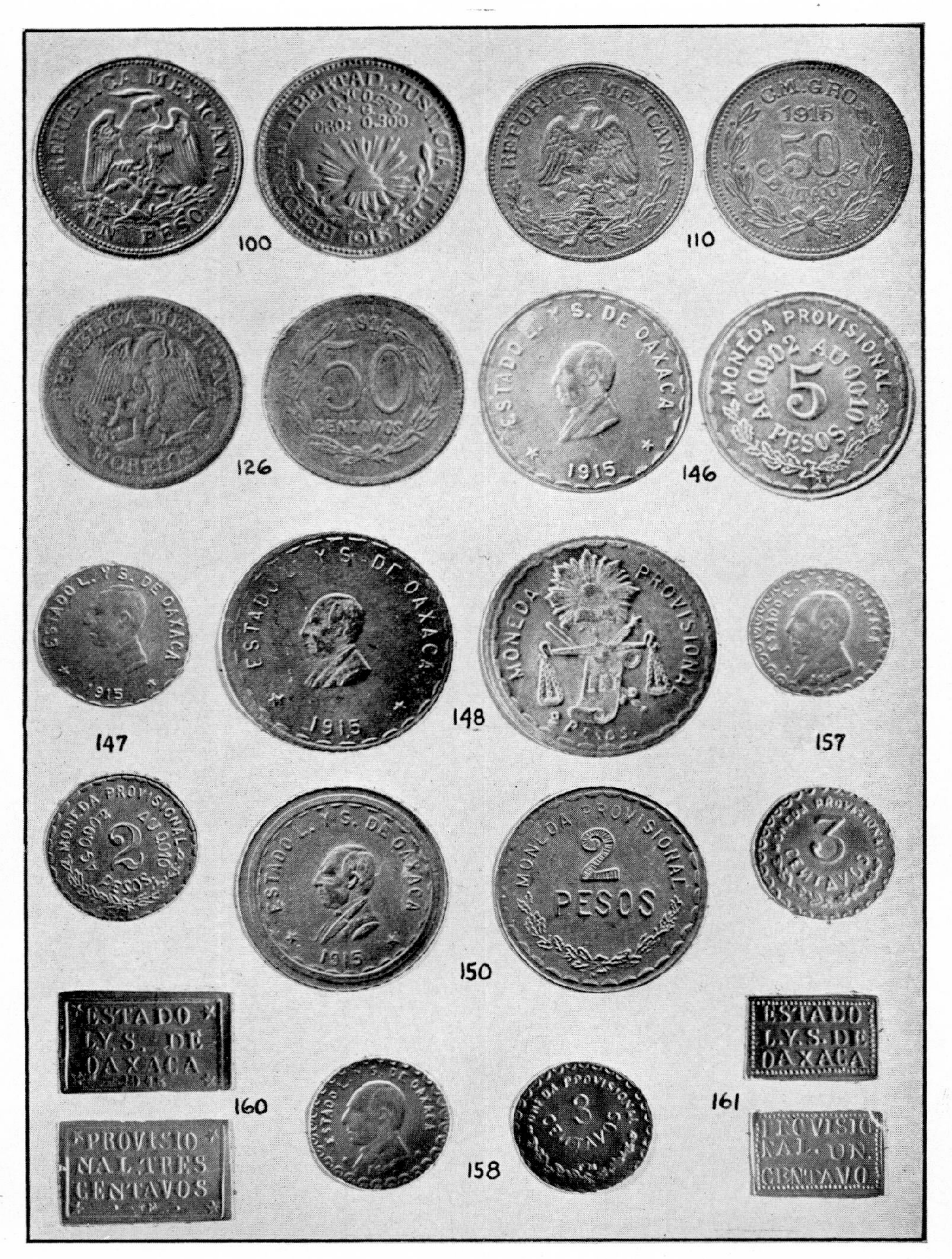
100
110
126
146
147
148
157
150
160
161
158
CM. GRO.
1915
50
CENTAVOS
ESTADO L. Y S. DE OAXACA
1915
MONEDA PROVISIONAL
AG. 0.902 AU. 0.010
5
PESOS
2
PESOS
3
CENTAVOS
ESTADO
L. Y. S. DE
OAXACA
PROVISIO
NAL TRES
CENTAVOS
PROVISIO
NAL. UN.
CENTAVO

MEXICO

GUERRERO

Zapata Coinage

93 1914 2 Pesos 3.00
94 1915 2 Pesos 3.00
96 1915 2 Pesos. Reduced size 2.00
99 1914 Peso 1.75
100 1915 Peso 1.50
102 1915 50 Centavos 3.50

COPPER

110 1915 50 Centavos 1.00
112 1915 20 Centavos 1.50
114 1915 10 Centavos 1.00
119 1915 5 Centavos 1.50

MORELOS

Zapata Coinage

COPPER

126 1915 50 Centavos 1.25
127 1915 20 Centavos 1.50
129 1916 10 Centavos 1.25
130 1915 2 Centavos 6.00

INDEPENDENT STATE OF OAXACA

GOLD

142 60 Pesos 1916. Bust of Juarez *l.* within wreath. ℞ Liberty cap and scales 400.00
Specimens are known in copper and silver.

Hereafter all coins are dated 1915; all have bust of Juarez *l.* except a few which are noted. There were many different dies made showing slight variations in bust.

143 20 Pesos. ℞ Value and partial wreath 30.00
144 10 Pesos. Similar 20.00
145 5 Pesos. Similar 10.00
The above three pieces are of very base gold.

SILVER

146 5 Pesos. ℞ Large 5 in center within two circular legends........ 4.00
147 2 Pesos. Similar but large 2. 23 mm. 2.50
148 2 Pesos. ℞ Liberty cap and scales. 2 PESOS at bottom. 35 mm. 2.00
149 2 Pesos. Similar but DOS PESOS at bottom 2.00
150 2 Pesos. ℞ Value in partial wreath. 31 mm. 2.50

151 1 Peso. Similar 1.25
152 50 Centavos. Similar 1.00
153 20 Centavos. Similar. Very rare ....
Many of the above specimens are known in copper.

COPPER

154 20 Centavos. Similar .... .50
155 10 Centavos. Similar .... .50
156 5 Centavos. Similar .... .50
157 3 Centavos. ℞ Similar but large flat top 3 .... .75
158 3 Centavos. ℞ Similar but small round top 3 .... .75
159 1 Centavo. ℞ 1c in monogram .75

Provisional Issue

160 3 Centavos 1915. Inscription on both sides. Rectangular 3.50
161 1 Centavo. Similar 2.00

MONACO

A small principality on the Mediterranean Sea on the south coast of France.
Mint: Paris. 100 Centimes = 1 Franc.

Albert I—1889-1922

GOLD

1 100 Francs 1901, 1904. Head *l.*
℞ Crowned arms in wreath............ 90.00

Louis II—1922-1949

ALUMINUM BRONZE

2 2 Francs 1924, 1926. Bowman *r.*
℞ Value and arms 1.00

3 1 Franc 1924, 1926. Similar ...... .50

4 50 Centimes 1924, 1926. Similar... .35

The coins of 1924 have, within inner circle, the words REMB. JUSQU'AU 31 X.BRE 1926.

Type—Head of Louis II. ℞ Arms in canopy

ALUMINUM BRONZE

5 2 Francs undated (1943) .... .50
6 1 Franc (1943) .... .35

ALUMINUM

7 2 Francs (1943) .... .50
8 1 Franc (1943) .... .25

9 5 Francs 1945 .... .75

COPPER-NICKEL

Type—Bust of Louis II.
℞ Value below arms and canopy

10 10 Francs 1946 .... .75
11 20 Francs 1947 .... 1.00

Rainier III—1949

COPPER-NICKEL

12 100 Francs 1950. Head. ℞ Rider

ALUMINUM BRONZE

13 50 Francs 1950. Head. ℞ Rider

14 20 Francs 1950. Head. ℞ Arms

15 10 Francs 1950. Head. ℞ Arms

MONGOLIA

A vast tract of land in central Asia bounded by Siberia on the north, China and Manchuria on the east and Sinkiang and Turkestan on the south. Nominally a dependency of China, but under USSR influence.

Mint: Leningrad. 100 Mung = 1 Tugrik.

1 1 Tugrik (1925). Buddhist symbols and insc. ℞ Value in wreath, inscription above 10.00

2 50 Mung. Similar 5.00

3 20 Mung. Similar. ℞ Value in wreath 2.50

4 15 Mung. Similar 2.00

5 10 Mung. Similar 1.50

COPPER

6 5 Mung. Similar to the silver...... 3.00

7 2 Mung. Similar 2.00

8 1 Mung. Similar 1.50

MONTENEGRO

(Now part of Yugoslavia)

On the Adriatic Sea in southern Europe. Former kingdom, proclaimed independent in 1941, under Italian protection. Now part of Yugoslavia Federal Peoples republic.

Mints: Vienna, Paris.

100 Paras = 1 Perper.

Nicholas I—1860-1918

Before 1910 with title of Prince and Lord of the Black Mountains. After 1910 with title of King.

GOLD

1	100 Perpera 1910. Head *r.* Arms on mantle on wreath	350.00
2	20 Perpera 1910. Similar	30.00
3	10 Perpera 1910. Similar	15.00
4	100 Perpera 1910. 50 Year Jubilee	500.00
	Commemorating 50 years of reign, also country assumed the dignity of a kingdom, 50th wedding anniversary	
5	20 Perpera 1910. Similar	30.00
6	10 Perpera 1910. Similar	15.00

SILVER

Type of gold coins

7	5 Perpera 1909, 1912, 1914	10.00
8	2 Perpera 1910, 1914. Similar	2.50
9	1 Perpera 1909, 1912, 1914	1.25

NICKEL

10	20 Para 1906, 1908, 1914. Arms on crowned two-headed eagle	.25
11	10 Para 1906-14. Similar	.20

BRONZE

12	2 Para 1906-14. Similar	.20
13	1 Para 1906, 1914. Similar	.15

MOROCCO

(Moghred-el-aksa, i.e., The Farthest West)

In northwest Africa bordering on the Mediterranean on the north and the Atlantic Ocean on the west. French protectorate.

Mints: Paris, Berlin, Birmingham, Poissy, Castelsarrazin

100 Mazunas = 1 Ryal or Piastre

Hassani Currency

A.H. 1320-37 = A.D. 1903-19

SILVER

Type—Moorish inscriptions in double lined circle. ℞ Six pointed star with date in center.

1	1 Ryal 1320, 21	3.50
2	½ Ryal 1320-23	1.50
3	¼ Ryal 1320-23	1.00
4	1/10 Ryal 1320, 21	.50
5	1/20 Ryal 1320, 21	.25

Type—Inscription, mint and date in interlaced lobed triangle. ℞ Inscription in wreath.

6	1 Ryal 1329	3.50
7	½ Ryal 1329	1.50
8	¼ Ryal 1329	1.00

Type—Six pointed star. ℞ Value in square.

9	1 Ryal 1330-37	3.50
10	½ Ryal 1330-37	1.50
11	¼ Ryal 1330-37	1.00
12	1/10 Ryal 1330-37	.50

The preceding coins were all demonetized in 1920 upon the adoption of the franc standard.

BRONZE

Type with Greek fret border

13	10 Mazunas 1320-23	.50
14	5 Mazunas 1320-23	.35
15	2 Mazunas 1320,21	.25
16	1 Mazuna 1320,21	.15

Type with five pointed star and lobed triangle

17 10 Mazunas 1330,31 .... .50
18 5 Mazunas 1330,31 .... .35
19 2 Mazunas 1330,31 .... .25
20 1 Mazuna 1331 .... .15

The Franc System

SILVER

21 20 Francs 1347,52 (1929,34) 3.50
22 10 Francs 1347,52,53 (1929,34,35) 2.00
23 5 Francs 1352,53 (1934,35) 1.00

NICKEL

24 1 Franc 1921-24 .... .50
25 50 Centimes 1921-24 .... .25

NICKEL-BRONZE

26 25 Centimes 1921-26 .... .15

BRONZE

27 10 Centimes 1340 (1922) .... .35
28 5 Centimes 1340 (1922) .... .25

New Coinage

COPPER-NICKEL

29 20 Francs 1947 ....
30 10 Francs 1947,48 ....

ALUMINUM BRONZE

31 5 Francs 1946,47 ....

32 2 Francs 1946,47 ....
33 1 Franc 1946 ....
34 50 Centimes 1946 ....

ALUMINUM

35 5 Francs 1950 ....
36 2 Francs 1950 ....
37 1 Franc 1950 ....

MOZAMBIQUE

Portuguese East Africa

In southeastern Africa extending from Cape Delgado to the Union of South Africa. Portuguese Colony.

Mint: Lisbon. 100 Centavos = 1 Escudo.

New State 1926

SILVER

Type—Arms on Cross. ℞ Square shield

1	10 Escudos 1935-37	2.00
2	5 Escudos 1935	1.00
3	2½ Escudos 1935,36	.75

COPPER-NICKEL

Type—Square shield. ℞ Value

4	1 Escudo 1936,37	.75
5	50 Centavos 1936,37	.35

BRONZE

Type of copper-nickel

6	20 Centavos 1936,37	.35
7	10 Centavos 1936,37	.25

New Silver Coinage

Type—Round shield crowned

8	10 Escudos 1938	2.00
9	5 Escudos 1938,49	1.00
10	2½ Escudos 1938,42	.75

BRONZE

Type—Round crowned shield. ℞ Value

11	1 Escudo 1945,46	.50
12	50 Centavos 1945	.35
13	20 Centavos 1941	.25
14	10 Centavos 1941,42	.20

NICKEL-BRONZE

15	1 Escudo 1950	.35
16	50 Centavos 1950	.20

BRONZE

17	20 Centavos 1949. Bronze	.15

MUSCAT and OMAN

An independent sultanate at easterly corner of Arabia
Mint: Bombay
200 Baizas = 1 Maria Theresa dollar

NICKEL

Dated A. H. 1359

1 50 Baizas 1940. Scalloped ....

2 20 Baizas 1940. Square ....

3 10 Baizas 1940. ....

Dated A. H. 1365 etc.

4 50 Baizas 1948. ....

5 20 Baizas 1946,48. Square ....

6 10 Baizas 1948. ....

7 5 Baizas 1946. Scalloped ....

8 2 Baizas 1946. Square ....

SILVER

9 Half Rial 1947 (1367) ....

NEPAL

An independent state in the Himalayas between India and Tibet.
Mints: Katmandu, Dhankuta, Butaul

Prithvi Bira Bikrama—1881-1911

The entire coinage of 1911 struck to commemorate the Durbar at time George V was proclaimed "Emperor of India."

GOLD

Type—Trident in inner circle.
℞ Sword in center.

1	4 Mohar 1833 Saka era = 1911 A. D. Weight 357 gr.	75.00
2	2 Mohar 1833 (1911)	35.00
3	1 Mohar 1833 (1911)	20.00
4	½ Mohar 1833 (1911)	12.50
5	¼ Mohar 1833 (1911)	7.50
6	⅛ Mohar 1833 (1911)	6.50
7	1/16 Mohar 1833 (1911)	5.00
8	1/32 Mohar Undated	5.00
9	1/64 Mohar Undated	5.00

SILVER

Type—Similar to gold but border frame, except on smaller pieces.

9a	4 Mohar 1833 (1911)	12.50
10	2 Mohar 1833	7.50
11	1 Mohar 1833	3.50
12	½ Mohar 1833	2.00
13	¼ Mohar 1833	1.25
14	⅛ Mohar 1833	1.00
15	1/16 Mohar. Undated	.75
16	1/32 Mohar. Undated	.75
17	1/64 Mohar. Undated	.75

COPPER

Type—Native inscription in square, obverse and reverse. Dates in Samvat era.

18	1 Dak 1968. = 1911 A.D. 26½ m.	1.25
19	1 Paissah 1968 23 m.	.75
20	½ Paissah 1968 19 m.	.75
21	¼ Paissah 1968 16 m.	.50

Tribhubana Bira Bikrama—1911

GOLD

Type of preceding coinage. Samvat dates.

22	Double Mohar 1975 Samvat = 1918 A. D.	50.00
23	1 Mohar 1969, 94	30.00
24	½ Mohar 1995 (1938)	15.00

SILVER

Type of preceding coinage. Samvat dates. between 1969 and 1989 = 1912 to 1932.

25	4 Mohar 1969	5.00
26	2 Mohar 1969-89	3.00
27	1 Mohar 1969	2.00
28	½ Mohar 1970	1.00

COPPER

29	1 Paisa 1971	1.00

30	1 Paisa 1975-86. New design	1.00

New Standard

100 Paisa = 1 Rupee

SILVER

Type—Trident in inner circle. ℞ Sword.

Samvat dates between 1989 and 2001 =
A. D. 1932-1944

31 1 Rupee 1989-2000 .... 2.00
32 50 Paisa 1997-2005 .... 1.00

33 20 Paisa 1992,93 .... .50

COPPER-NICKEL

34 5 Paisa, Samvat 2000 (1943) ...... .35

COPPER OR BRASS

Crossed swords. Samvat dates between 1989 and 2003.

35 5 Paisa 1995, 96 .... 1.00
36 2 Paisa 1992-2003 .... .50
37 1 Paisa 1991-2005 .... .25

Gyanendra Bira Bikrama

SILVER

38 1 Rupee 2007 (1950) ....

NETHERLANDS

(Koninkrijk der Nederlanden)

In northwestern Europe bounded by Germany on the east, Belgium on the south and the North Sea on the west and north. Kingdom.

Mints: Utrecht, Philadelphia. 100 Cent = 1 Guilder.

Wilhelmina 1890-1948

GOLD

1 10 Gulden 1911-13, 17. Bust *r.* with coronet. ℞ Crowned arms ... 15.00
2 5 Gulden 1912. Similar ... 10.00
3 10 Gulden 1925-27, 32, 33. Bare head ... 15.00

SILVER

Type: Young head with coronet. ℞ Crowned arms.

4 1 Guilder 1901, 1904-10 ... 1.25
5 ½ Guilder 1904-10 ... 1.00
6 25 Cents 1901-06. ℞ Value only .50
7 10 Cents 1901-06. ℞ Value only .25

Type: Bust *l.* with coronet. ℞ Crowned arms.

8 1 Guilder 1911-17 ... 1.00
9 ½ Guilder 1912-13, 1919 ... .75
10 25 Cents 1910-19, 1925 ... .50
11 10 Cents 1910-19, 1921, 1925 ... .25

Type: Bare head *l.* ℞ Crowned Arms.

12 2½ Gulden 1929-43 ... 2.50
13 1 Guilder 1922-46 ... 1.00
14 ½ Guilder 1921-30 ... .50
15 25 Cents 1925-46 ... .35
16 10 Cents 1925-46 ... .15

MINOR COINS

17 5 Cent. Copper Nickel 1907-09. Round Crown. ℞ Value ... .25

Type: Lion. ℞ Value

18 2½ Cent. Bronze 1903-06 .... .25
19 1 Cent. Bronze 1901-02, 1904-07. In 1901 there are two varieties .20
20 ½ Cent Bronze 1901, 1903, 1906 .15
21 5 Cent Copper Nickel 1913-44. Square with rounded corners. Orange branch. ℞ Value. The last few years are nickel silver .25

Type: Lion. ℞ Value. Similar to previous bronze but with larger lettering.

22 2½ Cent 1912-44 .... .25
23 1 Cent 1913-44 .... .20
24 ½ Cent 1909-38 .... .15

25 25 Cents 1948. Nickel ....

26 10 Cents 1948. Nickel ....

27 5 Cents 1948. Bronze ....

28 1 Cent 1948. Bronze ....

Juliana 1948-

Reverse types of previous issue

29 25 Cents 1950. Nickel ....
30 10 Cents 1950. Nickel ....
31 5 Cents 1950. Bronze ....
32 1 Cent 1950. Bronze ....

German Occupation—World War II

ZINC

01 25 Cents 1941-43. Ship .... .25
02 10 Cents 1941-43. Flower .... .20
03 5 Cents 1941-43. Hobbyhorse ... .15
04 2½ Cents 1941, 42. Birds .... .10
05 1 Cent 1941-44. Cross .... .10

NETHERLANDS EAST INDIES

(Nederlandsch-Indie)

An archipelago lying along the equator between the Asiatic mainland, the Philippines and Australia. Now the Republic of the United States of Indonesia a sovereign state of the Netherlands Union.

Mints: Utrecht, Philadelphia, San Francisco, Denver 100 Cents = 1 Guilder.

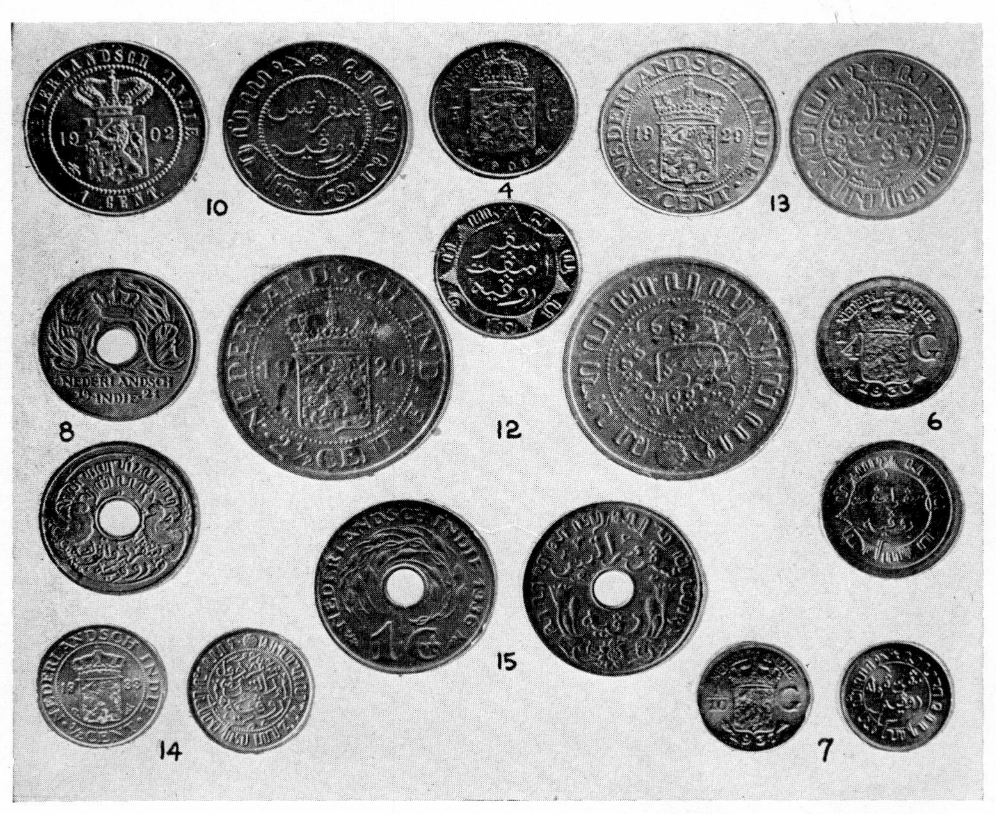

Trade Coin

GOLD

1 1 Ducat 1901-1937. Knight *r*. ℞ Ins. in ornamental cartouche 10.00

Wilhelmina—1890-1948

SILVER

No.	Description	Price
2	1/4 Guilder 1900-01. Crowned arms large Crown	.50
3	1/10 Guilder 1900-01. Similar	.30
4	1/4 Guilder 1903-09. Similar	.50
5	1/10 Guilder 1903-09. Similar	.30
6	1/4 Guilder 1910-45. Broad flan	.50
7	1/10 Guilder 1910-45. Similar	.30

COPPER-NICKEL

No.	Description	Price
8	5 Cents 1913, 1921-22. Crown over central hole.	.50

COPPER OR BRONZE

No.	Description	Price
9	2 1/2 Cents 1902-13.	.25
10	1 Cent 1901-12. Similar	.25
11	1/2 Cent 1902, 1908-09. Similar	.25
12	2 1/2 Cents 1914-20. Crown smaller, letters larger. ℞ Three line ins.	.25
13	1 Cent 1914-29. Similar	.25
14	1/2 Cent 1914-38. Similar	.25
15	1 Cent 1936-46.	.15
16	1/2 Cent 1945	.10
17	2 1/2 Cent 1945, 46	.15

NEWFOUNDLAND

An island in the Atlantic Ocean separated from Canada by the Strait of Belle Isle, the Gulf of St. Lawrence and Cabot Strait. A province of the Dominion of Canada.

Mints: London, Birmingham (H), Ottawa (C).

100 Cents=1 Dollar.

Edward VII

SILVER

1 50 Cents. 1904, 1907-09, Bust *r.* ℞ Value in scrolled circle 2.00

2 20 Cents. 1904. Similar. ℞ Value in circle 1.50

3 10 Cents 1903-04. Similar .... .75

4 5 Cents. 1903-04, 1908. Similar .... .75

BRONZE

5 1 Cent. 1904, 1907, 1909. Bust *r.* ℞ Crown and date in wreath .... .35

George V

SILVER

6 50 Cents. 1911, 1917-19. Bust *l.* ℞ Value in scrolled circle...... 1.50

7 25 Cents. 1917, 1919. Similar. ℞ Value in circle. 1.00

8 20 Cents. 1912. Similar 1.00

9 10 Cents. 1912, 1917, 1919. Similar .... .50

10 5 Cents. 1912, 1917, 1919, 1929. Similar .... .50

BRONZE

11 1 Cent. 1913, 1917, 1919-20, 1929, 1936. Similar. ℞ Crown and date in wreath .... .25

George VI

SILVER

12 10 Cents. 1938-47 .... .75

13 5 Cents. 1938-47 .... .50

BRONZE

14 1 Cent. 1938-44, 47 .... .50

NEW GUINEA

An Australian mandate. Bounded by Papua on the south and Dutch New Guinea on the west.
Mint: Melbourne.
English Coinage System. 12 pence = 1 Shilling.

George V

SILVER

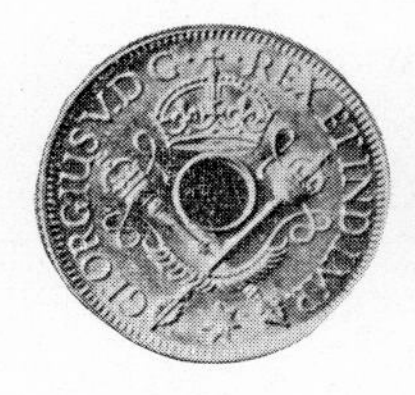

1 1 Shilling. 1935-36. Holed type. Crowned maces crossed. ℞ Ornaments in form of cross 1.50

COPPER-NICKEL

2 6 Pence. 1935. Holed type. Crown. G.R.I. and date. ℞ Eight lobed ornament .... .50

3 3 Pence. 1935. Similar. ℞ square and four points .... .25

4 Penny 1929. Type of shilling 2.50

5 Halfpenny 1929. Similar 1.50

Edward VIII

COPPER

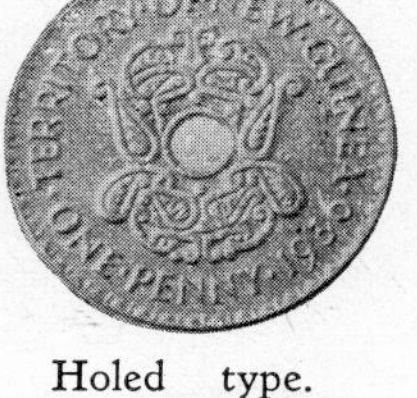

6 1 Penny. 1936. Holed type. Crowned ornament and E.R.I. ℞ Native ornament .... .75

George VI

Types of preceding reign.

SILVER

7 1 Shilling. 1938, 45 .... 1.25

COPPER-NICKEL

8 6 Pence. 1942, 43 .... .35
9 3 Pence 1944 .... .25

COPPER

10 1 Penny. 1938, 44 .... .25

NEW ZEALAND

In the South Pacific Ocean 1200 miles eastward from Australia. A self-governing British Dominion.

Mint: London.

English Coinage System. 12 pence = 1 Shilling.

George V

SILVER

1 1 Crown. 1935. Treaty of Waitangi. Bust *l.* ℞ Maori and Naval officer shaking hands 50.00

2 ½ Crown. 1933-35. Bust *l.* ℞ arms 3.00

3 1 Florin. 1933-36. Kiwi bird 2.00

4 1 Shilling. 1933-35. Maori warrior 1.00

5 6 Pence. 1933-36. Huia bird .... .50

6 3 Pence. 1933-36. War clubs .... .25

George VI

SILVER

7 Half Crown. 1937-46. Bare head *l.* ℞ Type of preceding issue as are all that follow 1.25

8 Florin. 1937 .... 1.00

9 Shilling. 1937-46 .... .50

10 6 Pence. 1937-46 .... .35

11 3 Pence. 1937-46 .... .25

12 Half Crown. 1940. Centennial issue. Maori woman stg. 2.50

COPPER

13 Penny. 1937-47. Tui bird .... .15

14 Halfpenny. 1937-47. Tiki .... .10

COPPER-NICKEL

Types of silver coins No. 7 to 11

15 ½ Crown 1947 ....
16 Florin 1947 ....
17 Shilling 1947 ....
18 6 Pence 1947 ....
19 3 Pence 1947 ....

With title — KING GEORGE THE SIXTH

20 ½ Crown 1948-50 ....
21 Florin 1948-50 ....
22 Shilling 1948-50 ....
23 6 Pence 1948-50 ....
24 3 Pence 1948-50 ....

BRONZE

25 Penny 1948-50 ....
26 Halfpenny 1949, 50 ....

COMMEMORATIVE COIN

27 Crown 1949. Silver ....

Struck to commemorate the proposed royal visit in 1949

NICARAGUA

(Republica de Nicaragua)

Situated between Honduras and Costa Rica in Central America.

Mints: Birmingham, Philadelphia.

100 Centavos = 1 Cordoba.

SILVER

Type—Bust of Cordoba ℞ Mountains.

1	1 Cordoba 1912	7.50
2	50 Centavos 1912, 29	2.50
3	25 Centavos 1912-36	1.50
4	10 Centavos 1912-36	1.00

COPPER-NICKEL

Same type as silver.

5	50 Centavos 1939, 46	.75
6	25 Centavos 1939, 46	.35
7	10 Centavos 1939, 46	.25
8	5 Centavos 1946	

9	5 Centavos 1912-40	.15

BRONZE

10	1 Centavo 1912-40	.10
11	½ Centavo 1912-37	.10

BRASS

Type of silver and copper-nickel.

12	25 Centavos 1943. Size 27 m.	.35
13	10 Centavos 1943. Size 24 m.	.25
14	5 Centavos 1943. Size 21 m.	.20
15	1 Centavo 1943. Arms ℞ Value...	.10

NORWAY

(Norge)

In northern Europe, occupying the western half of the Scandinavian Peninsula. Kingdom.
Mint: Kongsberg, Birmingham.
100 Ore = Krone.

Oscar II—1872-1905

GOLD

1 20 Kroner 1902. Head *l.* ℞ Crowned arms in wreath 35.00
2 10 Kroner 1902. Similar 20.00

SILVER

3 2 Kroner 1902, 04. Head *l.* ℞ Crowned arms in wreath 1.50
4 1 Krone 1901, 1904. Similar .75
5 50 Ore 1901-02, 1904. Similar... .35
6 25 Ore 1901-02, 1904. ℞ Value ... .25
7 10 Ore 1901, 1903. Crowned O. ℞ Crowned arms .... .15

BRONZE

8 5 Ore 1902. Crowned arms .... .15
9 2 Ore 1902. Similar .... .10
10 1 Ore 1902. Similar .... .10

Haakon VII—1905-

GOLD

11 20 Kroner 1910. St. Olaf standing 35.00
12 10 Kroner 1910. Similar 20.00

SILVER

13 2 Kroner 1906-07. (Commemorating Independence). 1.50

14 2 Kroner 1907. (Watch on the Border.) Similar but crossed guns under inscription 10.00
15 2 Kroner 1909-17 .... 2.00
16 2 Kroner 1914. (Centenary of Constitution) 2.00
17 1 Krone 1908-17. Head *r.* ℞ Crowned arms with Olaf order .75
18 50 Ore 1909-19. Similar .... .35
19 25 Ore 1909-19. Lion *l.* ℞ H7's in form of cross .... .25
20 10 Ore 1909-20. Crowned H 7. ℞ Value .... .15

COPPER-NICKEL

22 50 Ore 1920-23. Crowned arms ℞ H 7's in form of cross........ .25
23 50 Ore. Same type. Center hole... .25
24 25 Ore 1920-23. Same type as silver .... .15
25 25 Ore. Same type. Center hole... .15
26 10 Ore 1920-23. Same type as silver .... .10
The 25 and 50 Ore were perforated in 1924.
21 1 Krone 1925-40. 46. 47. Crowned H's in cross form ℞ Olaf order around center hole .50
27 50 Ore 1926-29. 39-41, 45-47 .... .25
Similar. Crown above hole
28 25 Ore 1924-29, 39, 40, 46, 47 .15
28a 10 Ore 1924-41, 45-47 .... .10

BRONZE

29 5 Ore 1907. Crowned arms. ℞ Value in wreath 15

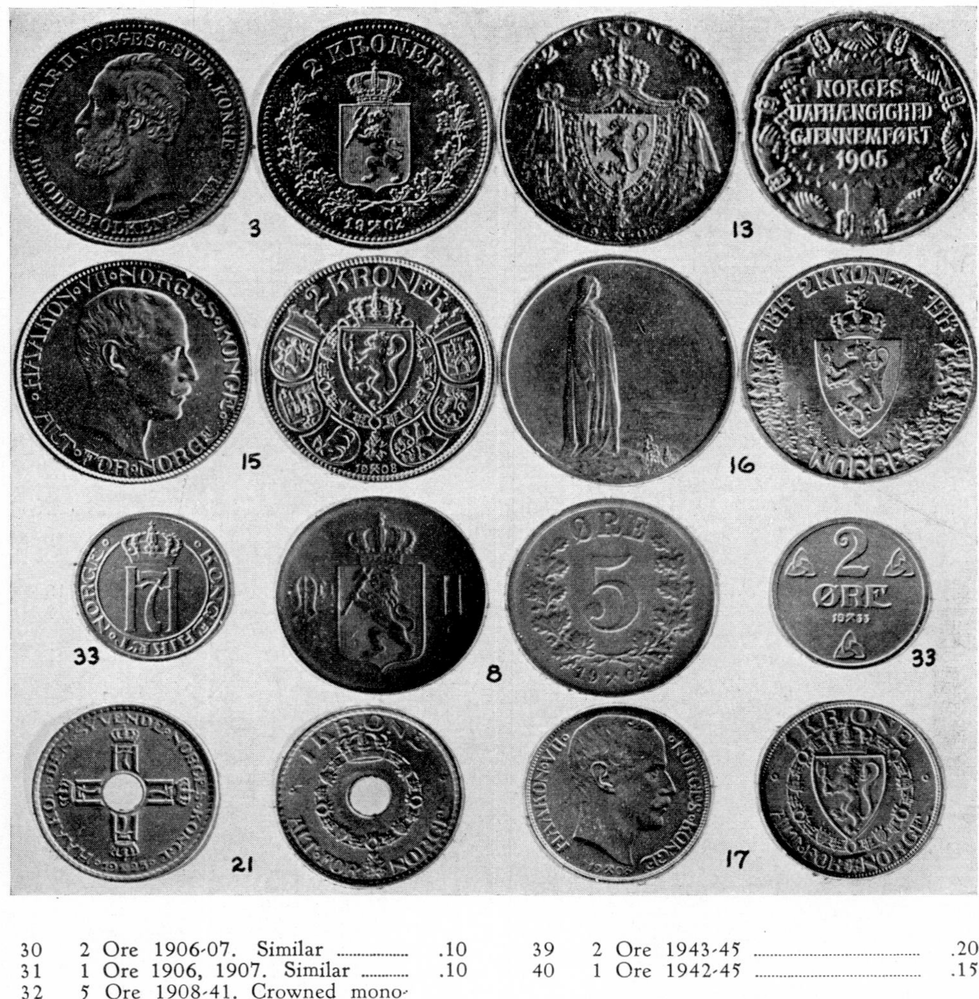

30 2 Ore 1906-07. Similar .10
31 1 Ore 1906, 1907. Similar .10
32 5 Ore 1908-41. Crowned monogram. ℞ Value and ornament .15
33 2 Ore 1908-41. Similar .10
34 1 Ore 1908-41. Similar .10

IRON

World War I

35 5 Ore 1917-20. Similar to above .25
36 2 Ore 1917-20. Similar to above .20
37 1 Ore 1918-20. Similar to above .15

World War II

Type—Arms. ℞ Value.

38 5 Ore 1941-45 .25
39 2 Ore 1943-45 .20
40 1 Ore 1942-45 .15

ZINC

Arms. ℞ Value. Without hole.

41 50 Ore 1941-45 .25
42 25 Ore 1943-45 .15
43 10 Ore 1941-45 .10

London War Coinage

NICKEL BRASS

Type of Oslo Mint

44 50 Ore 1942 .25
45 25 Ore 1942 .15
46 10 Ore 1942 .10

PAKISTAN

A self governing dominion in the British Commonwealth of nations. Consists of the former territories of British India—Baluchistan, East Bengal, North West Frontier, West Punjab and Sind.

Mints: Calcutta, Bombay, Lahore

12 Pies = 1 anna. 3 Pies = 1 Pice

16 annas = 1 Rupee

Type—Toughra. ℞ Star in crescent

NICKEL

1 1 Rupee 1948-50 ....

2 ½ Rupee 1948-50 ....

3 ¼ Rupee 1948-50 ....

COPPER-NICKEL

4 2 Annas 1948-50 ....

5 1 Anna 1948-50 ....

6 ½ Anna 1948-50 ....

BRONZE

7 1 Pice 1948-50 ....

PALESTINE

(Eretz Yisrael-Flstin)

Between the Mediterranean Sea and the River Jordan south of Syria in Western Asia.

Mint: London.

1000 Mils = 1 Pound.

SILVER

1	100 Mils 1927-42. Olive sprig	....	1.00
2	50 Mils 1927-42. Similar	....	.50

COPPER-NICKEL

3	20 Mils 1927-41. Holed type	....	.25
4	10 Mils 1927-42, 46, 47	....	.15
5	5 Mils 1927-41, 46, 47	....	.10

BRONZE

6	2 Mils 1927-46	....	.15
7	1 Mil 1927-46	....	.10
8	20 Mils 1942, 44. Type of No. 3		.25
9	10 Mils 1943. Type of No. 4	....	.15
10	5 Mils 1942-44. Type of No. 5		.10

PANAMA

(Republica de Panama)

In Central America between Costa Rica and Colombia.

Mints: Philadelphia, San Francisco.

100 Centesimos = 1 Balboa.

SILVER

Type: Bust of Balboa. ℞ Arms.

No.	Description	Price
1	50 Centesimos 1904, 05	1.50
2	25 Centesimos 1904	.75
3	10 Centesimos 1904	.35
4	5 Centesimos 1904	.25
5	2½ Centesimos 1904	.25

MINOR COINS

Type: Arms. ℞ Value.

No.	Description	Price
6	5 Centesimos. Copper Nickel 1929-32	.15
7	2½ Centesimos. Copper Nickel 1907, 1916	.10

Type: Bust of Balboa. ℞ Value.

No.	Description	Price
8	2½ Centesimos. Copper Nickel 1929	.15
9	½ Centesimo. Copper Nickel 1907	.15

Law of 1930

SILVER

No.	Description	Price
10	1 Balboa 1931, 1934, 1947. Bust of Balboa. ℞ Female. Figure and arms	3.50

Type: Bust of Balboa. ℞ Arms.

No.	Description	Price
11	½ Balboa 1930, 1932-34, 1947	1.00
12	¼ Balboa 1930-34. 1947	.50
13	1/10 Balboa 1930-34, 1947	.25

MINOR COINS

No.	Description	Price
14	1 Centesimo. Bronze 1935, 1937. Head of Urraca. ℞ Value	.15

Type: Bust of Balboa. ℞ Value

No.	Description	Price
15	2½ Centesimos. Copper Nickel 1940	.15
16	1¼ Centesimos. Bronze 1940	.15

PARAGUAY

(Republica del Paraguay)

One of the two inland countries of South America. Bounded by Bolivia, Brazil and Argentina.
Mints: Buenos Aires, Huguenin Freres & Co.
100 Centavos = 1 Peso.
100 Centimos = 1 Guarani.

COPPER-NICKEL

Type—Lion ℞ Value.

1	20 Centavos 1900, 03	.50
2	10 Centavos 1903	.35
3	5 Centavos 1903	.25

Type—Star in wreath ℞ Value.

4	20 Centavos 1908	.50
5	10 Centavos 1908	.40
6	5 Centavos 1908	.35
7	2 Pesos 1925	.50
8	1 Peso 1925	.40
9	50 Centavos 1925	.35

10	10 Pesos 1939	.75
11	5 Pesos 1939	.60

ALUMINUM

Type of preceding copper-nickel.

12	2 Pesos 1938	.50
13	1 Peso 1938	.35
14	50 Centavos 1938	.25

ALUMINUM BRONZE

15	50 Centimos 1944-47	
16	25 Centimos 1944-47	
17	10 Centimos 1944-47	
18	5 Centimos 1944-47	
19	1 Centimo 1944-47	

PERSIA

(Iran)

In Western Asia bordering on the Persian Gulf and the Gulf of Oman.

Mints: Teheran, Berlin, Birmingham, Brussels, Leningrad.

50 Dinars = 1 Shahi.
20 Shahis = 1 Kran.
10 Krans = 1 Toman.
100 Dinars = 1 Rial.
20 Rials = 1 Pahlevi (1937, 100 Rials = 1 Pahlevi.)
40 Puls = 1 Rial.

Muzaffar-ed-din Shah—1896-1907

GOLD

1 2 Tomans A.H. 1322 = 1904 A.D. Bust facing partly left. ℞ Persian inscription in wreath 25.00
2 1 Toman A.H. 1319, 1322=1901, 1904. Similar 12.50
3 2/5 Toman or 4 krans A.H. 1319, 1324=1901, 1906. Bust facing partly right. ℞ Inscription in wreath 7.50
4 ¼ Toman A.H. 1319, 1324=1901, 1906. Similar 3.00
5 2 Tomans A.H. 1322=1904. Similar. Commemorating the Royal birthday 50.00
6 1 Toman A.H. 1322=1904. Similar 20.00
7 ½ Toman A.H. 1324=1906. Lion in wreath. ℞ Inscription in wreath 6.00

SILVER

8 5 Krans A.H. 1320=1902. Lion. ℞ Inscription in wreath 7.50
9 2 Krans A.H. 1319=1901. Similar 1.50
10 ½ Kran A.H. 1322=1904. Similar .75
11 ¼ Kran. No date. Similar .35
12 3 Shahi. No date. Similar .25
13 5 Krans A.H. 1322=1904. Bust facing partly to right. ℞ Lion in wreath 12.50
Commemorating the Royal birthday.
14 2 Krans A.H. 1319-1324=1901-1906. Similar 1.50
15 1 Kran A.H. 1319-1324. Similar 1.00
16 ½ Kran A.H. 1323=1905. Similar .50

NICKEL

17 2 Shahi A.H. 1319, 1321-1323. Lion in wreath. ℞ Inscription in wreath .25
18 1 Shahi A.H. 1319, 1321-1323. Similar .15
Brussels mint.

Mohammad ali Shah—1907-1909

GOLD

18a 5 Tomans A.H. 1324 = 1907. Facing bust 100.00
19 2 Tomans A.H. 1326=1908. Bust facing partly left. ℞ Inscription in wreath 35.00
20 1 Toman A.H. 1326. Similar 15.00
21 ½ Toman A.H. 1326. Similar 10.00
22 1/5 Toman A.H. 1326. Similar 5.00
23 1 Toman A.H. 1327. Similar. ℞ Inscription in larger field in closed wreath 12.50
24 ½ Toman A.H. 1326. Similar 7.50
25 ¼ Toman A.H. 1326. Similar 4.50
26 ½ Toman A.H. 1324. Lion in wreath 7.50
Probably obverse die of previous reign.

SILVER

27 2 Krans A.H. 1326. Lion in wreath. ℞ Inscription in wreath 1.50
28 ½ Kran A.H. 1326. Similar .75
29 ¼ Kran A.H. 1326, 1327. Similar .35
30 3 Shahis. No date. Similar .25
31 2 Krans A.H. 1326. Bust facing partly left. ℞ Lion 2.00
32 1 Kran A.H. 1326, 1327. Similar 1.25
33 ½ Kran A.H. 1326, 1327. Similar .75

COPPER-NICKEL

34 2 Shahis A.H. 1327. Lion type .35
35 1 Shahi A.H. 1327. Similar .25

Ahmed Shah—1909-1925

GOLD

36 10 Tomans A.H. 1331=1913. Bust facing partly left. ℞ Inscription in wreath 100.00
Fifth year jubilee.
37 10 Tomans A.H. 1337=1919. Similar bust. ℞ Lion in wreath 100.00
Tenth year jubilee.

PERSIA

38 5 Tomans A.H. 1332. Lion. ℞ Inscription in wreath 50.00
39 5 Tomans A.H. 1332. Crown. ℞ Lion 75.00
Fifth Year jubilee. Die of 2 Kran piece.
40 5 Tomans A.H. 1334. Lion type 40.00
41 5 Tomans A.H. 1337. Bust facing partly left. ℞ Lion........ 65.00
42 5 Tomans A.H. 1337. Similar type 60.00
Dies of the silver 2 Kran piece.
43 2 Tomans A.H. 1333. Bust facing partly left, date in field. ℞ Inscription in wreath 35.00
Size of 1 Toman, but twice as thick.
44 2 Tomans A.H. 1337. Similar bust. ℞ Lion 20.00
45 1 Toman A.H. 1329-1332. Lion type 10.00
46 ½ Toman A.H. 1329-1332. Similar 5.00
47 1/5 Toman A.H. 1329-1332. Similar 2.50
48 1 Toman A.H. 1333-1344. Bust type 7.50
49 ½ Toman A.H. 1333-1343. Similar 3.50
50 1/5 Toman A.H. 1333-1343. Similar 2.50
51 1 Toman A.H. 1337. Bust. ℞ Lion 12.50
Tenth year jubilee.

SILVER

52 5 Krans A.H. 1332-1343. Bust. ℞ Lion 5.00
53 2 Krans A.H. 1328-1331. Lion type 1.00
54 1 Kran A.H. 1328-1330. Similar .50
55 ½ Kran A.H. 1330. Similar .... .35
56 ¼ Kran. Often undated. Similar .25
57 3 Shahis. Undated. Similar .... .25
58 2 Krans A.H. 1332-1344. Bust. ℞ Lion 1.50
59 1 Kran A.H. 1331-1344. Similar .75
60 ½ Kran A.H. 1332-1344. Similar .35
61 2 Krans A.H. 1337. Inscription around bust 1.50
Tenth year jubilee.
62 1 Kran A.H. 1337. Similar .... .75

COPPER-NICKEL

63 2 Shahi A.H. 1337. Lion type .25
64 1 Shahi A.H. 1337. Similar .... .15

BRONZE

65 100 Dinars A.H. 1330. Radiate head ....

Riza Shah Pahlevi—1925-1941

Solar year instituted. A.H. 1304=1926.

GOLD

66 1 Toman A.H. 1305. Lion type... 10.00
Distributed on first New Year's day.
67 5 Pahlevi A.H. 1305. Lion type 25.00
68 2 Pahlevi A.H. 1305. Similar...... 12.50
69 1 Pahlevi A.H. 1305. Similar...... 7.50
70 5 Pahlevi A.H. 1306, 1308. Bust in uniform 25.00
71 2 Pahlevi A.H. 1306-1308. Similar 12.50
72 1 Pahlevi A.H. 1306-1308. Similar 7.50
73 1 Pahlevi A.H. 1310. Head left. ℞ Lion 20.00
74 ½ Pahlevi A.H. 1310. Similar...... 12.50

SILVER

75 5 Krans A.H. 1304, 1305. Lion 2.50
76 2 Krans A.H. 1304, 1305 .... 1.50
77 1 Kran A.H. 1304, 1305 .... 1.00
78 ¼ Kran A.H. 1304, 1305 .... .75
79 5 Krans A.H. 1305. Similar. Date below wreath 2.50
80 2 Krans A.H. 1305 .... 1.50
81 1 Kran A.H. 1305, 1306 .... 1.00
82 ½ Kran A.H. 1305. Similar .... .75
83 ¼ Kran A.H. 1305. Similar .... .50
84 5 Krans A.H. 1306. Bust in uniform. ℞ Lion 5.00
85 2 Krans A.H. 1306. Similar...... 2.00
85a 1 Kran A.H. 1308 .... 1.00
86 5 Rials A.H. 1310-1312. Lion. ℞ Value in wreath 7.50
87 2 Rials A.H. 1310-1312. Similar 3.50
88 1 Rial A.H. 1310-1312. Similar... 2.00
89 ½ Rial A.H. 1310-1312. Similar... 1.00

COPPER-NICKEL

90 2 Shahi A.H. 1305. Lion type .20
91 1 Shahi A.H. 1305. Similar .... .15
92 25 Dinars A.H. 1310. Lion. ℞ Value in cartouche .... .25
93 10 Dinars A.H. 1310. Similar .... .20
94 5 Dinars A.H. 1310. Similar .... .15

BRONZE

95 2 Dinars A.H. 1310. Lion type .15
96 1 Dinar A.H. 1310. Similar........ .10
97 10 Shahi A.H. 1312. Lion. ℞ Value in cartouche .... .10

P E R S I A

IRAN

National name changed in 1935.

Riza Shah Pahlevi 1925-1941
Mohammed Riza Pahlevi 1942-

Type—Lion. ℞ Value in wreath.
100 Dinars = 1 Rial. 20 Rials = 1 Pahlevi.

GOLD

1	1 Pahlevi A.H. 1322, 23	
2	½ Pahlevi A.H. 1322, 23	

SILVER
Law of 1322 (1944)

3	10 Rials 1322-24	2.00
4	5 Rials 1322-24	1.00
5	2 Rials 1322-24	.50
6	1 Rial 1322-24	.25

MINOR COINS

Law of 1315 (1937)

7	50 Dinar 1315-21 Alum. Bronze:	
	(a) Copper	.25
8	10 Dinar 1315-21 Alum. Bronze	.20
9	5 Dinar 1315-21 Alum. Bronze	.15

PERU

(Republica del Peru)

On the west coast of South America.

Mints: Lima, Philadelphia, London, San Francisco.

10 Centavos = 1 Dinero. 10 Soles = 1 Libra. 100 Centavos = 1 Sol.

GOLD

1 1 Libra 1901-30. Indian head *r*. ℞ Arms in wreath 15.00

2 ½ Libra 1902-08. Similar 7.50

3 1/5 Libra 1906-30. Similar 5.00

5 5 Soles 1910. Patriotic issue. Similar 5.00

6 50 Soles 1930-31. Head of the Inca Manco Capoc. ℞ Inca symbol 250.00

SPECIAL GOLD ISSUE

Type—Seated figure as on 1 sol 1914-16. ℞ Arms.

B1 100 Gold soles 1950,51 ....

B2 50 Gold soles 1950,51 ....

B3 20 Gold soles 1950,51 .... Struck for purchasers of bullion

SILVER

Type: Seated Figure. ℞ Arms.

7 1 Sol 1914-16. 9 Decimos Fine...... 1.50
8 ½ Sol 1907-17 .... .75
9 1/5 Sol 1901-16 .... .35
10 1 Dinero (1/10 Sol) 1902-13, 1916 .... .20
11 ½ Dinero 1901-17 .... .15
12 1 Sol 1922-34. 5 Decimos fine...... 1.25

The issues struck at Philadelphia from 1923-26 do not have the assayer's initials.

13 ½ Sol 1922-35. Fineness not on coin .... .50

COPPER-NICKEL

15 20 Centavos 1918-26 .... .25
16 10 Centavos 1918-40 .... .15
17 5 Centavos 1918-40 .... .10

BRONZE

18 2 Centavos 1917-42 .... .15

19 1 Centavo 1901-42 .... .10
There are many varieties of the two preceding, some with date at top, others with date at bottom of coin. Also a great variety in the size of letters and thickness of metal.

19a 2 Centavos 1948,49 size reduced
19b 1 Centavo 1948,49 ....
19c 2 Centavos 1950. Zinc ....
19d 1 Centavo 1950. Zinc ....

BRASS

20 1 Sol 1943-49. Central Reserve Bank Issue .... .50

21 ½ Sol 1935-49. Similar .... .35
22 20 Centavos 1942-49. Type of copper-nickel coins .... .25
23 10 Centavos 1942-49. Similar .... .15
24 5 Centavos 1942-49. Similar .... .10

PHILIPPINE ISLANDS

Under the United States

A group of over 7000 islands in the Malay Archipelago in the North Pacific Ocean. Commonwealth.

Mints: Philadelphia, San Francisco (S), Manila (M after 1924).

100 Centavos = 1 Peso.

SILVER

Type—Female and volcano. ℞ U. S. Arms.

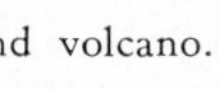

1	Peso 1903-06	2.00
2	50 Centavos 1903-06	1.00
3	20 Centavos 1903-06	.50
4	10 Centavos 1903-06	.25
5	Peso 1907-12. Size reduced	2.00
6	50 Centavos 1907-09, 20, 21	1.00
7	20 Centavos 1907-21, 29	.35

8	20 Centavos 1928. Reverse of 5 Centavos. Manila mint	
9	10 Centavos 1907-35	.20

COPPER-NICKEL

Type—Seated male figure. ℞ U. S. Arms.

10	5 Centavos 1903-28	.15

11	5 Centavos 1930-35. Size reduced	.15

BRONZE

Type of copper-nickel.

12	1 Centavo 1903-36	.15
13	½ Centavo 1903-08	.15

COMMONWEALTH OF THE PHILIPPINES

Mints: Manila, Philadelphia, Denver, San Francisco.

SILVER

Commemorating the establishment of the Commonwealth in 1935.

14 1 Peso 1936. Roosevelt and Quezon. ℞ Arms of Commonwealth 5.00

15 1 Peso 1936. Gov. Genl. Murphy and Pres. Quezon 5.00

16 50 Centavos 1936. Facing busts of Murphy and Quezon 2.50

REGULAR ISSUE

17 50 Centavos 1944, 45. Female and volcano. ℞ Arms 1.00

18 20 Centavos 1937, 38, 41, 44, 45. Similar .... .25

19 10 Centavos 1937, 38, 44, 45. Similar .... .15

COPPER-NICKEL

20 5 Centavos 1937, 38, 41. Seated male. ℞ Philippine arms .... .15

NICKEL-SILVER

21 5 Cents 1944, 45. Same type as copper-nickel .... .10

BRONZE

22 1 Centavo 1937-39, 41, 44, 45. Similar .... .10

REPUBLIC OF THE PHILIPPINES

MacArthur Commemorative Coins

SILVER

23 1 Peso 1947 .... 2.50

24 ½ Peso 1947 .... 1.25

1 ZŁOTY
11
5 ZŁOTYCH 5
9
RZECZPOSPOLITA POLSKA
1925
26
50 GROSZY
RZECZPOSPOLITA POLSKA
1925
HONOR I OJCZYZNA
1830
W SETNA
1930
ROCZNICE
POWSTANIA
5 5
ZŁOTYCH
13
14
7
RZECZPOSPOLITA POLSKA
10 ZŁOTYCH 10
14
2 GROSZE
31
5 GROSZY
30
1 GROSZ
32
RZECZPOSPOLITA POLSKA
12
RZECZPOSPOLITA POLSKA
1929
29
1 ZŁOTY
5 5
ZŁOTYCH
1928
12

P O L A N D

POLAND

German Occupation—World War I

Mints: Berlin (A), Hamburg (J).

Under the Military High Commander of the East. (Poland and Lithuania.)

IRON

1	3 Kopec 1916. Inscription. ℞ Value in cross	.50
2	2 Kopec 1916. Similar	.50
3	1 Kopec 1916. Similar	.40

Regency under Germany and Austria. (Krolestwo Polskie.)
Mint: Stuttgart (F).

IRON

4	20 Fenegow 1917-18. Eagle. ℞ Value	.50
5	10 Fenegow 1917-18. Similar	.50
6	5 Fenegow 1917-18. Similar	.35
6a	1 Fenig 1917	.50

POLAND

(Rzeczpospolita Polska)

In Central Europe, bounded on the north by Germany and on the east by the USSR.

Mints: Warsaw (Arrow-like mark), Brussels, London, Paris, Philadelphia, Utrecht, Vienna, Huguenin Freres & Co., King's Norton.

100 Groszy = 1 Zloty.

GOLD

7	20 Zlotych 1925. Head of Boleslaus I *l.* ℞ Eagle	35.00
8	10 Zlotych 1925. Similar	20.00

SILVER

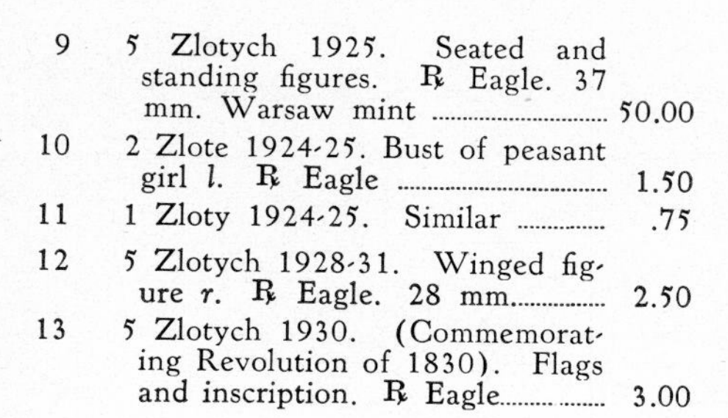

9	5 Zlotych 1925. Seated and standing figures. ℞ Eagle. 37 mm. Warsaw mint	50.00
10	2 Zlote 1924-25. Bust of peasant girl *l.* ℞ Eagle	1.50
11	1 Zloty 1924-25. Similar	.75
12	5 Zlotych 1928-31. Winged figure *r.* ℞ Eagle. 28 mm.	2.50
13	5 Zlotych 1930. (Commemorating Revolution of 1830). Flags and inscription. ℞ Eagle	3.00
14	10 Zlotych 1932-33. Female head *l.* Background of wheat ears. ℞ Eagle 34 mm.	5.00
15	5 Zlotych 1932-34. Similar	2.50
16	2 Zlote 1932-34. Similar. Warsaw	1.00

17	10 Zlotych 1933. (250th Anniv. Relief of Vienna). Bust of Jan Sobieski *r.* ℞ Eagle	7.50

18 10 Zlotych 1933. (Insurrection of 1863). Bust of Traugutt facing. ℞ Eagle 7.50

19 10 Zlotych 1934. (Entry into field of Rifle Corps Aug. 6, 1914). Head of Pilsudski *l.* ℞ Eagle on badge 8.00

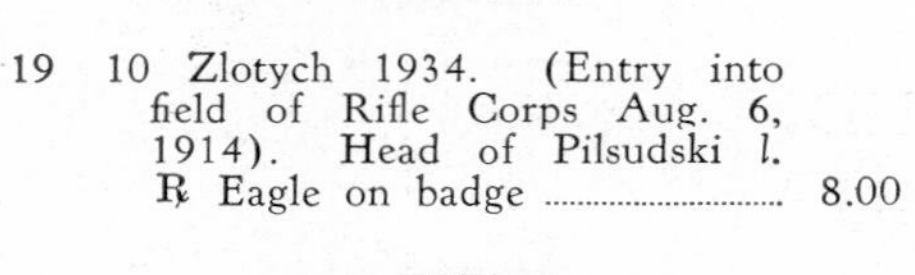

20 5 Zlotych 1934. Similar 2.00
21 10 Zlotych 1934-37. Similar, but no badge under eagle 3.50
22 5 Zlotych 1934-36. Similar 2.00

23 2 Zlote 1934. Similar .... .75

24 5 Zlotych 1936, 37. Sailing ship *l.* ℞ Eagle 5.00

25 2 Zlote 1936, 37. Similar 2.50

NICKEL

26 50 Groszy 1923. Eagle. ℞ Value in closed wreath .... .35
27 20 Groszy 1923. Similar .... .35
28 10 Groszy 1923. Similar .... .35
29 1 Zloty 1929. Eagle. ℞ Value in cartouche .... .25

BRONZE

30 5 Groszy 1923-38. Eagle ℞ Value on scroll .... .25
31 2 Groszy 1923-38. Similar .... .20
32 1 Grosz 1923-38. Similar .... .15

Coins of the first year are found in red and yellow bronze.

German Occupation—World War II

Types—Similar to regular issues.

33 50 Groszy 1938. Iron ....
34 20 Groszy 1939-45 (Dated 1923) Zinc ....
35 10 Groszy. Similar. Zinc ....
36 5 Groszy 1939. Zinc. Holed ....
37 1 Grosz 1939. Zinc ....

PORTUGAL

(Republica Portuguesa)

On the western part of the Iberian Peninsula in southwestern Europe.

A monarchy until 1910. Now a republic.

Mint: Lisbon (no mint Mark)

Monarchy — 1000 Reis = 1 Crown } 10 Tostões
Republic — 100 Centavos = 1 Escudo }

Carlos I—1889-1908

SILVER

1 500 Reis 1901-08. Bare head r. ℞ Crowned arms in wreath. 1.25
2 200 Reis 1901, 03. Head r. ℞ value in wreath .... .75

BRONZE

3 5 Reis 1901-06. Head. ℞ Value .25

Manuel II—1908-1910

SILVER

4 500 Reis 1908,09. Head l. ℞ Crowned arms in wreath 1.00
5 200 Reis 1909. Head l. ℞ Crowned value in wreath ...... .50
9 100 Reis 1909,10. Similar .... .35

Commemorative Coins

6 1000 Reis. Centenary of Peninsular War 10.00
7 500 Reis. Similar 2.50

8 500 Reis. Marquis de Pombal 5.00

BRONZE

10 5 Reis 1910. Head ℞ Value ...... .15

Republic 1910-1926

SILVER

11 1 Escudo (1914). Commemorating birth of the republic, October 5, 1910 .... 5.00

Regular Issue with Republic head

12 1 Escudo 1915, 16 .... 3.50
13 50 Centavos 1912-16 .... 1.00
14 20 Centavos 1913,16 .... .50
15 10 Centavos 1915 .... .25

ALUMINUM BRONZE

Type—Republic with Flag

20 1 Escudo 1924,26 .... .50
21 50 Centavos 1924,26 .... .25

COPPER-NICKEL

Type—Head of Republic. ℞ Value

22 4 Centavos 1917,19 .... .15
23 20 Centavos 1920-22 .... .25
24 10 Centavos 1920,21 .... .15

BRONZE

Type—Arms. ℞ Value

27 5 Centavos 1920-22 .... .20
28 2 Centavos 1918-21 .... .15
29 1 Centavo 1917-22 .... .10

Type—Head of Republic. ℞ Value

30 20 Centavos 1924,25 .... .20
31 10 Centavos 1924-26 .... .15
32 5 Centavos 1924,25 .... .10

IRON

Provisional Coin World War I

36 2 Centavos 1918. Arms. ℞ Value 1.00

REPUBLICA PORTUGUESA
5 DE OUTUBRO DE
1910
11
EMANVEL II PORTVG: ET ALGARB: REX
1910
6
REPUBLICA PORTUGUESA
1915
12
REPUBLICA PORTUGUESA
5
CENTAVOS
32
32
1 ESCUDO
CENTENARIO DA GUERRA PENINSULAR
1808 1814
1000 REIS
1 ESCUDO
REPUBLICA PORTUGUESA
1924
20
1 ESCUDO
CARLOS I REI DE PORTUGAL
1906
1
REPUBLICA PORTUGUESA
1927
25
1 ESCUDO
REPUBLICA PORTUGUESA
1916
14
20 CENTAVOS
REPUBLICA PORTUGUESA
4
CENTAVOS
1917
22
REPUBLICA PORTUGUESA
5
CENTAVOS
1921
27
500 REIS
EMANVEL II PORTVG: ET ALGARB: REX
1909
5
200
REIS
16
Republica Portuguesa
10
1928
REPUBLICA PORTUGUESA
1932
17
10$00

PORTUGAL

New State 1926

SILVER

16 10 Escudos 1928. Commemorating Battle of Ourique in 1139 .... 3.50

Type—Caraval. ℞ Arms over value

17	10 Escudos 1932-48	1.50
18	5 Escudos 1932-48	.75
19	2½ Escudos 1932-48	.50

NICKEL BRONZE

Type—Bust of Republic. ℞ Arms in wreath

25	1 Escudo 1927-45	.35
26	50 Centavos 1927-47	.20

BRONZE

Type—Head of Republic. ℞ Value

31a	10 Centavos 1930,38,40	.20
32a	5 Centavos 1927	.10

Type—Quinas cross. ℞ Value over wreath

34	XX Centavos 1942-49	.15
35	X Centavos 1942-50	.10

PORTUGUESE GUINEA

The Portuguese possessions on the west coast of Africa. Portuguese Colony.
Mint: Lisbon. 100 Centavos = 1 Escudo

1 2 3 4 5

COPPER-NICKEL

Type—Head of Republic. ℞ Arms and value.

1	1 Escudo 1933	.50
2	50 Centavos 1933	.35

BRONZE

Type—Younger head. ℞ Value.

3	20 Centavos 1933	.25
4	10 Centavos 1933	.20
5	5 Centavos 1933	.15

Fifth Centennial of Discovery

Type—Crowned shield. ℞ Value.

6	1 Escudo Bronze 1946	.50
7	50 Centavos 1946	.35

PORTUGUESE INDIA
(Estado da India)

The Portuguese possessions in India consisting of Diu in Gugerat, Damão and Goa on west coast of Indian Peninsula.

Mint: Lisbon

16 Tangas = 1 Rupia

Carlos I—1889-1908
SILVER

Type—Head r. ℞ Crowned arms in wreath

1 1 Rupia 1903-05 .... 3.50

BRONZE

Type—Similar. Date in Roman numerals. Without reverse wreath

2 ½ Tanga 1901,03 .... .75
3 ¼ Tanga 1901,03 .... .50
4 ⅛ Tanga 1901,03 .... .50
5 1/12 Tanga 1901,03 .... .50

Republic 1910-1926
SILVER

Type—Liberty head. ℞ Value in wreath

6 1 Rupia 1912 .... 3.50

New State 1926
SILVER

Type—Arms on cross. ℞ Shield over value

7 1 Rupia 1935 .... 2.50
8 ½ Rupia 1936,37 .... 3.50

COPPER-NICKEL

Type—Arms over date. ℞ Arms over value

9 4 Tangas 1934 .... 2.00
10 2 Tangas 1934 .... 1.50

BRONZE

Type of Preceding

12 1 Tanga 1934 .... 1.50

Modern Coinage

SILVER

Type—Arms on cross.
℞ Crowned round shield

13	1 Rupia. 1947,48	1.25

COPPER-NICKEL

Type—Crowned round shield. ℞ Value

14	½ Rupia 1947	.75
15	¼ Rupia 1947	.50

BRONZE

Type of Preceding

16	1 Tanga 1947	.25

REUNION ISLAND

(Ile de la Reunion)

Situated about 420 miles east of Madagascar. A French overseas department.

Mint: Paris

100 Centimes = 1 Franc

ALUMINUM

1	2 Francs 1949	
2	1 Franc 1949,50	

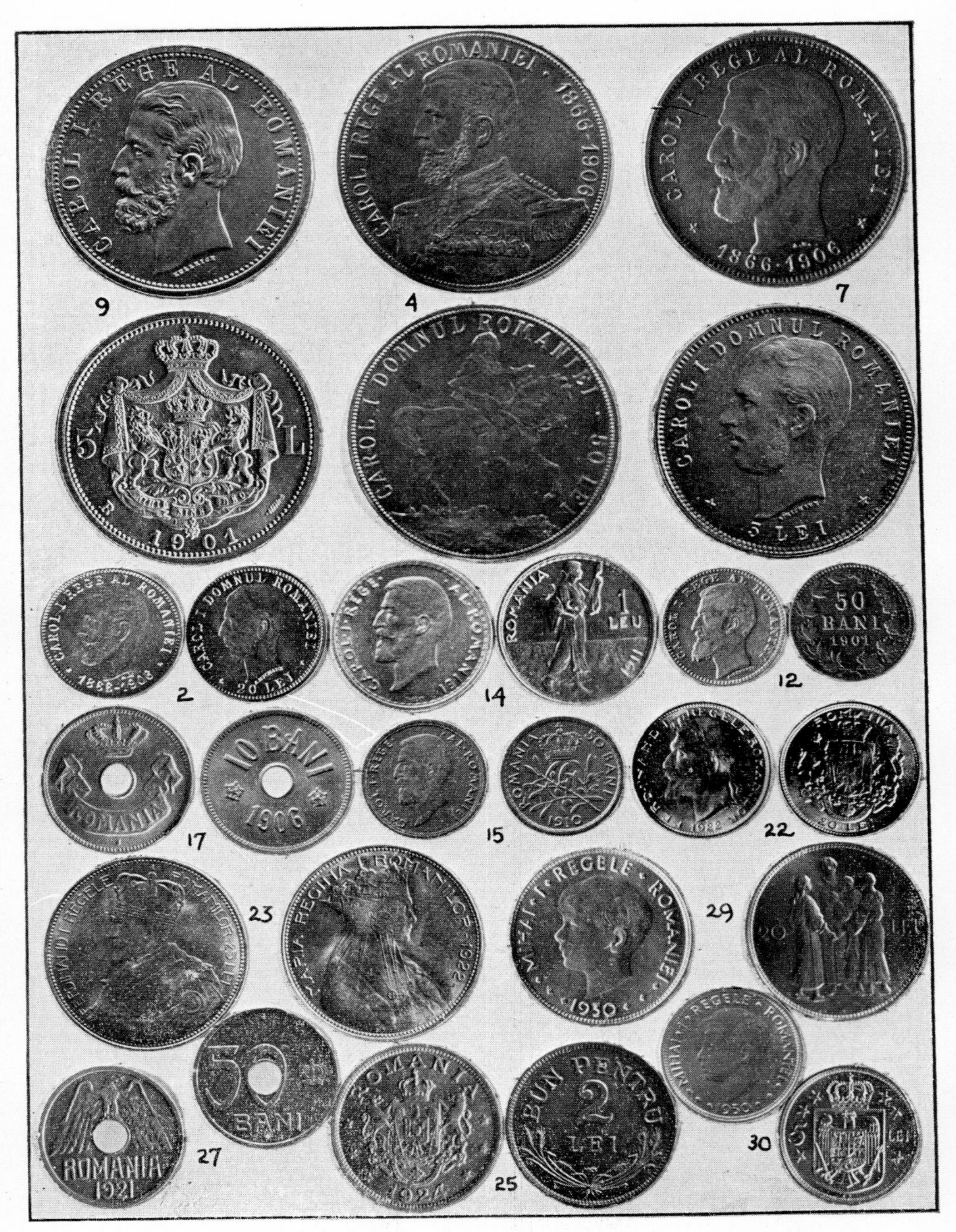
CAROL I REGE AL ROMANIEI
9
CAROL I REGE AL ROMANIEI · 1866-1906
4
CAROL I REGE AL ROMANIEI
1866·1906
7
5 L
1901
CAROL I DOMNUL ROMANIEI · 50 LEI
CAROL I DOMNUL ROMANIEI
5 LEI
2
20 LEI
14
ROMANIA
1 LEU
50
BANI
1901
12
ROMANIA
17
10 BANI
1906
15
50 BANI
1910
22
23
29
1930
ROMANIA
1921
27
50
BANI
ROMANIA
1924
25
BUN PENTRU
2
LEI
30

ROMANIA

ROMANIA

On the Black Sea in Central Europe. Kingdom until 1947. Now a People's Republic.

Mints: Brussels, London, Paris, Hamburg, King's Norton, Birmingham, Poissy, Huguenin Freres & Co.

100 Bani = 1 Leu.

Carol I—1866-1914

GOLD

1 100 Lei 1906. (Fortieth Anniversary of Reign.) Young head of Carol. ℞ Bearded head 150.00

2 20 Lei 1906. Similar 20.00

4 50 Lei 1906. Bust in uniform. ℞ Carol on horseback 50.00

5 25 Lei 1906. Bust in uniform. ℞ Crowned eagle 25.00

6 12½ Lei 1906. Similar 12.50

SILVER

7 5 Lei 1906. (40th Anniv.) Young head *l.* ℞ Bearded head *l.* 10.00

8 1 Leu 1906. Similar 1.00

9 5 Lei 1901. Head *l.* ℞ Crowned arms on mantle 20.00

10 2 Lei 1901. Similar 1.50

11 1 Leu 1901. Similar 1.00

12 50 Bani 1901. Similar. ℞ Value in wreath ..... .50

13 2 Lei 1910-12, 1914. Head *l.* ℞ Peasant woman walking *r.* 1.00

14 1 Leu 1910-12, 1914. Similar ..... .75

15 50 Bani 1910-12, 1914. Head *l.* ℞ Crowned olive branch ..... .50

COPPER-NICKEL

16 20 Bani 1906-07. Holed type. Crown and ROMANIA on ribbon. ℞ Value and date ..... .25

17 10 Bani 1905-07. Similar ..... .20

18 5 Bani 1905-07. Similar ..... .15

BRONZE

19 2 Bani 1901. Head *l.* ℞ Arms on mantle ..... .25

20 1 Bani 1901. Similar ..... .15

Ferdinand I—1914-1927

GOLD

21 100 Lei 1922. (Commemorating the coronation.) Laureated head *l.* ℞ Crowned arms. Lion supporters. 34 mm. 200.00

22 20 Lei 1922. Similar 35.00

23 50 Lei 1922. Crown bust *l.* of Ferdinand. ℞ Crowned bust *r.* of Marie. 40 mm. Broad and thin 85.00

24 25 Lei 1922. Similar. 30 mm 25.00

The above four pieces were struck at London in 1928.

COPPER-NICKEL

25 2 Lei 1924. Arms and supporters. ℞ Value in wreath...... .75

26 1 Leu 1924. Similar .... .40

ALUMINUM

27 50 Bani 1921. Holed type. Eagle ℞ Value .... .35

28 25 Bani 1921. Similar .... .25

Mihai I—1927-1930

NICKEL-BRASS

29 20 Lei 1930. Head *l.* ℞ Four figures 1.00

30 5 Lei 1930. Similar. ℞ Crowned arms .... .75

Carol II—1930-1940

SILVER

31 250 Lei 1935. Head *l.* ℞ Arms 6.00

32 100 Lei 1932. Head *r.* ℞ Arms value in wreath 4.00

32a 250 Lei 1939, 40. Head *r.* ℞ Arms 6.00

NICKEL

33 100 Lei 1936-40. Head *l.* ℞ Crowned arms in wreath 1.25

34 50 Lei 1937-40. Helmeted head *l.* ℞ Crowned arms in wreath 1.00

NICKEL-BRASS

35 20 Lei 1930. Head *l.* ℞ Interlaced C's on shield on eagle...... .50

36 10 Lei 1930. Similar .... .35

37 1 Leu 1938-41. Crown. ℞ Value .15

Commemorating the Centennial of birth of King Carol I, born April 20, 1839

GOLD

38 Galbeni 1939. King Carol II mounted *l.* ℞ Wolf of Rome across band 100.00

39 Galbeni 1939. Same obverse. ℞ Mower 100.00

40 100 Lei 1939. Head of Carol II. ℞ Value above arms 200.00

41 100 Lei 1939. Same obverse. ℞ Archangel behind shield 200.00

42 20 Lei 1939. Head of Carol II. ℞ Crowned arms between branches 50.00

43 20 Lei 1939. Same obverse. ℞ Eagle on shield 50.00

Little is known regarding the above set of gold coins. They seem to be of German origin.

The first two are medals but are included as they form part of the set.

The block illustrates coins 38 to 43

Mihai I (Second reign)—1941-47

SILVER

Type—Bare head. ℞ Arms.

51 500 Lei 1941-43. .835 fine 17.50

52 500 Lei 1944, 45. .700 fine 6.00

53 250 Lei 1941 .... 6.00

54 200 Lei 1942, 43 .... 2.50

NICKEL-IRON

55 100 Lei 1943-45. Head. ℞ Value

ZINC

Type—Crown. ℞ Value.

56 20 Lei 1942-46 ....

57 5 Lei 1942-46 ....

58 2 Lei 1941-47 ....

World War II Inflation

All denominations with bare head.

59 100,000 Lei 1946, 47. Silver. Female with arms and dove 17.50
60 25,000 Lei 1946. Silver. Value above branches 10.00
61 10,000 Lei 1947. Brass. Similar......
62 2,000 Lei 1946, 47. Brass. Arms......
63 500 Lei 1945, 46. Brass. Arms ....
64 500 Lei 1946, 47. Aluminum ....
65 200 Lei 1945. Brass ....

Reform of August 1947

66 5 Lei 1947. Aluminum ....
67 2 Lei 1947. Tombac ....
68 1 Leu 1947. Brass ....
69 50 Bani 1947. Brass ....

Peoples Republic

70 5 Lei 1948. Arms. ℞ Value. Aluminum bronze ....

71 1 Leu 1949. Oil derrick. Alum. bronze ....

RUSSIA

(Empire)

Mint: St. Petersburg.

100 Kopecks = 1 Rouble.

Nicholas II

GOLD

1 37½ Roubles (100 francs) 1902. Head *l.* ℞ Arms. Very rare 500.00

2 25 Roubles 1908. Similar. Very rare 400.00

3 10 Roubles 1901-04, 06, 10, 11. Similar 15.00

4 5 Roubles 1901-04, 06, 07, 09, 10. Similar 10.00

SILVER

5 1 Rouble 1901-15. Similar to gold 2.00

6 50 Kopecks 1901-14. Similar 1.00

7 25 Kopecks 1901. Similar 2.50

8 20 Kopecks 1901-16. Double eagle. ℞ Value in wreath ...... .50

9 15 Kopecks 1901-16. Similar ...... .35

10 10 Kopecks 1901-16. ...... .25

11 5 Kopecks 1901-14 ...... .20

The 15 and 10 Kopecks of 1916 were made at Osaka.

COPPER

12 5 Kopecks 1911, 12, 16. Eagle. ℞ Value ...... .35

13 3 Kopecks 1901-16. Similar ...... .25

14 2 Kopecks 1901-16. Similar ...... .15

15 1 Kopeck 1901-16. Similar ...... .10

16 ½ Kopeck 1908-16. H I I crowned. ℞ Value ...... .10

17 ¼ Kopeck 1909-16 Similar ...... .10

COMMEMORATIVE ROUBLES

18 1912. Commemorating centenary of victory over Napoleon. Crowned imperial eagle on circular background. ℞ Inscription in 7 lines 15.00

19 1912. Statue of Alexander III at Moscow. Head to *l.* ℞ View of statue 20.00

20 1913. Third centenary of Romanoff rule. Heads of Nicholas II and Michael Feodorovich. ℞ Imperial eagle 3.50

21 1914. Second centennial of Battle of Gangut. Bust of Peter I. ℞ Imperial eagle 100.00

6
2
6
8
10
20 КОПѢЕКЪ 1915
10 КОПѢЕКЪ 1915
5
РУБЛЬ 1912
1812
СЛАВНЫЙ ГОДЪ
СЕЙ МИНУЛЪ,
НО НЕ ПРОЙДУТЪ
СОДѢЯННЫЕ ВЪ
НЕМЪ ПОДВИГИ
1912
РУБЛЬ
1911 ГОДА
3 КОПѢЙКИ
13
18
13
19
20
21
ГАНГУТЪ
1714
1914
27 ІЮЛЯ
РУБЛЬ
1613 — 1913
МОНЕТА РУБЛЬ

RUSSIA

22
РУБЛЬ
1
1921
23
20
КОПЕЕК
1921
25
ОДИН
РУБЛЬ
1924
28
10
КОПЕЕК
32
32
10
КОПЕЕК
1923
27
50
1921
24
5
КОПЕЕК
1930
33
1924
29
5
КОПЕЕК
1924
47
СССР
3
КОПЕЙКИ
48
ОДИН
ПОЛТИННИК
3
КОПЕЙКИ
34
20
КОПЕЕК
1925
30
41
20

RUSSIA

SALVADOR

(Republica de El Salvador)

The smallest of the five Central American republics, on the Pacific Coast between Guatemala, Honduras and the Gulf of Fonseca.

Mints: Brussels, Birmingham, Hamburg, Philadelphia, San Francisco, Mexico.

100 Centavos = 1 Peso.
100 Centavos = 1 Colon.

GOLD

1 20 Colones 1925. (4th Centenary of San Salvador). Busts of Alvarada and Quinonez *l.* ℞ Arms in wreath. Mexico Mint Very rare 150.00

SILVER

2 1 Peso 1904-14. Head of Columbus. ℞ Arms 2.50

3 1 Colon 1925. 4th Centenary of San Salvador. Similar to No. 1... 20.00

Type: Arms. ℞ Value.

4 25 Centavos 1911 ..... .50

5 10 Centavos 1911 ..... .35

6 5 Centavos 1908, 1911 ..... .25

Type: New design of arms on obverse.

7 25 Centavos 1914 ..... .50

8 10 Centavos 1914 ..... .35

9 5 Centavos 1914 ..... .25

COPPER-NICKEL

Type: Head of Morazan. ℞ Value.

10 10 Centavos 1914-40 ..... .25

11 5 Centavos 1915-50 ..... .20

12 3 Centavos 1913, 1915 ..... .15

13 1 Centavo 1913-40 ..... .10

COPPER OR BRONZE

14 1/4 Real 1909. Arms in wreath. ℞ Value ..... .25

15 1 Centavo 1942, 1945, 47. Type of Copper nickel ..... .10

SILVER

16 25 Centavos 1943-44, 45. Type of Copper nickel ..... .50

SAN MARINO

Situated in the Apennines in the heart of Italy. Republic.

Mint: Rome.

100 Centesimi = 1 Lira.

GOLD

1 20 Lire 1925. Three towers. ℞ Standing saint 30.00

2 10 Lire 1925. Similar 15.00

SILVER

3 2 Lire 1906. Crowned arms. ℞ Value in wreath 1.00

4 1 Lira 1906. Similar .... .60

5 20 Lire 1931-37. Three feathers crowned. ℞ Half figure of St. Marinus facing 5.00

6 10 Lire 1931-38. Crowned arms. ℞ Female half figure 3.00

7 5 Lire 1931-38. Helmeted head in circle. ℞ Plow 1.50

BRONZE

8 10 Centesimi 1935-37. Crowned arms. ℞ Value .... .35

9 5 Centesimi 1935-37. Similar........ .25

SARAWAK

On the northwest coast of Borneo between the mountains and the China Sea. British Protectorate.

Mint: Birmingham.

100 Cents=1 Dollar.

Charles J. Brooke, Rajah. 1868-1917.

SILVER

1 50 Cents. 1900, 1906. Head *l.* ℞ Value in roped circle 3.50

2 20 Cents. 1900, 1906, 1910-11, 1913, 1915. Similar 2.00

3 10 Cents. 1900, 1906, 1910-11, 1913, 1915. Similar 1.25

4 5 Cents. 1907, 1911, 1913, 1915. Similar 1.25

Charles Vyner Brooke, Rajah. 1917-

SILVER

5 50 Cents. 1927. Head *r.* ℞ Value in roped circle 3.50

6 20 Cents. 1920, 1927. Similar 2.00

7 10 Cents. 1920. Similar 1.25

8 5 Cents. 1920. Similar 1.00

COPPER-NICKEL

9 10 Cents. 1920. 1921, 1927, 1934. Head *r.* ℞ Value in wreath........ .50

10 5 Cents. 1921, 1927. Similar .35

11 1 Cent. 1920-21. Similar .... .25

BRONZE

12 1 Cent. 1927-42 Head *r.* ℞ Value in wreath .... .25

13 ½ Cent. 1933. Similar .... .15

SAUDI ARABIA

(Al Mamlaka al'Arabiya as-Sa'udiya)

Comprises the sultanate of Nejd and the Kingdom of Hejaz and its dependencies. Hejaz lies on the southwest part of Arabia from the Egyptian line to Asir along the Red Sea.

Mints: Birmingham, London, Philadelphia, Bombay.

2 Girsh Darij = 1 Girsh Miri.

22 Girsh Miri (Piastre) = 1 Riyal

Abdul Aziz a-Sa'ud—1926-

SILVER

1   1 Riyal 1346-48 A.H. = 1928-30 A.D. Arabic inscription in circle and above. Swords in cartouche at bottom, palm trees at sides. ℞ Similar 7.50

2   ½ Riyal. Same dates. Similar 2.50

3   ¼ Riyal. Same dates. Similar 1.50

Mecca Pilgrim Currency

4   1 Rupee 1346, 47 A.H. Arabic inscription, center blank. ℞ Inscription and value 3.00

5   ½ Rupee 1346, 47 A.H. Similar... 2.00

6   ¼ Rupee 1346, 47 A.H. Similar... 1.25

COPPER-NICKEL

7   1 Girsh 1344-1356 A.H. .... .25
8   ½ Girsh .... .20
9   ¼ Girsh .... .15

SILVER

Reduced standard. Smaller size.

10   Riyal 1355-1366 A.H. 1.25
11   ½ Riyal .... .75
12   ¼ Riyal .... .50

SERBIA

A former kingdom which with other states united to form the present state of Yugoslavia in southeastern Europe.

Mints: Vienna, Kremnitz, Paris, Gorham Mfg. Co., N. Y.

40 Paras = 1 Dinar.

Peter I—1903-1918

SILVER

1 5 Dinars 1904. Centenary of the Karageorgowiczs. Two heads r. ℞ Crowned arms in mantle... 10.00

2 2 Dinars 1904, 05, 12, 15-17. Head r. ℞ Value in wreath 2.00

3 1 Dinar 1904, 05, 12, 15-17. Similar 1.00

4 50 Paras 1904, 12, 15-17. Similar .35

COPPER-NICKEL

5 20 Paras 1912, 17. Crowned eagle. ℞ Value .... .25

6 10 Paras 1912, 17. Similar .... .20

7 5 Paras 1904, 12, 17. Similar .15

BRONZE

8 2 Paras 1904. Crowned eagle. ℞ Value .... .10

SEYCHELLES

Approximately one hundred islands in the Indian Ocean near Mauritius off the coast of Africa. British Crown Colony.

Mint: London

100 Cents = 1 Rupee

George VI

SILVER

Type—Crowned head *l.* ℞ Value.

No.	Coin	Price
1	1 Rupee 1939	3.00
2	½ Rupee 1939	2.00
3	25 Cents 1939, 43, 44	1.00

NICKEL-BRONZE

No.	Coin	Price
4	10 Cents 1939, 43, 44	.50

BRONZE

No.	Coin	Price
5	5 Cents 1948	.25
6	2 Cents 1948	.20
7	1 Cent 1948	.15

SIAM

(Prades Thai or Muang-Thai)

In southeastern Asia occupying the western part of the Indo-Chinese Peninsula.
Mints: Bangkok, Paris, Birmingham, Brussels, Philadelphia, Osaka, Hamburg.
64 Atts = 1 Tical or Bat. 100 Satangs = 1 Tical.

P'ra Paramin Maha Chulalongkorn 1868-1910

SILVER

1 Tical 1901-1907. Bust to *l*. ℞ Arms. Bangkok mint 2.50
2 ¼ Tical (Salung) 1901-1909. Similar. Bangkok mint .... .75
3 ⅛ Tical (Fuang) 1901-1908. Similar. Bangkok .... .50

4 Tical 1909. Older bust to *l*. ℞ Three headed elephant. Rare ......

COPPER-NICKEL

5 10 Satangs 1908, 1909. Name and value. ℞ Chakra containing date .... .25
6 5 Satangs 1908, 1909. Similar .15

BRONZE

7 2 Atts 1903, 1904, 1906. Bust of king *l*. ℞ Allegorical figure of Siam st'd *r*. 1.00
8 1 Att 1903, 1904, 1906. Similar .50
9 ½ Att 1906. Similar .... .35
10 1 Satang 1908, 1909. Similar to No. 5 .... .15

P'ra Paramin Maha Vajiravudh (Rama VI)—1910-1925

11 1 Tical 1910, 1913-1918. Bust to *r*. ℞ Three headed elephant... 2.50
12 ½ Tical 1915-23. Similar 1.00
13 ¼ Tical 1915-24. Similar .... .50

COPPER-NICKEL

14 10 Satangs 1910-22. Type of preceding reign .... .20
15 5 Satangs 1910-22 .... .15

BRONZE

16 1 Satang 1910-24. Type of preceding reign .... .15

P'ra Paramin Maha Prajadhipok 1925-33

SILVER

17 ½ Tical 1929-1932. Bust in uniform *l.* ℞ Elephant *l.* 2.00
18 ¼ Tical 1926, 1929-1932. Similar 1.50

COPPER-NICKEL

19 5 Satangs 1926-1929. Type of preceding reign .... .15

BRONZE

20 1 Satang 1926-1929. Type of preceding .... .10

Ananda Mahidol 1933-46

SILVER

21 10 Satangs 1941 .... .75
22 5 Satangs 1941 .... .50

COPPER-NICKEL

23 10 Satangs 1936, 38 .... .20
24 5 Satangs 1936, 38 .... .15

BRONZE

25 1 Satang 1936, 38 .... .15
26 ½ Satang 1937 .... .10

27 1 Satang 1941 .... .35

TIN COMPOSITION

28 10 Satangs 1942. (2485) .... .35
29 5 Satangs 1942 .... .25
30 1 Satang 1942. Not holed .... .20

The following with Western figures in denominations and dates. 1944 = 2487. All holed except 1 Satang.

31 20 Satangs 1944, 45 .... .50
32 10 Satangs 1944, 45 .... .35
33 5 Satangs 1944, 45 .... .25
34 1 Satang 1944 .... .20

With young bust of Ananda

35 25 Satangs 1946 .... .75
36 10 Satangs 1946 .... .35
37 5 Satangs 1946 .... .25

With older bust of Ananda

38 50 Satangs 1946 .... 1.00
39 25 Satangs 1946 .... .75
40 10 Satangs 1946 .... .35
41 5 Satangs 1946 .... .25

28 35 30

31 39 38

SOMALIA

On the east coast of Africa between British Somaliland and Kenya.

Under Italian trusteeship

Mint: Rome

100 Centesimi = 1 Somalo

SILVER

Type — Lioness. R Value

1 1 Somalo 1950 ....

2 50 Centesimi 1950 ....

BRONZE

Type — Elephant head. R Value

3 10 Centesimi 1950 ....

4 5 Centesimi 1950 ....

5 1 Centesimo 1950 ....

SOUTH AFRICAN REPUBLIC

Mint: Pilgrims Rest.

GOLD

The Veld Pond

1 1 Pond. 1902. ZAR in monogram. 1902. R EEN POND...... 50.00

There is a dangerous counterfeit of this coin.

SOUTH AFRICA

(Union of South Africa)

A self-governing Dominion within the British Commonwealth of Nations, includes the former Colonies of the Cape of Good Hope, Natal, the Transvaal and the Orange Free State.

Mint: Pretoria.

British Coinage system. 12 pence = 1 shilling. 20 shillings = 1 pound.

George V

GOLD

British sovereigns were struck at Pretoria from 1925 to 1932.

Mint mark—SA.

SILVER

With Zuid Africa

All coins with crowned bust *l.*

1 2½ Shillings. 1923-30. Crowned arms 1.50

2 1 Florin. 1923-30. Arms 1.00

3 1 Shilling. 1923-30. Hope standing with anchor, within circle .... .50

There were some slight changes made on the reverse in 1926.

4 6 Pence. 1923-24. Value in closed wreath .... .50

5 6 Pence. 1925-30. Six bundles of sticks around a flower .... .35

6 3 Pence. 1923-24. Value in closed wreath .... .25

7 3 Pence. 1925-30. Three bundles of sticks around flower .... .25

With Suid Africa

8 2½ Shillings. 1931-36. Similar to previous piece but with slight changes on reverse 1.50

9 2 Shillings. 1931-36. Similar to previous piece but 2 SHILLING in place of FLORIN 1.00

10 1 Shilling. 1931-36. Similar but Hope not in circle .... .50

11 6 Pence. 1931-36. Similar but 6D in place of 6 PENCE .... .35

12 3 Pence. 1931-36. Similar but 3D in place of 3 PENCE .... .25

BRONZE

With Zuid Africa

13 1 Penny. 1923-30. Ship .... .20
14 ½ Penny. 1923-30. .... .15
15 ¼ Penny. 1923-30. Two birds ...... .10

With Suid Africa

Word "Penny" abbreviated

Types of preceding

16 1 Penny. 1931-36 .... .20

17 ½ Penny. 1931-36 .... .15
18 ¼ Penny. 1931-36 .... .10

George VI

Obverse type—Bare head

SILVER

19 2½ Shillings. 1937-47. Crowned arms 1.25

20 2 Shillings. 1937-47. Arms 1.00

21 1 Shilling. 1937-47. Hope .... .50
22 6 Pence. 1937-47. Six bundles of sticks around a flower .... .35
23 3 Pence. 1937-47. Three bundles of sticks around a flower .... .25

BRONZE

24 1 Penny. 1937-47. ℞ Ship right .20
25 ½ Penny. 1937-47. Similar .... .15
26 ¼ Penny. 1937-47. Similar ℞ Two birds .... .10

Commemorative Crown

27 5 Shillings 1947. Bare head l. ℞ Springbok. Struck to commemorate the Royal Visit to South Africa 2.50

With title — GEORGIVS SEXTVS REX

Types of preceding issue

SILVER

28 Crown 1948-50 .... 2.00
29 ½ Crown 1948-50 .... 1.25
30 2 Shillings 1948-50 .... 1.00
31 1 Shilling 1948-50 .... .50
32 6 Pence 1948-50 .... .35
33 3 Pence 1948-50 .... .25

BRONZE

34 1 Penny 1948-50 .... .20
35 ½ Penny 1948-50 .... .15
36 ¼ Penny 1948-50 .... .10

SOUTHERN RHODESIA

In the central part of South Africa. British Crown Colony.
Mint: London.
British Coinage system. 12 pence = 1 Shilling. 20 Shillings = 1 Pound.

George V

SILVER

1 ½ Crown. 1932-36. Bust *l.* ℞ Crowned arms 2.50

2 1 Florin. 1932, 34-36. Antelope ... 1.50
3 1 Shilling. 1932-36. Stone bird ... 1.00

4 6 Pence. 1932-36. ℞ Axes .... .60
5 3 Pence. 1932-36. Three spears ... .35

COPPER-NICKEL

6 1 Penny. 1934-36. Holed type. Crowned rose .... .35
7 ½ Penny. 1934, 36. Similar .... .25

George VI

SILVER

Types of preceding reign.

8 ½ Crown. 1937-46 .... 2.00
9 1 Florin. 1937-46 .... 1.50
10 1 Shilling. 1937-46 .... 1.00
11 6 Pence. 1937-46 .... .50
12 3 Pence. 1937-46 .... .35

COPPER-NICKEL

Types of silver coins

13 ½ Crown 1947 ....
14 1 Florin 1947 ....
15 1 Shilling 1947 ....
16 6 Pence 1947 ....
17 3 Pence 1947 ....

NICKEL-BRONZE

Types of preceding reign.

18 Penny. 1937-44, 47 .... .25
19 ½ Penny. 1938-44 .... .15
Some of the dates after 1942 are in bronze.

With title — KING GEORGE THE SIXTH

COPPER-NICKEL

20 ½ Crown 1948, 49, 50 ....
21 1 Florin 1948, 49, 50 ....
22 1 Shilling 1948, 49, 50 ....
23 6 Pence 1948, 49, 50 ....
24 3 Pence 1948, 49, 50 ....

BRONZE

25 Penny 1949, 50 ....

SPAIN

(Espana)

Occupies most of the Iberian Peninsula in southwestern Europe. Nationalist government.
Mint: Madrid.
100 Centimos = 1 Peseta.

Alfonso XIII—1886-1931

GOLD

1 20 Pesetas 1904. Young head *r.* ℞ Arms 100.00

SILVER

2 2 Pesetas 1905. Bust *l.* in uniform. ℞ Arms 1.50

3 1 Peseta 1901, 02. Young boy's head .... .75

4 1 Peseta 1902-1905. Bust *l.* in uniform .... .75

5 50 Centimos 1904, 1905, 1910, 1911. Similar .... .50

6 50 Centimos 1926, 1927. Mature head *l.* ℞ Crowned arms without pillars .... .35

NICKEL BRONZE

7 25 Centimos 1925, 1926. Galleon. ℞ Value .... .35

8 25 Centimos 1927, 1928. Crown, hammer and olive. ℞ Value. Holed center .... .50

BRONZE

9 2 Centimos 1904, 1906, 1911-1913. Bust *r.* in uniform .... .35

10 1 Centimo 1906, 1911-1913. Similar .... .25

The dates 1911-13 show an older bust.

Republic 1931-37

SILVER

11 1 Peseta 1933, 1934. Seated figure *l.* ℞ Arms 2.50

NICKEL BRONZE

12 25 Centimos 1934, 1935. Female holding branch. ℞ Value. Holed center .... .50

BRASS

13 1 Peseta 1937. Female head *l.* ℞ Value and grape spray 1.00

BRONZE

14 50 Centimos 1937. Seated figure... 1.00

15 25 Centimos 1938. Chains 1.00

IRON

16 5 Centimos 1937. Hispania head... 1.00

Nationalist Government—1937-

COPPER-NICKEL

17 25 Centimos 1937. Arrows and sun .50

ALUMINUM

18 10 Centimos. 1940-48. Horseman .50

19 5 Centimos. 1940-48. Similar ...... .25

ALUMINUM BRONZE

20 1 Peseta 1944-47. Arms. ℞ Value .75

21 1 Peseta 1947. Head of Gen. Franco ....

NICKEL

22 5 Pesetas 1949. Head of Gen. Franco ....

STRAITS SETTLEMENTS

(British Malaya)

In the southeastern part of Asia on the Malay Peninsula. Formerly a British Crown Colony.
Mints: London, Bombay, Birmingham, Calcutta.
100 Cents=1 Dollar.

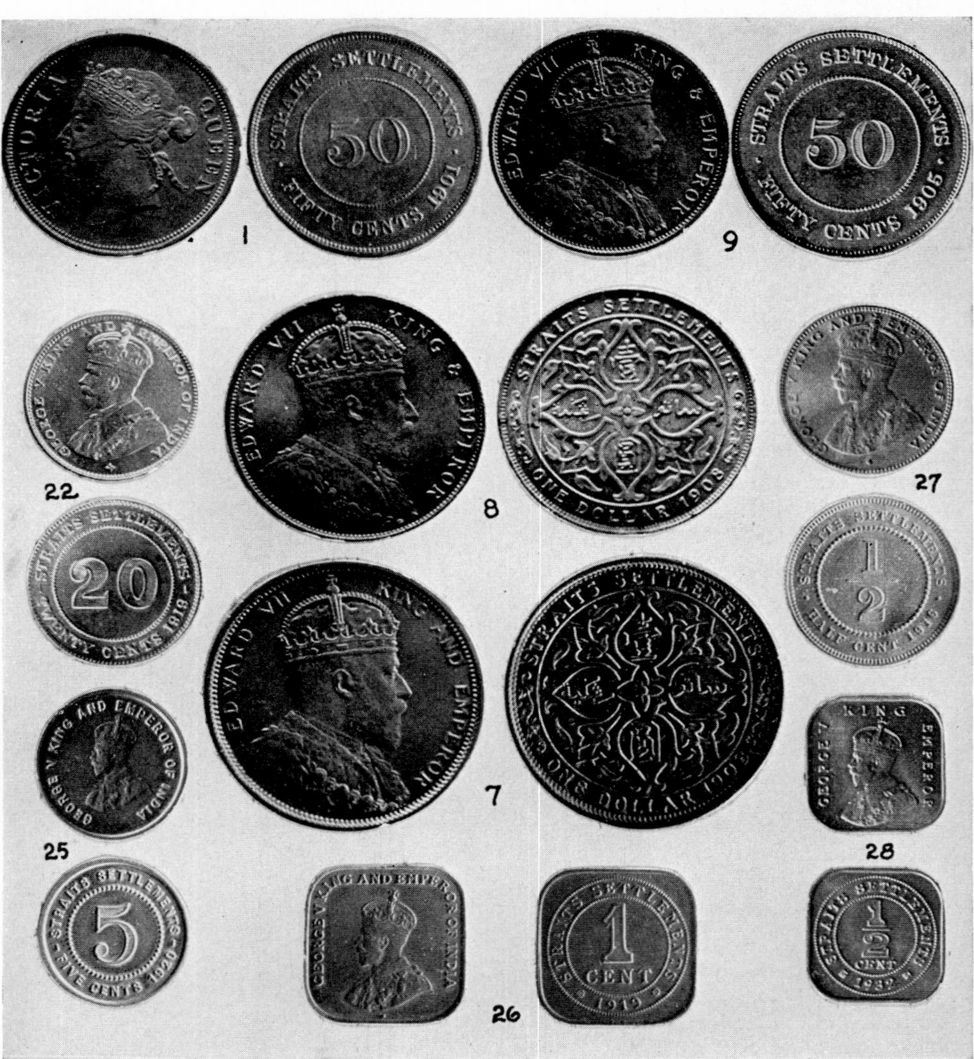

Victoria

SILVER

1 50 Cents. 1901. Head *l.* ℞ Value in circle 1.50

2 20 Cents. 1901. Similar 1.00

3 10 Cents. 1901. Similar .... .50

4 5 Cents. 1901. Similar .... .25

COPPER

5 1 Cent. 1901. Head *l.* ℞ Value in circle .... .35

6 ¼ Cent. 1901. Similar .... .25

Edward VII

SILVER

7 1 Dollar. 1903-04. Crowned bust *r.* ℞ Value in Chinese and Malay in ornamental panels........... 5.00

8 1 Dollar. 1907-09. Similar but size reduced 5.00

9 50 Cents. 1902 - 03, 1905 - 06. Crowned bust *r.* ℞ Value in circle 1.50

10 50 Cents. 1907-09. Similar but size reduced 1.00

11 20 Cents. 1902-10. Similar .... .60

12 10 Cents. 1902-10. Similar .... .35

13 5 Cents. 1902-03, 1910. Similar... .25

COPPER

14 1 Cent. 1902-05, 1907-09. Bust *r.* Value in circle .... .25

15 ½ Cent. 1908. Similar .... .15

16 ¼ Cent. 1902, 1905, 1908. Similar .... .15

George V

SILVER

17 1 Dollar. 1919 - 21, 1925 - 26. Crowned bust *l.* ℞ Value in Chinese and Malay in ornamental panels 25.00

18 50 Cents. 1920 - 21. Crowned bust *l.* ℞ Value in circle........... 1.50

19 20 Cents. 1911-38. Similar .... .75

20 10 Cents. 1911-28. Similar .... .50

21 5 Cents. 1911-38 .... .75

Fractional coins dated 1918-1920 have a small cross under bust indicating that coins are only 400 fine. The later coins are 600 fine.

COPPER-NICKEL

25 5 Cents. 1920-21, 1926. Bust *l.* ℞ Value in circle ....

COPPER

26 1 Cent. 1919-20, 1926. Square, round corners. Bust *l.* ℞ Value in double circle .... .15

27 ½ Cent. 1913, 1916. Round. Bust *l.* ℞ Value in circle............ .75

28 ½ Cent. 1932. Square, round corners. Similar. .... .15

29 ¼ Cent. 1916. Round. Similar...... .75

OSCAR II SVERIGES OCH NORGES KONUNG
2 KRONOR
4
OSCAR II SVERIGES KONUNG
2 KRONOR
1907
5
KONUNG OSCAR II DROTTNING SOFIA
DEN 6 JUNI 1857-1907
6
400 ÅRSMINNE AV GUSTAF VASAS BEFRIELSEVERK
GUSTAF V SVERIGES KONUNG
19 21
23
GUSTAF V SVERIGES KONUNG
1924
22
MED FOLKET FÖR FOSTERLANDET
2 KR
24
1
SVERIGES VÄL
9
19
19 16
SVERIGE
27
19 20
30
20 KRONOR
50 ÖRE
1907
50 ÖRE
50 ÖRE
SVERIGES VÄL
16
5 ÖRE
20
KRONOR
5
MED FOLKET FÖR FOSTERLANDET
19 18
33
5
FEM ÖRE

S W E D E N

SWEDEN
(Sverige)

Occupies the eastern and largest part of the Scandinavian peninsula in northwest Europe.
Mint: Stockholm.
100 Ore = 1 Krona.

Oscar II—1872-1907

GOLD

No.	Description	Price
1	20 Kronor 1901, 1902. Head *r.* ℞ Crowned arms	25.00
2	10 Kronor 1901. Similar	12.50
3	5 Kronor 1901. Head *r.* ℞ Value in wreath	6.50

SILVER

No.	Description	Price
4	2 Kronor 1903, 1904. Head *l.* ℞ Arms with supporters	1.25
5	2 Kronor 1906, 1907. Older head with pointed beard	1.25
6	2 Kronor 1907. Golden wedding of Oscar II and Sofia	1.50
7	1 Krona 1901, 1903, 1904. Type of No. 4	.75
8	1 Krona 1906, 1907. Type of No. 5	.75
9	50 Ore 1906, 1907. Crowned cypher. ℞ Value	.35
10	25 Ore 1902, 1904, 1905, 1907. Similar	.25
11	10 Ore 1902-1904. BRODRAFOLKENS VAL.	.15
12	10 Ore 1907. SVERIGES VAL.	.15

BRONZE

No.	Description	Price
13	5 Ore 1901-1905. Similar. BRODRAFOLKENS VAL.	.15
14	5 Ore 1906, 1907. SVERIGES VAL.	.15
15	2 Ore 1901, 1902, 1904, 1905. Type of No. 13	.10
16	2 Ore 1906, 1907. Type of No. 14	.10
17	1 Ore 1901-1905. Type of No. 13	.10
18	1 Ore 1906, 1907. Type of No. 14	.10

Gustavus V—1907-50

GOLD

No.	Description	Price
19	20 Kronor 1925. Head *r.* ℞ Crowned Arms	30.00
20	5 Kronor 1920. Head *r.* ℞ Value	7.50

SILVER

No.	Description	Price
21	5 Kronor 1935. Head *l.* ℞ Arms. Com. Fifth centennial of the Riksdag.	6.00
22	2 Kronor 1910-39. Head *l.* ℞ Arms	1.25
23	2 Kronor 1921. Head of Gustaf Vasa *r.* ℞ Arms. Com. Fourth centennial of political liberty.	2.50
24	2 Kronor 1932. Bust of Gustaf II Adolf *r.* ℞ Inscription on panel. Third centennial of his death.	2.50

No.	Description	Price
25	2 Kronor 1938. Head *l.* ℞ Ship. Com. Third centennial of Swedish settlement in Delaware.	2.00
26	1 Krona 1910-39. Type of No. 22	.50
27	50 Ore 1911-39. Crowned arms. ℞ Value	.30
28	25 Ore 1910-38. Similar	.20
29	10 Ore 1911-36. Similar	.15

NICKEL BRONZE

Type—Crowned G5. ℞ Value.

No.	Description	Price
30	50 Ore 1920, 21, 24, 40, 46, 47	.35
31	25 Ore 1921, 40, 41, 46, 47	.25
32	10 Ore 1920-25, 40, 41, 46, 47	.15

BRONZE

Type—Crowned cypher. ℞ Value and three crowns.

33	5 Ore 1909-42, 50	.15
34	2 Ore 1909-42, 50	.10
35	1 Ore 1909-42, 50	.10

IRON

Type of bronze coins.

World War I Issue

36	5 Ore 1917-19	.25
37	2 Ore 1917-19	.20
38	1 Ore 1917-19	.15

New Coinage

SILVER

39	2 Kronor 1940-50. Older head	1.25
40	1 Krona 1940-50. Similar	.50
41	50 Ore 1943-50. Crown. ℞ Value	.35
42	25 Ore 1939-50. Similar	.25
43	10 Ore 1937-50. Similar	.15

IRON

World War II Issue
Type of bronze coins

44	5 Ore 1942-50	.15
45	2 Ore 1942-50	.10
46	1 Ore 1942-50	.10

SWITZERLAND

(Schweiz—Suisse—Svizzera)

Between France, Italy and Germany in central Europe. Republic.

Mint: Berne.

100 Centimes or Rappens = 1 Franc.

GOLD

1 100 Francs 1925. Peasant girl head *l.* ℞ Value and radiant cross above Edelweiss spray. Rare (5000 struck) 125.00

2 20 Francs 1901-16, 1922, 1925-27, 1930, 1935. Similar. ℞ Shield and value 15.00

3 10 Francs 1911-16, 1922. Similar. ℞ Similar to the 100 Francs........ 7.50

4 100 Francs 1934. Fribourg Shooting Piece. Type of 5 Francs...... 75.00

5a 100 Francs 1939. Lucerne Shooting Festival 50.00

SILVER

5 5 Francs 1904, 1907-08, 1916. Female head *l.* ℞ Shield in wreath 2.00

6 2 Francs 1901-48. Standing female *l.* ℞ Value in wreath........ 1.00

7 1 Franc 1901-45. Similar .... .50

8 ½ Franc 1901-48. Similar .... .25

9 5 Francs 1922-23. Male bust to *r.* ℞ Shield. Sprays at sides. Val. at top. 5 Fr. 2.00

10 5 Francs 1924-26, 1928. Similar but 5 FR. 2.00

11 5 Francs 1931-49. Size reduced........ 1.50

12 5 Francs 1934. (Fribourg Shooting piece.) Standing soldier. ℞ Crowned arms 4.00

13 5 Francs 1936. (Premium for the armament fund.) Kneeling figure to *r.* ℞ Inscription in square 2.50

14 5 Francs 1939. Lucerne Shooting Festival 4.00

15 5 Francs 1939. Zurich Exposition 2.50

15a 5 Francs 1939. Laupen Commemorative 4.50

15b 5 Francs 1941. 650 Years of Confederation 2.50

15c 5 Francs 1944. Fifth Centennial Battle of St. Jakob an der Birs... 2.50

15d 5 Francs 1948. Centennial of Swiss Confederation 2.50

COPPER-NICKEL

16 20 Centimes 1901-36, 39-45. Female head to *r.* ℞ Value in wreath .... .20

17 10 Centimes 1901-32, 39-49 Similar .... .15

18 5 Centimes 1901-32, 39-49 Similar .... .10

NICKEL

19 10 Centimes 1933-37 .... .15

20 5 Centimes 1933-37 .... .10

BRASS

21 10 Centimes 1918-19. Same .... .10

22 5 Centimes 1918. Same .... .10

BRONZE-ZINC

23 2 Centimes, bronze 1902-41. Shield. (a) zinc 1942-44 .... .10

24 1 Centime, bronze 1902-41. Shield. (a) zinc 1942-45 .... .10

25 2 Centimes, bronze 1948. Cross .10

26 1 Centime, bronze 1948,49. Cross .10

SYRIA
(Suriya)

In the Mediterranean Sea in western Asia. A former province of the old Turkish Empire. A republic under French influence from 1920 to 1943. Now an independent republic.

Mints: Paris, Birmingham

100 Piastres = 1 Lira

SILVER

1	50 Piastres 1929-37	1.25
2	25 Piastres 1929-38	.50
3	10 Piastres 1929	.35

ALUMINUM BRONZE

4	5 Piastres 1926-41	.35
5	2 Piastres 1926	.25

VARIOUS METALS

6	1 Piastre 1929-37, nickel-br. 1940 zinc	.20
7	½ Piastre 1935,36, nickel-br.	.15
8	½ Piastre 1921,22 nickel-br. Bank of Syria	.20
9	2½ Piastres 1940 aluminum bronze	.25

The 1 and 2½ piastres have center holes

Local Provisional Coinage
World War II

P1	2½ Piastres. Aluminum	
P2	1 Piastre. Aluminum	
P3	½ Piastre. Aluminum	

New Republican Coinage
SILVER

11	1 Lira 1950	
12	50 Piastres 1947	
13	25 Piastres 1947	

COPPER-NICKEL

14	10 Piastres 1948	

15 5 Piastres 1948 ....

16 2½ Piastres 1948 ....

GOLD

17 1 Pound 1950 ....

18 ½ Pound 1950 ....

TARIM

(Southern Arabia)

Mint: Birmingham.

SILVER

1 1/6 Straits Dollar 1898-1924. Arabic inscription in circle and wreath. ℞ 24 in Arabic in circle and wreath 7.50

2 1/12 Straits Dollar. Similar but 12 on reverse 6.00

3 1/24 Straits Dollar. Similar but 6 on reverse 5.00

These pieces all bear the Arabic date 1315 or 1897 of our era, and were struck in 1898, 1900, 1902, 1904 and 1924 at Birmingham for the firm of Alkaff & Co. of Singapore which had them made for use of their Tarim Kinsmen in the Hadhramaut. The figures on the reverse probably represent the values in Chomsihs or cents. In 1926 and 1927 similar silver pieces were made at Birmingham, dated in Arabic 1344 (1925 A.D.) but bearing the following denominations in Arabic: 60, 45, 30, 20, 15, 10, 8, 5 and 4 (Chomsihs).

4
5
7
8
11
12
13
14
15
16
17
18

TIBET

In Central Asia extending eastwards between the Himalaya and Kwen-lun Mountains to the borders of Chinghai and Sikong. A semi-independent state nominally under control of China.

Mint: Cheng-too.

Kuang Hsu 1875-1908

Coins struck in Szechuen province, China for use in Tibet

1 Rupee 1903 .... 3.00
2 ½ Rupee 1903 .... 15.00

3 ¼ Rupee 1903 .... 15.00

See also under China

Hsuan Tung 1909-1911

4 1 Srang. Year I (1908/9). Silver (4)
5 5 Sho 1908/9. Similar. Silver ......
6 1 Sho 1908/9. Similar. Silver ......
7 2 Sho. Without date. Silver ....
8 1 Sho. Similar. Silver (7) ....
9 1 Skar. Similar. Copper ....

It has been determined that No. 8 on the plate is a pattern.

Tibetan Type

10 1 Srang 1909. Silver (5) ....
11 7½ Skar 1909. Copper ....
12 2½ Skar 1909. Copper ....

Transitional Silver Coins (Undated)

No. 13 type coined 1750 to 1950.
No. 14, 15 Coined 1908 to 1912.

13 1 Tangka ....

14 1 Tangka ....

15 5 Sho ....

Autonomous Coins

Types Struck 1913 to 1918

16 5 Sho. Silver (11) ....
17 5 Skar. Copper (14) ....
18 2½ Skar. Copper (15) ....

The numbers in brackets refer to numbers on plate.

Types coined 1918 to 1922

19 20 Srang 1918-20. Gold ....
20 1 Sho. Copper (16) ....
21 7½ Skar. Copper (17) ....
22 5 Skar. Copper (18) ....

Types coined 1923 to 1928

20a 1 Sho. Copper ....
20b 1 Sho. Copper ....
Both of preceding, varieties of No. 20

Types coined 1932 to 1938

23 3 Srang 1933, 34. Silver (12) ......
24 3 Srang 1935-38. Silver (13) ......
25 1½ Srang 1936-38. Silver ....

26 1 Sho 1932-38. Copper ....

Types coined 1946-1948

27 10 Srang 1948, 49. Silver ....

28 5 Sho. Copper ....

29 3 Sho. Copper ....

The numbers in brackets refer to numbers on plate.

TIMOR

Portuguese Timor consists of the eastern portion of the island of Timor in the Malay Archipelago.
Mint—Lisbon. 100 Avos = 1 Pataca.

New State 1926

SILVER

1 50 Avos 1945, 48. Arms on cross. 1.00

NICKEL-BRONZE

2 20 Avos 1945. Republic bust. 2.00

BRONZE

3 10 Avos 1945,48. Quinas cross. .. 1.00

TOGO

On the Gulf of Guinea in western Africa. French Mandate.
Mints: Paris, Vincennes 100 Centimes = 1 Franc

ALUMINUM BRONZE

1 2 Francs 1924,25 .... 2.00
2 1 Franc 1924,25 .... 1.50
3 50 Centimes 1924-26 .... 1.00

ALUMINUM

4 2 Francs 1948 ....
5 1 Franc 1948 ....

TONKIN

A state of French Indo-China. French Protectorate.

ZINC

1 1/600 Piastre 1905. Square hole. French and Chinese inscriptions .35

See Indo-China.

TUNIS
(Afrikiya—Tunisie)

On the Mediterranean Sea in northern Africa. French Protectorate.

Mints: Paris, Castelsarrazin, Beaumont-le-Roger

100 Centimes = 1 Franc

First Issue

GOLD

1 20 Francs. 1901-04 .... 15.00
Struck in specimen sets 1901-28

2 10 Francs. Very rare ....
Struck only in specimen sets 1901-28

SILVER

3 2 Francs 1901-28 .... 1.00

4 1 Franc 1901-28 50
5 50 Centimes 1901-28 .... .35

Some dates struck only in specimen sets

BRONZE

6 10 Centimes 1903-17 .... .35
7 5 Centimes 1903-17 .... .25

New Standard

GOLD

8 100 Francs 1930,32,34 .... 60.00

SILVER

9 20 Francs 1930,32,34 .... 15.00

10 10 Francs 1930,32,34 .... 7.50

11 20 Francs 1935 .... 2.00
12 10 Francs 1935 .... 1.00
13 5 Francs 1935,36 .... .50

14 20 Francs 1939 .... 7.50
15 10 Francs 1939 .... 3.00
16 5 Francs 1939 .... 2.00

ALUMINUM BRONZE

Jeton Currency

17 2 Francs 1921-46 .... .25
18 1 Franc 1921-46 .... .20
19 50 Centimes 1921-46 .... .15

NICKEL-BRONZE

Holed Centers

20 25 Centimes 1919-38 .... .20

21 10 Centimes 1918-38 .... .15
22 5 Centimes 1918-38 .... .10

The size was slightly reduced in 1920. Both sizes in that year.

Modern Coinage

ALUMINUM BRONZE

Type of No. 14

23 5 Francs 1946 .... .75

ZINC

24 20 Centimes 1942-46 .... .20
25 10 Centimes 1941-46 .... .15

COPPER-NICKEL

26 20 Francs 1950 ....

TURKEY

(Turkiye Cumhuriyeti)

Between the Mediterranean and Black Seas in southeastern Europe and Western Asia.

Mints: Constantinople (Istanbul), Ankara.

40 Paras = 1 Piastre. 100 Piastres = 1 Lira or Pound.

The Turkish coins are dated in the same way as those of Egypt.

Abd-ul-Hamid II—1876-1909
Accession date A.H. 1293

GOLD

1 500 Piastres 1901-1909. Toughra above crossed branches. ℞ Inscription in wreath 100.00

2 250 Piastres 1901-1909. Similar...... 50.00

3 100 Piastres 1901-1909. Similar...... 20.00

4 50 Piastres 1901-1909. Similar...... 10.00

5 25 Piastres 1901-1909. Similar...... 5.00

6 500 Piastres "Monnaie de luxe." Trophy of arms, ornamental border. ℞ Inscription in wreath. Broad flan 100.00

7 250 Piastres. Similar 50.00

The last two were specially struck for presentation in the harems and are often mounted.

SILVER

8 20 Piastres 1906-1908. Toughra within ring of stars and crescents 2.50

8a 10 Piastres 1906-1909. Similar...... 1.25

9 5 Piastres 1901-1909. Similar...... .50

10 2 Piastres 1901-1909. Similar...... .25

11 1 Piastre 1901-1909. Similar...... .20

BILLON OR COPPER

12 10 Paras 1901-05. Similar .... .15

13 5 Paras 1901-05. Similar .... .10

Mohammed V—1909-1918
Accession date A.H. 1327

GOLD

16 500 Piastres 1910-1913. Type of preceding issue 100.00

17 250 Piastres 1910-1913. Similar...... 40.00

18 100 Piastres 1910-1913. Similar...... 15.00

19 50 Piastres 1910-1913. Similar........ 7.50

20 25 Piastres 1910-1913. Similar........ 3.50

21 12½ Piastres 1911, 1913. Similar 2.00

During 1910 and 1911 all of the gold coins were struck with the names of the cities visited by the Sultan — Kossova, Monastir, Brousse, Adrianople, Salonica. Some of them are quite rare. The "monnaies de luxe" were also struck during this reign.

SILVER

22 20 Piastres 1918. Border of stars and crescents ....

23 10 Piastres 1910, 1911, 1913. Similar 1.00

24 5 Piastres 1910, 1911, 1913. Similar .... .50

25 2 Piastres 1910, 1911, 1913, 1918. Similar .... .35

26 1 Piastre 1910, 1911. Similar..... .25

NICKEL

27 40 Paras 1909, 1911 - 1913. Toughra in circle. ℞ Value in circular wreath .... .25

28 20 Paras 1909-1916. Similar.......... .20

29 10 Paras 1909-1916. Similar.......... .15

30 5 Paras 1909-1911, 1916. Similar .10

Mohammed VI—1918-1921

Accession date A.H. 1336

GOLD

31 500 Piastres 1919-1921. Similar to previous type 100.00

32 250 Piastres 1919-1921. Similar... 35.00

33 100 Piastres 1919-1921. Similar... 15.00

34 50 Piastres 1919-1921. Similar... 7.50

35 25 Piastres 1919-1921. Similar... 3.50
The "monnaies de luxe" were also struck during this reign.

SILVER

Mint records show that a few 2, 5 and 10 piastre pieces were coined in 1919.

COPPER-NICKEL

36 40 Paras 1921, 1922. Type of preceding issue .... .25

Republic 1923-

GOLD

37 500 Piastres 1926-1929. Star above crescent, Turkish date. ℞ Inscription in wreath, Christian date 125.00

38 250 Piastres 1927-1928. Similar... 50.00

39 100 Piastres 1926-1928. Similar... 20.00
40 50 Piastres 1927-1928. Similar... 8.50
41 25 Piastres 1925-1929. Similar... 5.00
42 500 Piastres "monnaie de luxe." 1928 Inscription in wreath, star, crescent and sunburst above. ℞ Ornamental wreath, Christian date ... 80.00
43 250 Piastres 1928. Similar ... 35.00
44 100 Piastres 1928. Similar ... 12.50
45 50 Piastres 1928. Similar ... 7.50
46 25 Piastres 1928. Similar ... 3.50

The last set struck at Ankara.

MINOR COINS

Type: Wheat spray. ℞ Value and oak spray.

50 25 Piastres. Nickel 1925, 26 ... .50
50a 25 Piastres. Copper-Nickel 1927, 28 ... .35
54 10 Piastres. Aluminum Bronze 1924-26 ... .25
55 5 Piastres. Aluminum Bronze 1924-26 ... .20
56 2 Piastres (100 paras). Aluminum Bronze 1926, 27 ... .15

Law of June 7, 1933

(All coins with Gregorian dates)

100 Kurus = 1 Lira

SILVER

57 100 Kurus 1934. Head of Kemal Ataturk. ℞ Value ... 2.50

Type—New head of Ataturk. ℞ Value.

58 1 Lira 1935-37 ... 2.00
59 50 Kurus 1935-37 ... 1.00
60 25 Kurus 1935-37 ... .75

61 1 Lira 1940-41. Head of Ismet Inonu ... 2.00

MINOR COINS

Type: Crescent and star. ℞ Value.

51 10 Kurus. Copper-Nickel 1935-40 .35
63 5 Kurus. Copper-Nickel 1935-40 .25
64 1 Kurus. Copper-Nickel 1935-37 .15

65 1 Kurus. Copper-Nickel 1938-42 Scalloped edge ... .15
66 10 Paras. Aluminum Bronze 1940, 42 ... .15

Post War Coinage

SILVER

67 1 Lira 1947, 48 ...
68 50 Kurus 1947-49 ...

BRASS

69 25 Kurus 1948, 49 ...
70 10 Kurus 1949 ...
71 5 Kurus 1949 ...
72 2½ Kurus 1948, 49 ...
73 1 Kurus 1947-49 ...

UNITED STATES OF AMERICA

Mints: Philadelphia, Denver (D), New Orleans (O), Closed in 1909; San Francisco (S).

100 Cents = 1 Dollar.

GOLD

1 20 Dollars. 1901-1907. .... 60.00

2 10 Dollars. 1901-1907 .... 30.00

3 5 Dollars. 1901-1908 .... 15.00

4 2½ Dollars. 1901-1907. Similar. Philadelphia mint only 10.00

5 20 Dollars. 1907. Date MCMVII. Standing Liberty. ℞ Eagle. High relief 125.00

6 20 Dollars. 1907, 1908. Arabic date. Lower relief 60.00

7 20 Dollars. 1908-1916, 1920-1933. Motto added on reverse 60.00

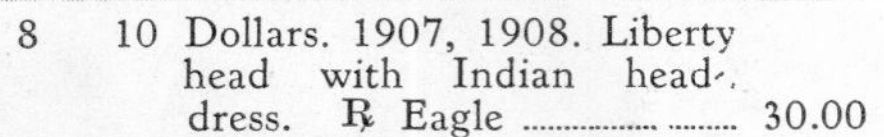

8 10 Dollars. 1907, 1908. Liberty head with Indian headdress. ℞ Eagle 30.00

9 10 Dollars. 1908-1916, 1920, 1926, 1930, 1932, 1933. With motto added on reverse 30.00

10 5 Dollars. 1908-1916, 1929. Indian head. ℞ Eagle........ 15.00

11 2½ Dollars. 1908-1915, 1926-1929. Similar 7.50

COMMEMORATIVE GOLD COINS

12 1903 Dollar. Louisiana Purchase Exposition. Bust of Jefferson 15.00

13 1903 Same. Bust of McKinley...... 15.00

14 1904 Dollar. Lewis & Clark Exposition 60.00

15 1905 Dollar. Same type 60.00

16 1915 Dollar. Pan. Pacific Exposition 10.00

17 1915 Quarter Eagle (2½ Dol.) Pan. Pacific 60.00

18 1916 Dollar. McKinley Memorial 15.00

19 1917 Dollar. Same type 17.50

20 1922 Dollars. Grant Memorial...... 30.00

21 1922 Dollar. Same with star.......... 25.00

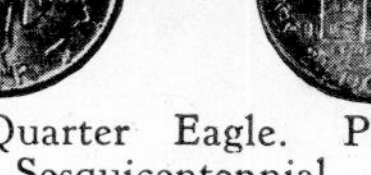

22 1926 Quarter Eagle. Philadelphia Sesquicentennial 15.00

PANAMA PACIFIC EXPOSITION FIFTY DOLLAR PIECES

23 1915 Round planchet 650.00

24 1915 Octagonal planchet 550.00

SILVER

25 Dollar. 1901-1904. 1921 .... 2.50

26 Half Dollar. 1901-1915 .... 4.00

27 Quarter Dollar. 1901-1916 .... 3.00

28 Dime. 1901-1916 .... 2.00

29 Dollar. 1921-1928, 1934, 35 .... 2.00

30 Half Dollar. 1916-1921, 1934-47 1.25

31 Quarter Dollar 1916, 1917. (1916 is rare) 2.50

32 Quarter Dollar. 1917-1921, 1923-1930 modified type, stars below eagle 1.50

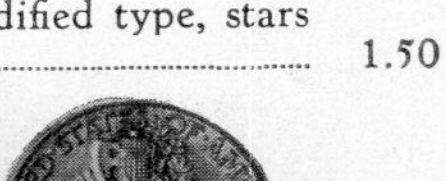

33 Dime. 1916-21, 23-31, 34-45 .... .25

34 Half Dollar. 1948-50 ....

35 Quarter Dollar. 1932-50. Washington head ....

36 Dime. 1946-50. Roosevelt head

COPPER-NICKEL

41 5 Cents. 1901-1912 .... 1.00

42 5 Cents. 1913-38 .... .35

43 5 Cents. 1938-50 Jefferson head. ℞ Monticello ....

The coinage from 1942 to 1945 with a large mint mark over Monticello has a silver composition.

BRONZE

45 Cent. 1901-1909. Indian head .... .35

46 Cent 1909-50. Lincoln head ....

The coins dated 1943 were struck on steel planchets with a zinc coating.

COMMEMORATIVE HALF DOLLARS

There are numerous date and mint varieties. Values quoted are for the commonest variety in mint condition.

51 1915 Panama - Pacific Exposition 20.00

55 1921 Missouri Centennial 30.00

52 1918 Illinois Centennial. Lincoln head 3.50

56 1921 Alabama Centennial 12.50

53 1920 Maine Centennial 6.00

57 1922 Grant Memorial 3.50

54 1920, 21 Pilgrim Tercentenary 2.50

58 1923 Monroe Doctrine Centennial 3.50

59 1924 Huguenot-Walloon Tercentenary 4.50

63 1925 Fort Vancouver Centennial 17.50

60 1925 Lexington-Concord Sesquicentennial 3.50

64 1926 Philadelphia Sesquicentennial 3.50

61 1925 Stone Mountain Memorial 1.50

65 1926-39 Oregon Trail Memorial... 2.50

62 1925 California Diamond Jubilee 6.00

66 1927 150th Anniversary of Battle of Bennington 7.50

67 1928 150th Anniversary of Discovery of Hawaii 32.50

68 1934 Maryland Tercentenary 4.00

69 1934-38 Texas Centennial 2.00

70 1934-38 Daniel Boone Bicentennial 2.50

71 1935 Connecticut Tercentenary 8.50

72 1935-39 Arkansas Centennial 3.00

73 1935 Hudson, N. Y., Sesquicentennial 15.00

74 1935, 36 California-Pacific Exposition 2.50

75 1935 Old Spanish Trail 1535-1935 .... 15.00

76 1936 Rhode Island Tercentenary 3.50

77 1936 Great Lakes Exposition 2.00

78 1936 Wisconsin Centennial 3.00

79 1936 Cincinnati Musical Center 10.00

80 1936 Long Island Tercentenary... 2.50

81 1936 York County, Me. Centennial 3.00

82 1936 Bridgeport, Ct. Centennial 3.00

83 1936 Lynchburg, Va. 150th Anniversary 4.00

87 1936 Columbia, S. C. 150th Anniversary 4.50

84 1936 Elgin, Ill. Centennial 3.50

88 1936 Arkansas. Jos. T. Robinson head 2.50

85 1936 Albany, N. Y. 250th Anniversary 6.00

89 1937 Roanoke, N. C. 305th Anniversary 4.00

86 1936 San Francisco-Oakland Bridge 4.50

90 1936 Delaware Tercentenary 4.00

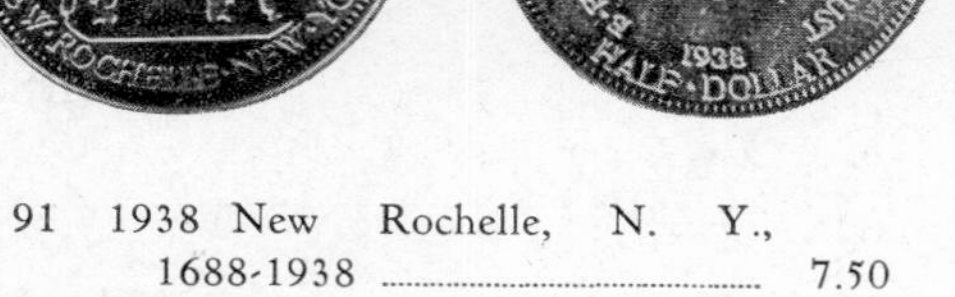

91 1938 New Rochelle, N. Y., 1688-1938 .... 7.50

94 1937 Battle of Antietam 1862-1937 .... 12.50

92 1936 Battle of Gettysburg. 1863-1938 .... 6.00

95 1946 Iowa State Centennial 5.00

93 1936 Norfolk, Va. Bicentennial...... 6.00

96 1946-50 Booker T. Washington Memorial 1.50

URUGUAY

(Republica Oriental del Uruguay)

In South America between Argentina and Brazil on the Atlantic Ocean.

Mints. Paris, Buenos Aires, Santiago, Berlin, Vienna, Société Francaise de Monnayage, Paris.

100 Centesimos = 1 Peso.

GOLD

1 5 Pesos 1930. Head of Artigàs *r.* ℞ Value in laurel and sun rays. Centenario 35.00

SILVER

2 Peso 1917. Bust of Artigas 6.00
3 50 Centesimos 1916, 17. Similar...... 1.50
4 20 Centesimos 1920. Similar 1.00
5 20 Centesimos 1930. Centenario... .75

ALUMINUM-BRONZE

Type—Liberty head. ℞ Jaguar.

6 10 Centesimos 1930. Centenario... .50
6a 10 Centesimos 1936. Reduced size .25

COPPER-NICKEL

Type—Sun. ℞ Value.

7 5 Centesimos 1901-41 .... .20
8 2 Centesimos 1901-41 .... .15
9 1 Centesimo 1901-36 .... .10

NEW SILVER COINAGE

10 1 Peso 1942-44. Head of Artigas 3.00
11 50 Centesimos 1943, 44. Artigas...... 1.50

12 20 Centesimos 1942. Liberty head .50

BRONZE

Type of copper-nickel.

13 5 Centesimos 1944-49 .... .15
14 2 Centesimos 1943-49 .... .10

VATICAN CITY

(Citta del Vaticana)

In western Italy, directly outside the western boundary of Rome.
Mint: Rome. 100 Centesimi = 1 Lira.

Pope Pius XI

GOLD

1 100 Lire 1929-1934. Bust *r.* ℞ Standing figure of Christ 25.00

2 100 Lire 1933. (Holy Year Jubilee issue). Similar but dated 1933-1934 .... 25.00

2a 100 Lire 1936, 37. Reduced size. Weight 5.15 gr. 20.00

SILVER

3 10 Lire 1929-37 Bust *l.* ℞ Seated Madonna 1.50

4 10 Lire 1933. (Jubilee issue). Similar but 1933-1934 .... 1.50

5 5 Lire 1929-37. Bust *l.* ℞ St. Peter in boat .... .75

6 5 Lire 1933. (Jubilee issue). Similar but 1933-1934 .... .75

NICKEL

7 2 Lire 1929-37. ℞ Good shepherd with lamb .... .50

8 2 Lire 1933. (Jubilee issue). Similar, 1933-1934 .... .50

9 1 Lira 1929-37. Arms. ℞ Virgin standing .... .35

10 1 Lira 1933 (Jubilee issue). Similar. 1933-1934 .... .35

11 50 Centesimi 1929-37. Arms. ℞ Archangel Michael .... .30

12 50 Centesimi 1933. (Jubilee issue). Similar. 1933-1934 .30

13 20 Centesimi 1929-37. ℞ Bust of St. Paul *l.* .25

14 20 Centesimi 1933 (Jubilee issue). Similar. 1933-1934 .25

BRONZE

15 10 Centesimi 1929-37. Arms. ℞ Bust of St. Peter *r.* .25

16 10 Centesimi 1933. (Jubilee issue). Similar, 1933-1934 .25

17 5 Centesimi 1929-37. Arms. ℞ Olive spray .15

18 5 Centesimi 1933. (Jubilee issue). Similar. 1933-1934 .15

Sede Vacante

SILVER

Type—Arms of Cardinal Pacelli. ℞ Dove.

19 10 Lire 1939 2.00

20 5 Lire 1939 1.25

Pope Pius XII

Type of preceding coinage of Pius XI.

GOLD

21 100 Lire 1939-41 20.00

SILVER

22 10 Lire 1939-41 1.50

23 5 Lire 1939-41 .75

NICKEL

24 2 Lire 1939 .50

25 1 Lire 1939 .35

26 50 Centesimi 1939 .25

27 20 Centesimi 1939 .20

BRONZE

28 10 Centesimi 1939 .15

29 5 Centesimi 1939 .10

ACMONITAL
(Stainless steel)

30 2 Lire 1940, 41 .75

31 1 Lire 1940, 41 .50

32 50 Centesimi 1940, 41 .35

33 20 Centesimi 1940, 41 .25

BRASS

34 10 Centesimi 1940, 41 .15

35 5 Centesimi 1940, 41 .10

New Types 1942-46

Same metals as preceding issue

35a 100 Lire 1942-49 15.00

36 10 Lire. Bust *l.* ℞ Caritas 1.50

37	5 Lire. Similar	75
38	2 Lire. Arms. ℞ Justice	.50
39	1 Lira. Similar	.35
40	50 Centesimi. Similar	.25
41	20 Centesimi. Similar	.20
42	10 Centesimi. Bust *l.* ℞ Dove	.15
43	5 Centesimi. Similar	.10

Types adopted in 1947
ALUMINUM

44 10 Lire 1947-49. Caritas ....

45 5 Lire 1947-49. Caritas ....

46 2 Lire 1947-49. Justice ....

47 1 Lira 1947-49. Justice ....

Holy Year Issue
GOLD

48 100 Lire 1950. Pope opening Holy Door ....

ALUMINUM

49 10 Lire 1950. Gate of Heaven ......

50 5 Lire 1950. Similar ....

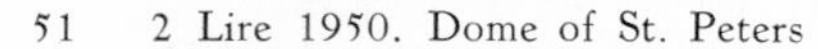

51 2 Lire 1950. Dome of St. Peters

52 1 Lira 1950. Holy Door ....

VENEZUELA

(Estados Unidos de Venezuela)

On the Caribbean Sea on the north coast of South America. Republic.

Mints: Paris, Philadelphia, Denver

100 Centimos = 1 Bolivar.

All of the gold and silver coins of this country have the head of Bolivar on obverse and the arms on reverse. The head is to *r.* on gold and to *l.* on silver.

8 9 3

GOLD

1	20 Bolivares 1901-1905, 1910-1912	15.00
2	10 Bolivares 1930.	10.00

SILVER

3	5 Bolivares 1901-37	2.50
4	2 Bolivares 1903-47	1.25
5	1 Bolivar 1901-47	.75
6	½ Bolivar (50 Centimos) 1901-47	.35
7	¼ Bolivar (25 Centimos) 1901-49	.25

MINOR COINS

Type: Shield of Arms. ℞ Value in wreath.

8	12½ Centimos. Copper-Nickel 1925-38	.25
9	5 Centimos. Copper-Nickel 1915-38	.10

Type: Different shield.

10	12½ Centimos. Brass 1944-45; (a) Copper-Nickel 1947, 49	.25
11	5 Centimos. Brass 1944-45; (a) Copper-Nickel 1947, 49	.10

YEMEN

In Arabia on the Red Sea north of the British Protectorate of Aden.

Mint: Sana'a.

40 Bogaches or 20 Guerches = 1 Imadi.

2 Halala = 1 Bogach.

Iman Yahya ibn Mohammad—

A.H. 1322-1367

SILVER

1 1 Imadi 1342 A.H. = 1924. Arabic inscription in circle, crescent and at bottom. ℞ Inscription in circle 10.00

2 ¼ Imadi 1341 A.H. = 1923. Similar 2.50

3 4 Bogaches (1/10 Imadi) 1339-49 A.H. (1921-1931). Similar 2.00

4 2 Bogaches (1/20 Imadi) 1337-51 A.H. (1918-1932). Similar 1.50

5 ¼ Imadi 1352 A.H. = 1933. Similar. ℞ Inscription in circle and four lobes 1.50

6 4 Bogaches 1352 A.H. Similar 1.25

7 2 Bogaches 1352 A.H. Similar 1.25

COPPER

8 1 Bogach 1341 A.H. = 1923. Similar 2.00

9 1 Halala. Similar 1.50

10 ½ Halala. Similar 1.50

Dates to 1366 A.H. have been noted on coins No. 5 to 10.

Ahmad Hamid al-Din 1948-

Types similar to preceding reign.

SILVER

11 1 Ryal (Imadi) A.H. 1367 (1948)

12 ½ Imadi 1949 ....

13 ¼ Imadi 1948 ....

14 ⅛ Imadi 1949 ....

15 1/16 Imadi 1949 ....

BRONZE

16 1 Bogach 1949 ....

YUGOSLAVIA

(Kraljevina Jugoslavja)

On the Adriatic Sea in southern Europe. Kingdom of the Serbs, Croats, and Slovenes.

Changed in 1945 to a Democratic Federative State.

Mints: Belgrade, London, Paris, Philadelphia, Vienna.

100 Paras = 1 Dinar.

Alexander I—1921-34

GOLD

1 20 Dinars 1925. Head *l.* ℞ Value in wreath 25.00

2 4 Ducats 1931-32. Conjoined busts of king and queen *l.* ℞ Crowned Eagle 75.00

3 1 Ducat 1926, 1931. Head of Alexander *l.* ℞ Eagle 15.00

SILVER

4 50 Dinars 1932, 1933. Head *l.* ℞ Eagle 5.00

5 20 Dinars 1931-1933. Similar 1.50

6 10 Dinars 1931, 1932. Similar 1.00

NICKEL BRONZE

7 2 Dinars 1925. Head *l.* ℞ Value in wreath .... .35

8 1 Dinar 1925, 1926. Similar .... .25

9 50 Para 1925, 1926. Similar .... .20

10 25 Para 1920. Arms. ℞ Value .... .20

ZINC

11 10 Para 1920, 21. Similar .... .15

12 5 Para 1920, 21. Similar .... .10

Peter II—1934-45

SILVER

13 50 Dinars 1938. Head *r.* ℞ Arms 3.00

14 20 Dinars 1938. Head *l.* ℞ Arms 1.50

NICKEL

15 10 Dinars 1938. Head *r.* ℞ Value .... .50

ALUMINUM-BRONZE

Type—Crown. ℞ Value.

16 2 Dinars 1938 .... .35
17 1 Dinar 1938 .... .25
18 50 Para 1938 .... .15

19 25 Para 1938 .... .15

Peoples Republic 1945

ZINC

20 5 Dinars 1945 ....
21 2 Dinars 1945 ....
22 1 Dinar 1945 ....
23 50 Para 1945 ....

World War II Coinages

Croatia

Created as an independent state in 1941 with the Duke of Aosta proclaimed as king

ZINC

2 Kune 1941 ....

Serbia

Republic under German occupation
Mint: Budapest (BP)

ZINC

10 Dinar 1943 ....
2 Dinar 1942 ....
1 Dinar 1942 ....

ZANZIBAR

An island 23 miles off the eastern coast of Africa. British Protectorate.

Mint: Birmingham.

100 Cents = 1 Rupee.

NICKEL

1 20 Cents 1908. Inscription. R
Palm tree 12.50

BRONZE

2 10 Cents 1908. Similar 7.50
3 1 Cent 1908. Similar 5.00

	0	1	2	3	4	5	6	7	8	9	10
ARABIC	٠	١	٢	٣	٤	٥	٦	٧	٨	٩	١٠
PERSIAN	۰	۱	۲	۳	۴	۵	۶	۷	۸	۹	۱۰
CHINESE	令	一	二	三	四	五	六	七	八	九	十
SIAMESE	๐	๑	๒	๓	๔	๕	๖	๗	๘	๙	๑๐
INDIAN	०	१	२	३	४	५	६	७	८	९	१०

This chart of numerals will enable the collector to determine the dates found on most coins of the world. Many countries using Arabic or Persian numerals give the year in the Mohammedan Era or Era of the Hegira (A.H.). This begins on the 16th of July A.D. 622, the day following the flight of Mohammed from Mecca to Medina. The years of the Hegira are lunar years of 354 days. The year 1357 A.H. is equivalent to 1938 A.D. The Hegira date is rectified by taking 3 per cent of it (41) subtracting it from 1357 and adding 622.

Example: 3% of 1357=40.71 or 41
1357— 41=1316
1316+622=1938 A.D.

In India several different eras are used. The Samvat of Vikramaditya begins B.C. 57. The Saka Era of Salivanhn begins A.D. 78. The respective issues bearing these dates are mentioned as they occur in the text.

Two eras may be found on the coins of Siam. The first is the Buddhist Era which begins B.C. 543. Thus a coin of 1917 A.D. might bear the Buddhist date (B.E.) 2460. Other coins are dated according to the founding of Bangkok in 1782. A coin of 1901 A.D. would bear the Siamese numerals (R.S.) 119.

Some coins of the Chinese Empire bear the year of issue and are dated according to their system of the sexagenary cycle. Such coins of the Republic that are dated begin with the first year or 1912 A.D. Chinese dates read from right to left.

LIST OF DENOMINATIONS

Afghani—Afghanistan.
Amani—Afghanistan.
Angolar—Angola.
Anna—Bahawalpur; Burma; Gwalior; Hyderabad; India; Indore; Jaipur; Jodhpur; Mewar; Sailana; Pakistan.
Ashrafi—Bahawalpur; Hyderabad.
Att—Siam.
Aurar—Iceland.
Avo—Timor.
Baizas—Muscat.
Balboa—Panama.
Bani—Roumania.
Bat—Siam.
Belga—Belgium.
Besa—Ethiopia; Italian Somaliland.
Bit—Danish West Indies.
Bogach—Yemen.
Bolivar—Venezuela.
Boliviano—Bolivia.
Candareen—China.
Cash—China; Chinese Turkestan; Pudukota; Travancore.
Cent — British Honduras; British North Borneo; Canada; Ceylon; China; Curacao; Danish West Indies; Dutch East Indies; East Africa; Ethiopia; Haiti; Hong Kong; Indo-China; Kiao (Chau); Liberia; Malaya; Mauritius; Netherlands; Newfoundland; Sarawak; Seychelles; Straits Settlements; U.S.A.; Zanzibar.
Centas—Lithuania.
Centavo—Angola; Argentina; Bolivia; Brazil; Chile; Cape Verde Islands; Colombia; Costa Rica; Cuba; Dominican Republic; Ecuador; Guatemala; Honduras; Mexico; Mozambique; Nicaragua; Paraguay; Peru; Philippine Islands; Portugal; Portuguese Guinea; St. Thomas & Prince Islands; Salvador.
Centesimi—Italy; San Marino; Somalia; Vatican City.
Centesimo—Panama; Uruguay.
Centime — Belgian Congo; Belgium; Cameroons; France; French Equat. Africa; French West Africa; Ghent; Guadeloupe; Indo-China; Luxemburg; Monaco; Morocco; Switzerland; Togo; Tunis.
Centimo—Costa Rica; Paraguay; Spain; Venezuela.
Chervonetz—Russia.
Chiao—China; Manchukuo.
Chon—Korea.
Chuckram—Travancore.
Colon—Costa Rica; Salvador.
Condor—Chile; Ecuador.
Cordoba—Nicaragua.
Corona—Austria.
Crown—Australia; Great Britain; New Zealand; South Africa.
Cruzeiro—Brazil.
Daler—Danish West Indies.
Dime—U.S.A.
Dinar—Hejaz; Persia; Serbia; Yugoslavia.
Dinero—Peru.
Dirhem—Iraq.
Dokda—Kutch; Junagadh.
Dollar—British Trade; Canada; China; Straits Settlements; U.S.A.
Dong—Indo-China.
Double—Guernsey.
Drachma—Crete; Greece.
Ducat—Austria; Czecho-Slovakia; Dutch East Indies; Yugoslavia.
Escudo—Cape Verde Islands; Mozambique; Portugal; Portuguese Guinea; St. Thomas and Prince Islands.
Eyrir—Iceland.
Fanam—Travancore.
Farthing—Great Britain; Irish Free State; Jamaica; Malta; South Africa.
Fen—China; Manchukuo.
Fenegow—Poland.
Filler—Hungary.
Fils—Iraq; Jordan.
Florin—Australia; East Africa; Fiji; Great Britain; Irish Free State; New Zealand; South Africa; Southern Rhodesia.
Forint—Hungary.
Franc — Algeria; Belgian Congo; Belgium; Cameroons; Danish West Indies; France; French Equatorial Africa; French Somaliland; French West Africa; Guadeloupe; Luxemburg; Madagascar; Martinique; Monaco; Morocco; Reunion Island; St. Pierre and Miquelin; Switzerland; Togo; Tunis.
Franka Ari—Albania.
Franken—Lichtenstein.
Fuang—Siam.
Fun—Korea.
Girsh—Hejaz; Saudi Arabia.
Gourde—Haiti.
Groschen—Austria.
Groszy—Poland.
Guerche—Egypt; Ethiopia; Yemen.
Guilder — Curacao; Dutch East Indies; Netherlands.
Gulden—Danzig; Netherlands.
Halala—Yemen.
Haler—Czecho-Slovakia.
Hao—Indo-China.
Heller—Austria; German East Africa.
Imadi—Yemen.
Kopec—Poland.
Kopeck—Russia.
Kori—Kutch.
Korona—Czecho-Slovakia; Hungary.

Kran—Persia.
Krona—Iceland; Sweden.
Krone—Austria; Denmark; Greenland; Lichtenstein; Norway.
Kroon—Estonia.
Kune—Croatia.
Kuru—Turkey.
Lari—Maldive Islands.
Lats—Latvia.
Lek—Albania.
Lempira—Honduras.
Lepta—Crete; Greece.
Leu (lei)—Roumania.
Leva—Bulgaria.
Li—Manchukuo.
Libra—Peru.
Lira—Turkey; Syria.
Lire—Italy; Italian Somaliland; San Marino; Vatican City.
Litas—Lithuania.
Mace—China; Chinese Turkestan.
Macuta—Angola.
Mark—Estonia; Germany.
Markka—Finland.
Matona—Ethiopia.
Maundy Money—Great Britain.
Mazuna—Morocco.
Mil—Israel; Palestine.
Millieme—Egypt.
Milreis—Angola; Brazil; Portugal.
Miscal—Chinese Turkestan.
Mohar—Nepal.
Mohur—Bikanir; India; Cooch Behar; Gwalior; Hyderabad; Rajkot.
Mung—Mongolia.
Ore—Denmark; Faroe Islands; Greenland; Norway; Sweden.
Pahlevi—Persia.
Pai—Hyderabad.
Paissa—Afghanistan; Bahawalpur; Bhutan; Rutlam.
Paissah—Nepal.
Para—Hejaz; Montenegro; Serbia; Turkey; Yugoslavia.
Pengo—Hungary.
Penni—Finland.
Penny, Pence — Australia; British Guiana; British West Africa; Fiji; Great Britain; Irish Free State; Jamaica; New Guinea; New Zealand; Nigeria; South Africa; Southern Rhodesia.
Perpera—Montenegro.
Peseta—Spain.
Peso—Argentina; Chile; Colombia; Cuba; Dominican Republic; Guatemala; Honduras; Mexico; Paraguay; Philippine Islands; Salvador; Uruguay.
Pfennig—Danzig; Germany.
Piastre—Cyprus; Egypt; Indo-China; Lebanon; Syria; Tonkin; Turkey.
Pice—Bahawalpur; India; Jodhpur; Pakistan; Tonk.
Pie—India.
Pond—South African Republic.
Pound—Syria.
Prutah—Israel.
Pul—Afghanistan.
Quetzal—Guatemala.
Qindar—Albania.
Qiran—Afghanistan.
Real—Guatemala; Salvador.
Reichspfennig—Germany.
Reis—Angola; Azores; Brazil; Portugal.
Rentenpfennig—Germany.
Rial—Muscat; Persia.
Rin—Japan.
Rixdollar—Curacao.
Riyal—Hejaz; Iraq; Saudi Arabia.
Rouble—Russia.
Rupee — Afghanistan; Bahawalpur; Bikanir; Bhutan; Bundi; German East Africa; Gwalior; Hyderabad; India; Indore; Jaipur; Mauritius; Mewar; Nepal; Pakistan; Saudi Arabia; Seychelles; Tibet; Travancore.
Rupia—Italian Somaliland; Portuguese India.
Rupie—German East Africa.
Ryal—Morocco.
Salung—Siam.
Santims—Latvia.
Sapeque—Annam; Indo-China.
Satang—Siam.
Schilling—Austria.
Sen—Japan.
Senti—Estonia.
Shahi—Afghanistan; Persia.
Shilling — Australia; British West Africa; Cyprus; East Africa; Fiji; Great Britain; Irish Free State; Jersey; New Guinea; New Zealand; South Africa; Southern Rhodesia.
Sho—Tibet.
Skar—Tibet.
Sol—Peru.
Somalo—Somalia.
Sovereign—Australia; Great Britain.
Srang—Tibet.
Stotinki—Bulgaria.
Sucre—Ecuador.
Tael—China; Chinese Turkestan.
Talari—Eritrea; Ethiopia.
Tanga—Portuguese India.
Tangka—Tibet.
Tical—Siam.
Toman—Persia.
Trambiya—Kutch.
Tugrik—Mongolia.
Wark—Ethiopia.
Won—Korea.
Xu—Indo-China.
Yang—Korea.
Yen—Japan.
Zloty—Poland.

INDEX

INDEX